MICROBIOLOGY AND PARASITOLOGY FOR ENVIRONMENTAL ENGINEERING

MICROBIOLOGY AND PARASITOLOGY FOR ENVIRONMENTAL ENGINEERING

Editor
Charles Monterio

DPH
DISCOVERY PUBLISHING HOUSE
INDIA

Published by:

DISCOVERY PUBLISHING HOUSE
4383/4B, Ansari Road, Darya Ganj
New Delhi-110 002 (India)
Phone : +91-11-23279245; 23253475; 43596065
Mobile : +91 9811179893 / +91 9871656464
E-mail : discoverybooksindia@gmail.com
orderdphbooks@gmail.com
namitwasan9@gmail.com
web : www.discoverypublishinggroup.com

Microbiology and Parasitology for Environmental Engineering
Edited by: **Charles Monterio**

Reprinted: **2026**

International Standard Book Number: **978-81-19205-68-4** (Hardback)

Printed at:
Infinity Imaging Systems
Delhi (INDIA)

PREFACE

The environment is everything that surrounds an organism or group of organisms, including the natural world, built or technological world, and social and cultural conditions. Humans are part of the environment and rely on it for their survival and growth. Microbes play a critical role in sustaining the planet by cycling energy and nutrients and impacting climate change through their impact on organic matter. Microbial diversity includes various aspects such as morphological, structural, metabolic, ecological, or evolutionary diversity. The central question in microbial ecology is understanding the relationships between the composition of microbial communities and their functional processes. Microorganisms have enabled feasible and cost-effective solutions to environmental problems that would have been impossible with physical and chemical engineering methods alone.

Recent scientific progress has applied microbial technologies to environmental management and biotechnology, addressing the harmful effects of soil erosion, sediment migration, chemical fertilizers, pesticides, and improper waste treatment. Hybrid applications that combine microbial methods with physical and chemical ones offer promising solutions to environmental problems. Although highly effective microorganisms have been cultured for various applications, they are only a small fraction of those found in the natural world. The untapped potential of microorganisms is vast, with new species continually discovered through culture-independent approaches such as metagenomics. Therefore, understanding and utilizing microbial diversity and its potential benefits are critical for sustaining the planet and solving environmental problems. As our knowledge of microbial ecology advances, we can continue to develop innovative solutions that combine microbial, physical, and chemical methods to address environmental challenges.

This book focuses on environmental microbiology and covers the important microorganisms involved in this field, the environments in which they are found, monitoring methodologies, and the potential effects of microorganisms on human activities. The book addresses new challenges in modern environmental microbiology, including pathogens and bioremediation, and highlights how molecular genetics and biotechnological tools have enhanced these subject areas. Molecular ecology, which involves investigating diversity in the environment and exploiting it for new natural products and activities, is also covered. In addition, the book provides a practical understanding of microorganisms in civil engineering processes and their functions in environmental engineering systems. It is a useful resource for both students and practitioners in the field of environmental microbiology and civil engineering.

Editor

CONTENTS

1 Bioremediation Techniques for Polluted Environment: Concept, Advantages, Limitations and Prospects

Indu Sharma

Department of Biotechnology, Maharishi Markandeshwar (Deemed to be University), Mullana, Ambala, Haryana, India

ABSTRACT

Environmental pollution has been rising in the past few decades due to increased anthropogenic activities. Bioremediation is an attractive and successful cleaning technique to remove toxic waste from polluted environment. Bioremediation is highly involved in degradation, eradication, immobilization, or detoxification diverse chemical wastes and physical hazardous materials from the surrounding through the all-inclusive and action of microorganisms. The main principle is degrading and converting pollutants to less toxic forms. Bioremediation can be carried out ex-situ and in-situ, depending on several factors, which include but not limited to cost, site characteristics, type, and concentration of pollutants. Hence, appropriate bioremediation technique is selected. Additionally, the major methodologies to develop bioremediation are biostimulation, bioaugmentation, bioventing, biopiles, and bioattenuation provided the environmental factors that decide the completion of bioremediation. Bioremediation is the most effective, economical, eco-friendly management tool to manage the polluted environment. All bioremediation techniques have its own advantage and disadvantage because it has its own specific applications.

Keywords: *Bioremediation, Environment, Pollutants soil, Ground water, Waste-water, Applications, Limitations*

INTRODUCTION

Bioremediation and natural reduction are also seen as a solution for emerging contaminant problems; microbes are very helpful to remediate the contaminated environment. Number of microbes including aerobic, anaerobic bacteria and fungi are involved in bioremediation process. Bioremediation is highly involved in degradation, eradication, immobilization, or detoxification diverse chemical wastes and physical hazardous materials from the surrounding through the all-inclusive and action of microorganisms. The main principle is degrading and converting pollutants to less toxic forms. There are two types of factors these are biotic and abiotic conditions are determine rate of degradation. Currently, different methods and strategies are applied for bioremediation process.

ENVIRONMENTAL POLLUTION

Environmental pollution has been on the rise in the past few decades due to increased human activities such as population explosion, unsafe agricultural practices, unplanned urbanization, deforestation, rapid industrialization and non-judicious use of energy reservoirs and other anthropogenic activities. Among the pollutants that are of environmental and public health concerns due to their toxicities are: chemical fertilizer, heavy metals, nuclear wastes, pesticides, herbicides, insecticides greenhouse gases, and hydrocarbons. Thousands of hazardous waste sites have been identified and estimated is that more will be identified in the coming decades. Release of pollutants into the environment comes from illegal dumping by chemical companies and industries. Many of the techniques utilized for site clean-up in the past, such as digging up the contaminated soil and hauling it away to be land filled or incinerated have been prohibitively expensive and do not provide permanent solution. More recent techniques such as vapor extraction and soil venting are cost effective but incomplete solution.

Definition of Bioremediation

Bioremediation is a process where biological organisms are used to remove or neutralize an environmental pollutant by metabolic process. The "biological" organisms include microscopic organisms, such as fungi, algae and bacteria, and the "remediation"—treating the situation.

In the Earth's biosphere, microorganisms grow in the widest range of habitats. They grow in soil, water, plants, animals, deep sea, and freezing ice environment. Their absolute numbers and their appetite for a wide range of chemicals make microorganisms the perfect candidate for acting as our environmental caretakers.

"Bioremediation is a waste management technique that includes the use of living organisms to eradicate or neutralize pollutants from a contaminated site."

"Bioremediation is a 'treatment techniques' that uses naturally occurring organisms to break down harmful materials into less toxic or non-toxic materials."

Bioremediation

Bioremediation technologies came into extensive usage and continue growing today at an exponential rate. Remediation of polluted sites using microbial process (bioremediation) has proven effective and reliable due to its eco-friendly features. In the past two decades, there have been recent developments in bioremediation techniques with the decisive goal being to successfully restore polluted environments in an economic, eco-friendly approach. Researchers have developed different bioremediation techniques that restore polluted environments. The micro-organisms used in bioremediation can be either indigenous or non-indigenous added to the contaminated site. Indigenous microorganisms present in polluted environments hold the key to solving most of the challenges associated with biodegradation and bioremediation of pollutant [1]. Environmentally friendly and cost effective are among the major advantages of bioremediation compared to both chemical and physical methods of remediation.

A mechanism of bioremediation is to reduce, detoxify, degrade, mineralize or transform more toxic pollutants to a less toxic. The pollutant removal process depends mainly on the pollutant nature, which includes pesticides, agrochemicals, chlorinated compounds, heavy metals, xenobiotic compounds, organic halogens, greenhouse gases, hydrocarbons, nuclear waste, dyes plastics and sludge. Cleaning technique apply to remove toxic waste from polluted environment. Bioremediation is highly involved in degradation, eradication, immobilization, or detoxification diverse chemical wastes and physical hazardous materials from the surrounding through the all-inclusive and action of microorganisms (Figure 1).

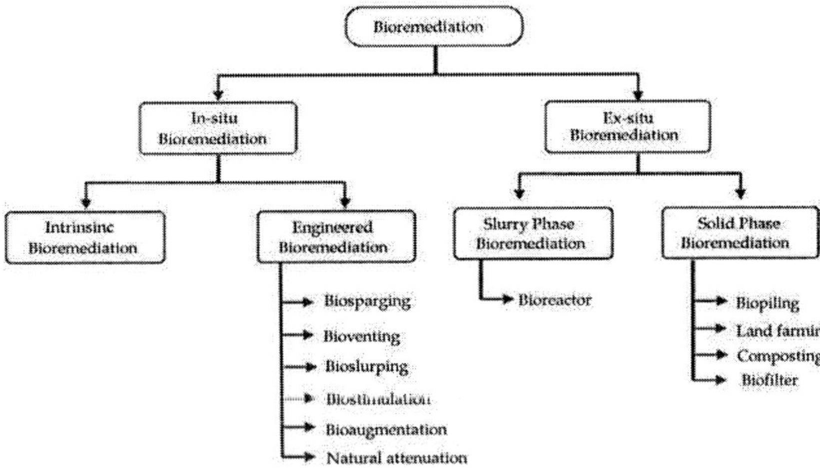

Figure 1. Bioremediation approaches for environmental clean-up.

MICROORGANISMS USED IN BIOREMEDIATION

Microorganisms play an important role on nutritional chains that are important part of the biological balance in life. Bioremediation involves the removal of the contaminated materials with the help of bacteria, fungi, algae and yeast. Microbes can grow at below zero temperature as well as extreme heat in the presence of hazardous compounds or any waste stream. The two characters of microbes are adaptability and biological system made them suitable for remediation process [2]. Carbon is the main requirement for microbial activity. Bioremediation process was carried out by microbial consortium in different environments.

These microorganisms comprise *Achromobacter*, *Arthrobacter*, *Alcaligenes*, *Bacillus*, *Corynebacterium*, *Pseudomonas,* *Flavobacterium*, *Mycobacterium*, *Nitrosomonas*, *Xanthobacter*, etc. [3].

There are groups of microbes which are used in bioremediation such as:

- **Aerobic:** aerobic bacteria have degradative capacities to degrade the complex compounds such as *Pseudomonas, Acinetobacter, Sphingomonas, Nocardia, Flavobacterium, Rhodococcus*, and *Mycobacterium.* These microbes have been reported to degrade pesticides, hydrocarbons, alkanes, and polyaromatic compounds. Many of these bacteria use the contaminants as carbon and energy source.
- **Anaerobic:** anaerobic bacteria are not as regularly used as aerobic bacteria. There is an increasing interest in aerobic bacteria used for bioremediation of chlorinated aromatic compounds, polychlorinated biphenyls, and dechlorination of the solvent trichloroethylene and chloroform, degrading and converting pollutants to less toxic forms.

Factors Affecting Microbial Bioremediation

Bioremediation process is degrading, removing, changing, immobilizing, or detoxifying various chemicals and physical pollutants from the environment through the activity of bacteria, fungi, algae and plants. Enzymatic metabolic pathways of microorganisms facilitate the progress of biochemical reactions that help in degradation of the pollutant. Microorganisms are act on the pollutants only when they have contact to the compounds which help them to generate energy and nutrients to multiply cells. The effectiveness of bioremediation depends on many factors; including, the chemical nature and concentration of pollutants, the physicochemical characteristics of the environment, and their accessibility to existing microorganisms [4].

The factors are mainly microbial population for degrading the pollutants, .the accessibility of contaminants to the microbial population and environment factors like type of soils, pH, temperature, oxygen and nutrients.

Biotic or Biological Factors

Biotic factors are helpful for the degradation of organic compounds by microorganisms with insufficient carbon sources, antagonistic interactions among microorganisms or the protozoa and bacteriophages. The rate of contaminant degradation is frequently dependent on the concentration of the contaminant and the amount of catalyst present in biochemical reaction. The major biological factors are included enzyme activity, interaction (competition, succession, and predation), mutation, horizontal gene transfer, its growth for biomass production, population size and its composition [5, 6].

Abiotic or Environmental Factors

The interaction of environmental contaminants with metabolic activity, physicochemical properties of the microorganisms targeted during the process. The successful interaction between the microbes and pollutant depends on the environmental situations. Microbial growth and activity are depended on temperature, pH, moisture, soil structure, water solubility, nutrients, site conditions, oxygen content and redox potential, deficiency of resources and physico-chemical bioavailability of pollutants, concentration, chemical structure, type, solubility and toxicity. This above factors are control degradation kinetics [5, 7].

Biodegradation of pollutant can occur under range of pH (6.5–8.5) is generally optimal for biodegradation in most aquatic and terrestrial environment. Moisture affects the metabolism of contaminant because it depends on the kind and amount of soluble constituents that are accessible as well as the pH and osmotic pressure of terrestrial and aquatic systems [8].

BIOREMEDIATION TECHNIQUE

Superficially, bioremediation techniques can be carried out ex-situ and in-situ site of application (Figure 1). Pollutant nature, depth and amount of pollution, type of environment, location, cost, and environmental policies are the selection standards that are considered for selecting any bioremediation technique. Performance based on oxygen and nutrient concentrations, temperature, pH, and other abiotic factors that determine the success of bioremediation processes [9, 10].

Ex-situ bioremediation techniques involve digging pollutants from polluted sites and successively transporting them to another site for treatment. Ex-situ bioremediation techniques are regularly considered based on the depth of pollution, type of pollutant, degree of pollution, cost of treatment and geographical location of the polluted site. Performance standards also regulate the choice of ex-situ bioremediation techniques.

Solid-phase Treatment

Solid-phase bioremediation is an ex-situ technology in which the contaminated soil is excavated and placed into piles. It is also includes organic waste like leaves, animal manures and agriculture wastes, domestic, industrial wastes and municipal wastes. Bacterial growth is moved through pipes that are distributed throughout the piles. Air pulling through the pipes is necessary for ventilation and microbial respiration. Solid-phase system required huge amount of space and cleanups require more time to complete as compared to slurry-phase processes. Solid-phase treatment processes include biopiles, windrows, land farming, composting, etc. [11].

Slurry-phase Bioremediation

Slurry-phase bioremediation is a relative more rapid process compared to the other treatment processes. Contaminated soil is combined with water, nutrient and oxygen in the bioreactor to create the optimum environment for the microorganisms to degrade the contaminants which are present in soil. This processing involves the separation of stones and rubbles from the contaminated soil. The added water concentration depends on the concentration of pollutants, the biodegradation process rate and the physicochemical properties of the soil. After completion of this process the soil is removed and dried up by using vacuum filters, pressure filters and centrifuges. The subsequent procedure is soil disposition and advance treatment of the resultant fluids.

TYPES OF BIOREMEDIATIONS

There are far more than nine types of bioremediation, but the following are the most common ways in which it is used.

Biopile

Bioremediation includes above-ground piling of dug polluted soil, followed by aeration and nutrient amendment to improve bioremediation by microbial metabolic activities. This technique comprises aeration, irrigation, nutrients, leachate collection and treatment bed systems. This specific ex-situ technique is progressively being measured due to its useful features with cost effectiveness, which allows operative biodegradation conditions includes pH, nutrient, temperature and aeration are effectively controlled. The biopile use to treat volatile low molecular weight pollutants; it can also be used effectively to remediate polluted very cold extreme environments [12, 13, 14]. The flexibility of biopile allows remediation time to be shortened as heating system can be integrated into biopile design to increase microbial activities and contaminant availability thus increasing the rate of biodegradation [15]. Additionally, heated air can be injected into biopile design to deliver air and heat in tandem, in order to facilitate enhanced bioremediation. Bulking agents such as straw saw dust, bark or wood chips and other organic materials have been added to enhance remediation process in a biopile construct. Although biopile systems connected to additional field ex-situ bioremediation techniques, such as land farming, bioventing, biosparging, robust engineering, maintenance and operation cost, lack of power supply at remote sites, which would facilitate constant air circulation in contaminated piled soil through air pump. Additional, extreme heating of air can lead to soil drying undertaking bioremediation, which will inhibit microbial activities and which stimulate volatilization than biodegradation [16].

Windrows

Windrows is bioremediation techniques depends on periodic rotating the piled polluted soil to improve bioremediation by increasing microbial degradation activities of native and transient hydrocarbonoclastic present in polluted soil. The periodic turning of polluted soil increase in aeration with addition of water, uniform distribution of nutrients, pollutants and microbial degradation activities, accordingly increase the rate of bioremediation, which can be proficient through acclimatization, biotransformation and mineralization. Windrow treatment as compared to biopile treatment, showed higher rate of hydrocarbon removal however, the effectiveness of the windrow for hydrocarbon removal from the soil [17]. However, periodic turning associated with windrow treatment not the best selection method to implement in bioremediation of soil polluted with toxic volatiles compounds. The use of windrow treatment has been associated in greenhouse gas (CH_4) release due to formation of anaerobic zone inside piled polluted soil, which frequently reduced aeration [18].

Land Farming

Land farming is the simplest, outstanding bioremediation techniques due to its low cost and less equipment requirement for operation. It is mostly observed in ex-situ bioremediation, while in some cases of in-situ bioremediation technique. This consideration is due to the site of treatment. Pollutant depth is important in land farming which can be carried out ex-situ or in-situ. In land farming, polluted soils are regularly excavated and tilled and site of treatment speciously regulates the type of bioremediation. When excavated polluted soil is treated on-site, it is ex-situ as it has more in common than other ex-situ bioremediation techniques. Generally, excavated polluted soils are carefully applied on a fixed layer support above the ground surface to allow aerobic biodegradation of pollutant by autochthonous microorganisms [19]. Over all, land farming bioremediation technique is very simple to design and implement, requires low capital input and can be used to treat large volume of polluted soil with minimal environmental impact and energy requirement [20].

Bioreactor

Bioreactor is a vessel in which raw materials are converted to specific product(s) following series of biological reactions. There are different operational modes of bioreactors, which include: batch, fed-batch, sequencing batch, continuous and multistage. Bioreactor provides optimal growth conditions for bioremediation. Bioreactor filled with polluted samples for remediation process. The bioreactor based treatment of polluted soil has several advantages as compared to ex-situ bioremediation procedures. Bioreactor-based bioremediation process having excellent control of pH, temperature, agitation and aeration, substrate and inoculum concentrations efficiently reduces bioremediation time. The ability to control and manipulate process parameters in a bioreactor implies that biological reactions. The flexible nature of bioreactor designs allows maximum biological degradation while minimizing abiotic losses [21].

1. Advantages of ex-situ bioremediation
   - Suitable for a wide range of contaminants

- Suitability relatively simple to assess from site investigation data
- Biodegradation are greater in a bioreactor system than or in solid-phase systems because the contaminated environment is more manageable and more controllable and predictable.

2. Disadvantages
   - Not applicable to heavy metal contamination or chlorinated hydrocarbons such as trichloroethylene.
   - Non-permeable soil requires additional processing.
   - The contaminant can be stripped from soil via soil washing or physical extraction before being placed in bioreactor.

In-situ Bioremediation Techniques

These techniques comprise treating polluted substances at the pollution site. It does not need any excavation and by little or no disturbance in soil construction. Perfectly, these techniques should to be cost effective compared to ex-situ bioremediation techniques. Some in-situ bioremediation techniques like bioventing, biosparging and phytoremediation may be enhanced, while others may be progress without any form of improvement such as intrinsic bioremediation or natural attenuation. In-situ bioremediation techniques have been effectively used to treat chlorinated solvents, heavy metals, dyes, and hydrocarbons polluted sites [22, 23, 24].

Types of in-situ Bioremediation

In-situ bioremediation is two types; these are intrinsic and engineered bioremediation.

Intrinsic Bioremediation

Intrinsic bioremediation also known as natural reduction is an in-situ bioremediation technique, which involves passive remediation of polluted sites, without any external force (human intervention). This process deals with stimulation of indigenous or naturally occurring microbial population. The process based on both microbial aerobic and anaerobic processes to biodegrade polluting constituents containing those that are recalcitrant. The absence of external force implies that the technique is less expensive compared to other in-situ techniques.

Engineered in-situ Bioremediation

The second approach involves the introduction of certain microorganism to the site of contamination. Genetically Engineered microorganisms used in the in-situ bioremediation accelerate the degradation process by enhancing the physicochemical conditions to encourage the growth of microorganisms.

Bioventing

Bioventing techniques involve controlled stimulation of airflow by delivering oxygen to unsaturated (vadose) zone in order to increase activities of indigenous microbes for bioremediation. In bioventing, amendments are made by adding nutrients and moisture to increase bioremediation. That will achieve microbial transformation of pollutants to a harmless state. This technique has gained popularity among other in-situ bioremediation techniques [25].

Bioslurping

This technique combines vacuum-enhanced pumping, soil vapor extraction and bioventing to achieve soil and ground water remediation by indirect providing of oxygen and stimulation of contaminant biodegradation [26]. This technique is planned for products recovery from remediating capillary, light non-aqueous phase liquids (LNAPLs), unsaturated and saturated zones. This technique used to remediate soils which are contaminated with volatile and semi-volatile organic compounds. The method uses a "slurp" that spreads into the free product layer, which pulls up liquids from this layer. The pumping machine transports LNAPLs to the surface by upward movement, where it becomes separated from air and water. In this technique, soil moisture bounds air permeability and declines oxygen transfer rate, which reducing microbial activities. Although this technique is not suitable for low permeable soil remediation, it is cost effective operation procedure due to less amount of ground water, minimizes storage, treatment and disposal costs.

Biosparging

This technique is similar to bioventing in this air is injected into soil subsurface to improve microbial activities which stimulate pollutant removal from polluted sites. However, in bioventing, air is injected in saturated zone, which can help in upward movement of volatile organic compounds to the unsaturated zone to stimulate biodegradation process. The efficiency of biosparging depends on two major factors specifically soil permeability and pollutant biodegradability. In bioventing and soil vapor extraction (SVE), biosparing operation is closely correlated technique known as in-situ air sparging (IAS), which depend on high air-flow rates for volatilization of pollutant, whereas biosparging stimulates biodegradation. Biosparging has been generally used in treating aquifers contaminated with diesel and kerosene.

Phytoremediation

Phytoremediation is depolluting the contaminated soils. This technique based on plant interactions like physical, chemical, biological, microbiological and biochemical in contaminated sites to diminish the toxic properties of pollutants. Which is depending on pollutant amount and nature, there are several mechanisms such as extraction, degradation, filtration, accumulation, stabilization and volatilization involved in phytoremediation. Pollutants like heavy metals and radionuclides are commonly removed by extraction, transformation and sequestration. Organic pollutants hydrocarbons and chlorinated compounds are mostly removed by degradation, rhizoremediation, stabilization and volatilization, with mineralization being possible when some plants such as willow and alfalfa are used [27, 28].

Some important factors of plant as a phytoremediator include: root system, which may be fibrous or tap depending on the depth of pollutant, above ground biomass, toxicity of pollutant to plant, plant existence and its adaptability to predominant environmental conditions, plant growth rate, site monitoring and above all, time mandatory to achieve the preferred level of cleanliness. In addition, the plant must be resistant to diseases and pests [29]. In phytoremediation removal of pollutant includes uptake, translocation from roots to shoots. Further, translocation and accumulation depends on transpiration and partitioning [30]. However, the process is possible to change, depending on other factors such as nature of contaminant and plant. The mostly plants growing in any polluted site are good phytoremediators. Therefore, the success of any phytoremediation method mainly depends on improving the remediation potentials of native plants growing in polluted sites either by bioaugmentation with endogenous or exogenous plant. One of the major advantages of using plants to remediate polluted site is that some precious metals can bioaccumulate in some plants and recovered after remediation, a process known as phytomining.

Permeable Reactive Barrier (PRB)

This technique is commonly observed as a physical method for remediating contaminated groundwater. However, biological mechanisms are precipitation degradation and sorption of pollutant removal used in PRB method. The substitute terms such as biological PRB, bio-enhanced PRB, passive bioreactive barrier, have been suggested to accommodate the biotechnology and bioremediation aspect of the technique. In general, PRB is an in-situ technique used for remediating heavy metals and chlorinated compounds in groundwater pollution [31, 32].

Advantages of in-situ Bioremediation

- In-situ bioremediation methods do not required excavation of the contaminated soil.
- This method provides volumetric treatment, treating both dissolved and solid contaminants.
- The time required to treat sub-surface pollution using accelerated in-situ bioremediation can often be faster than pump and treat processes.
- It may be possible to completely transform organic contaminants to innocuous substances like carbon dioxide, water and ethane.
- It is a cost effective method because there is minimal site disruption.

Limitation of in-situ Bioremediation

- Depending on specific site, some contaminants may not be absolutely transformed to harmless products.
- If transformation stops at an intermediate compound, the intermediate may be more toxic and/or mobile than parent compound some are recalcitrant contaminants cannot be biodegradable.
- When incorrectly applied, injection wells may become blocked by profuse microbial growth due to addition of nutrients, electron donor and electron acceptor.
- Heavy metals and organic compounds concentration inhibit activity of indigenous microorganisms.
- In-situ bioremediation usually required microorganism's acclimatization, which may not develop for spills and recalcitrant compounds.

BIOREMEDIATION PROSPECTS

Bioremediation techniques are varied and have demonstrated effective in restoring polluted sites. Microorganisms play fundamental role in bioremediation; consequently, their diversity, abundance and community structure in polluted environments offer insight into the chance of any bioremediation technique providing other environmental factors, which can inhibit microbial activities. Advanced Molecular techniques such as 'Omics' includes genomics, proteomics, metabolomics and transcriptomics have contributed towards microbial identification, functions, metabolic and catabolic pathways, with microbial based methods. Nutrient availability, low population or absence of microbes with degradative capabilities, and pollutant bioavailability may delay the achievement of bioremediation. Since bioremediation depends on microbial process, biostimulation and bioaugmentation approaches speed up microbial activities in polluted sites. Biostimulation increase microbial activities by the addition of nutrients to a polluted sample. Microorganisms are abundantly present in different type of environmental condition, it is noticeable that pollutant degrading microbes are naturally present in polluted contaminated sites, their growth and metabolic activities may depends on pollutant type and concentration; later, we can use of agro-industrial wastes, which contains nitrogen, phosphorus and potassium as a nutrient source most polluted sites. Microbial consortium has been reported to degrade pollutants more efficiently than pure isolates [33].

This activity due to metabolic diversities of individual isolates, which potency create from their isolation source, adaptation process, pollutant composition, and synergistic effects, which may lead to complete and rapid degradation of pollutants when such isolates are mixed together [34]. Additional so, both bioaugmentation and biostimulation were effective in removing pollutant such as polyaromatic hydrocarbons (PAHs) from heavily polluted sample compared to non-amended setup (control) [35].

Although bioaugmentation has recognized effective method, it has been shown to increase the degradation of many compounds. If proper biodegrading microorganisms are not present in soil or if microbial populations decreased because of contaminant toxicity, specific microorganisms can be added as "introduced organisms" to improve the current populations and the possibility that the inoculated microorganisms may not survive in the new environment make bioaugmentation a very uncertain method. This process is known as bioaugmentation. Bioremediation technique in which natural or genetically engineered bacteria with unique metabolic profiles are used to treat sewage or contaminated water or soil. The use of alginate, agar, agarose, gelatin, gellan gum and polyurethane as carrier materials solve some of the challenges associated with bioaugmentation [36].

Biosurfactants are chemical equivalents having ecofriendly and biodegradable properties. However, high construction cost and low scalability application of biosurfactants to polluted site are uneconomical. Agro-industrial wastes combination are nutrient sources for development of biosurfactant producers during fermentation process. Application of several bioremediation techniques will help increase remediation efficiency [37].

Enhancing bioremediation ability with organized use of genetically engineered microorganisms (GEM) is a favorable approach. This is due to possibility of engineering a designer biocatalyst target pollutant including recalcitrant compounds by combining a novel and efficient metabolic pathways, widening the substrate range of existing pathways and increasing stability of catabolic activity [38].

However, parallel gene transfer and multiplication of GEM in an environmental application are encouraging approach. Bacterial containment systems, in which any GEM escaping an environment to reconstruct polluted environment.

Further, derivative pathway of genetically engineering microorganisms with a target polluted compound using biological approach could increase bioremediation efficiency. Nanomaterials decline the toxicity of pollutant to microorganisms because nanomaterials having increase surface area and lower activation energy, which reduce time and cost of bioremediation [39].

BIOREMEDIATION APPLICATIONS

Bioremediation must be considered as appropriate methods that can applied to all states of matter in the environment

- Solids (soils, sediment and sludge)
- Liquids (ground water, surface water and industrial waste water
- Gases (industrial air emissions)
- Sub-surface environments (saturated and vadose zones).

The general approaches to bioremediation are the (i) intrinsic (natural) bioremediation, (ii) biosimulation (environmental modifications, through nutrient application and aeration, and (iii) bioaugmentation (addition of microbes).

The biological community exploited for bioremediation generally consists of the native soil microflora. However, higher plants can also be manipulated to enhance toxicant removal (phytoremediation), especially for remediation of metal contaminated soils.

Advantage and Disadvantage

All bioremediation techniques have its own advantage and disadvantage because it has its own specific applications.

The Advantage of Bioremediation

- It is a natural process; it takes a little time, as an adequate waste treatment process for contaminated material such as soil. Microbes able to degrade the contaminant, the biodegradative populations become reduced. The treatment products are commonly harmless including cell biomass, water and carbon dioxide.
- It needs a very less effort and can commonly carry out on site, regularly without disturbing normal microbial activities. This also eradicates the transport amount of waste off site and the possible threats to human health and the environment.
- It is functional in a cost effective process as comparison to other conventional methods that are used for clean-up of toxic hazardous waste regularly for the treatment of oil contaminated sites. It also supports in complete degradation of the pollutants; many of the toxic hazardous compounds can be transformed to less harmful products and disposal of contaminated material.
- It does not use any dangerous chemicals. Nutrients especially fertilizers added to make active and fast microbial growth. Because of bioremediation change harmful chemicals into water and harmless gases, the harmful chemicals are completely destroyed.
- Simple, less labor intensive and cheap due to their natural role in the environment.
- Contaminants are destroyed, not simply transferred to different environmental.
- Nonintrusive, possibly allowing for continued site use.
- Current way of remediating environment from large contaminates and acts as ecofriendly sustainable opportunities.

The Disadvantage of Bioremediation

- It is restricted for biodegradable compounds. Not all compounds are disposed to quick and complete degradation process.
- There are particular new products of biodegradation may be more toxic than the initial compounds and persist in environment.

- Biological processes are highly specific, ecofriendly which includes the presence of metabolically active microbial populations, suitable environmental growth conditions and availability of nutrients and contaminants.
- It is demanding to encourage the process from bench and pilot-scale to large-scale field operations. Contaminants may be present as solids, liquids and gases. It often takes longer than other treatment preferences, such as excavation and removal of soil or incineration.
- Research is needed to develop and engineer bioremediation technologies that are appropriate for sites with complex mixtures of contaminants that are not evenly dispersed in the environment.

Limitations of Bioremediation

Bioremediation is limited to those compounds that are biodegradable. This method is susceptible to rapid and complete degradation. Products of biodegradation may be more persistent or toxic than the parent compound in the environment.

Specificity

Biological processes are highly specific. Important site factors mandatory for success include the presence of metabolically capable microbial populations, suitable environmental growth conditions, and appropriate levels of nutrients and contaminants.

Scale up Limitation

It is difficult to scale up bioremediation process from batch and pilot scale studies applicable to large scale field operations.

Technological Advancement

More research is required to develop modern engineer bioremediation technologies that are suitable for sites with composite combinations of contaminants that are not equally distributed in the environment. It may be present as solids, liquids and gases forms.

Time Taking Process

Bioremediation takes longer time compare to other treatment options, such as excavation and removal of soil from contaminated site.

Regulatory Uncertainty

We are not certain to say that remediation is 100% completed, as there is no accepted definition of clean. Due to that performance evaluation of bioremediation is difficult, and there is no acceptable endpoint for bioremediation treatments.

CONCLUSION

Biodegradation is very fruitful and attractive option to remediating, cleaning, managing and recovering technique for solving polluted environment through microbial activity. The speed of undesirable waste substances degradation is determined in competition with in biological agents like fungi, bacterial, algae inadequate supply with essential nutrient, uncomfortable external abiotic conditions (aeration, moisture, pH, temperature), and low bioavailability. Bioremediation depending on several factors, which include but not limited to cost, site characteristics, type and concentration of pollutants. The leading step to a successful bioremediation is site description, which helps create the most suitable and promising bioremediation technique (ex-situ or in-situ). Ex-situ bioremediation techniques tend to be more costly due to excavation and transportation from archeological site. However, they can be used to treat wider range of pollutants. In contrast, in-situ techniques have no extra cost for excavation; however, on-site installation cost of equipment, attached with effectively and control the subsurface of polluted site can reduce some ineffective in-situ bioremediation methods. Geological characteristics of polluted sites comprising soil, pollutant type and depth, human habitation site and performance of every bioremediation technique should be integrated in determining the most appropriate and operative bioremediation technique to successfully treatment of polluted sites.

REFERENCES

1. Verma JP, Jaiswal DK. Book review: Advances in biodegradation and bioremediation of industrial waste. Frontiers in Microbiology. 2016;6:1-2. DOI: 10.3389/fmicb.2015.01555
2. Prescott LM, Harley JP, Klein DA. Microbiology. 5th ed. New York: McGraw Hill; 2002. pp. 10-14
3. Singh R, Singh P, Sharma R. Microorganism as a tool of bioremediation technology for cleaning environment: A review. International Academy of Ecology and Environmental Science. 2014;4(1):1-6
4. El Fantroussi S, Agathos SN. Is bioaugmentation a feasible strategy for pollutant removal and site remediation? Current Opinion in Microbiology. 2005;8:268-275. Available at: https://goo.gl/y6kLsc
5. Madhavi GN, Mohini DD. Review paper on parameters affecting bioremediation. International Journal of Life Science and Pharma Research. 2012;2:77-80. Available at: https://goo.gl/tBP2C6
6. Boopathy R. Factors limiting bioremediation technologies. Bioresource Technology. 2000;74:63-67. Available at: https://goo.gl/eQhPh7
7. Adams GO, Fufeyin PT, Okoro SE, Ehinomen I. Bioremediation, biostimulation and bioaugmention: A review. International Journal of Environmental Bioremediation & Biodegradation. 2015;3:28-39. Available at: https://goo.gl/9XY7ni
8. Cases I, de Lorenzo V. Genetically modified organisms for the environment: Stories of success and failure and what we have learned from them. International Microbiology. 2005;8:213-222. Available at: https://goo.gl/3oaxJT
9. Frutos FJG, Pe'rez R, Escolano O, Rubio A, Gimeno A, Fernandez MD, et al. Remediation trials for hydrocarbon-contaminated sludge from a soil washingprocess: Evaluation of bioremediation technologies. Journal of Hazardous Materials. 2012;199:262-271. DOI: 10.1016/j.jhazmat.2011.11.017
10. Smith E, Thavamani P, Ramadass K, Naidu R, Srivastava P, Megharaj M. Remediation trials for hydrocarbon-contaminated soils in arid environments: Evaluation of bioslurry and biopiling techniques. Integrated Journal of Biodeterioration Biodegradation. 2015;101:56-65. DOI: 10.1016/j.ibiod.2015.03.029
11. Kulshreshtha A, Agrawal R, Barar M, Saxena S. A review on bioremediation of heavy metals in contaminated water. IOSR Journal of Environmental Science Toxicology and food Technology (IOSR-JESTFT). 2014;8(7):44-50
12. Gomez F, Sartaj M. Optimization of field scale biopiles for bioremediation of petroleum hydrocarbon contaminated soil at low temperature conditions by response surface methodology (RSM). Integrated Journal of Biodeterioration Biodegradation. 2014;89:103-109. DOI: 10.1016/j.ibiod.2014.01.010
13. Dias RL, Ruberto L, Calabró A, Balbo AL, Del Panno MT, Mac Cormack WP. Hydrocarbon removal and bacterial community structure in on-site biostimulated biopile systems designed

for bioremediation of diesel-contaminated Antarctic soil. Polar Biology. 2015;38:677-687. DOI: 10.1007/s00300-014-1630-7

14. Whelan MJ, Coulon F, Hince G, Rayner J, McWatters R, Spedding T, et al. Fate and transport of petroleum hydrocarbons in engineered biopiles in polar regions. Chemosphere. 2015;131:232-240. DOI: 10.1016/j.Chemosphere.2014.10.088
15. Aislabie J, Saul DJ, Foght JM. Bioremediation of hydrocarbon contaminated polar soils. Extremophiles. 2006;10:171-179. DOI: 10.1007/s00792-2005-0498-4
16. Sanscartier D, Zeeb B, Koch I, Reimer K. Bioremediation of diesel-contaminated soil by heated and humidified biopile system in cold climates. Cold Regions Science and Technology. 2009;55:167-173. DOI: 10.1016/j.coldregions.2008.07.004
17. Coulon F, Al Awadi M, Cowie W, Mardlin D, Pollard S, Cunningham C, et al. When is a soil remediated? Comparison of biopiled and windrowed soils contaminated with bunker-fuel in a full-scale trial. Environmental Pollution. 2009;158:3032-3040. DOI: 10.1016/j.envpol.2010.06.001
18. Hobson AM, Frederickson J, Dise NB. CH_4 and N_2O from mechanically turned windrow and vermincomposting systems following in-vessel pre-treatment. Waste Management. 2005;25:345-352. DOI: 10.1016/j.wasman.2005.02.015
19. Silva-Castro GA, Uad I, Gònzalez-Lòpez J, Fandiño CG, Toledo FL, Calvo C. Application of selected microbial consortia combined with inorganic and oleophilic fertilizers to recuperate oil-polluted soil using land farming technology. Clean Technology of Environment Policy. 2012;14:719-726. DOI: 10.1007/s10098-011-0439-0
20. Maila MP, Colete TE. Bioremediation of petroleum hydrocarbons through land farming: Are simplicity and cost-effectiveness the only advantages? Review. Environmental Science Biotechnology. 2004;3:349-360. DOI: 10.1007/s111157-004-6653
21. Mohan SV, Sirisha K, Rao NC, Sarma PN, Reddy SJ. Degradation of chlorpyrifos contaminated soil by bioslurry reactor operated in sequencing batch mode: Bioprocess monitoring. Journal of Hazardous Materials. 2004;116:39-48. DOI: 10.1016/j.jhazmat.2004.05.037
22. Folch A, Vilaplana M, Amado L, Vicent R, Caminal G. Fungal permeable reactive barrier to remediate groundwater in anartificial aquifer. Journal of Hazardous Materials. 2013;262:554-560. DOI: 10.1016/j.jhazmat.2013.09.004
23. Frascari D, Zanaroli G, Danko AS. In situ aerobic cometabolism of chlorinated solvents: A review. Journal of Hazardous Materials. 2015;283:382-399. DOI: 10.1016/j.jhazmat.2014.09.041
24. Roy M, Giri AK, Dutta S, Mukherjee P. Integrated phytobial remediation for sustainable management of arsenic in soil and water. Environment International. 2005;75:180-198. DOI: 10.1016/j.envint.2014.11.010
25. Höhener P, Ponsin V. In situ vadose zone bioremediation. Current Opinion in Biotechnology. 2014;27:1-7. DOI: 10.1016/j.copbio.2013.08.018
26. Gidarakos E, Aivalioti M. Large scale and long term application of bioslurping: The case of a Greek petroleum refinery site. Journal of Hazardous Materials. 2007;149:574-581. DOI: 10.1016/j. jhazmat.2007.06.110
27. Meagher RB. Phytoremediation of toxic elemental organic pollutants. Currant Opinion Plant Biology. 2000;3:153-162. DOI: 10.1016/S1369-5266(99)00054-0
28. Kuiper I, Lagendijk EL, Bloemberg GV, Lugtenberg BJJ. Rhizoremediation: A beneficial plant-microbe interaction. Molecular Plant Microbe Interactions. 2004;7:6-15. DOI: 10.1094/MPMI.2004.17.1.6

29. Lee JH. An overview of phytoremediation as a potentially promising technology for environmental pollution control. Biotechnology and Bioprocess Engineering. 2013;18:431-439. DOI: 10.1007/s12257-013-0193-8

30. Miguel AS, Ravanel P, Raveton M, A comparative study on the uptake and translocation of organochlorines by Phragmites australis. Journal of Hazardous Materials. 2013;244:60-69. DOI: 10.1016/j.jhazmat.2012.11.025

31. Thiruvenkatachari R, Vigneswaran S, Naidu R. Permeable reactive barrier for groundwater remediation. Journal of Industrial and Engineering Chemistry. 2007;14:145-156. DOI: 10.1016/j.jiec.2007.10.001

32. Obiri-Nyarko F, Grajales-Mesa SJ, Malina G. An overview of permeable reactive barriers for in situ sustainable groundwater remediation. Chemosphere. 2014;111:243-259. DOI: 10.1016/j.chemosphere.2014.03.112

33. Silva-Castro GA, Uad I, Gonzalez-Lopez J, Fandino CG, Toledo FL, Calvo C. Application of selected microbial consortia combined with inorganic and oleophilic fertilizers to recuperate oil-polluted soil using land farming technology. Clean Technology of Environmental Policy. 2012;14:719-726. DOI: 10.1007/s10098-011-0439-0

34. Bhattacharya M, Guchhait S, Biswas D, Datta S. Waste lubricating oil removal in a batch reactor by mixed bacterial consortium: A kinetic study. Bioprocess and Biosystems Engineering. 2015;38:2095-2106. DOI: 10.1007/s00449-015-1449-9

35. Sun G-D, Xu Y, Jin J-H, Zhong Z-P, Liu Y, Luo M, et al. Pilot scale ex situ bioremediation of heavily PAHs-contaminated soil by indigenous microorganisms and bioaugmentation by a PAHs-degrading and bioemulsifier-producing strain. Journal of Hazardous Materials. 2012;233:72-78. DOI: 10.1016/j.jhazmat.2012.06.060

36. Tyagi M, da Fonseca MMR, de Carvalho CCCR. Bioaugmentation and biostimulation strategies to improve the effectiveness of bioremediation processes. Biodegradation. 2011;22:231-241. DOI: 10.1007/s10532-010-9394-4

37. Cassidy DP, Srivastava VJ, Dombrowski FJ, Lingle JW. Combining in situ chemical oxidation, stabilization, and anaerobic bioremediation in a single application to reduce contaminant mass and leachability in soil. Journal of Hazardous Materials. 2015;297:347-355. DOI: 10.1016/j.jhazmat.2015.05.030

38. Paul D, Pandey G, Pandey J, Jain RK. Accessing microbial diversity for bioremediation and environmental restoration. Trends in Biotechnology. 2005;23:135-142

39. Rizwan M, Singh M, Mitra CK, Morve RK. Ecofriendly application of nanomaterials: Nanobioremediation. Journal of Nanoparticles. 2014:1-7. DOI: 10.1155/2014/431787

2

Microbial Bioremediation and Different Bioreactors Designs Applied

Memory Tekere

Environmental Science Department, University of South Africa, Johannesburg, South Africa

ABSTRACT

Microbial remediation of pollutants involves the use of microorganisms to degrade pollutants either completely to water and carbon dioxide (for organic pollutants) or into less toxic forms. In the case of nonbiodegradable inorganic compounds, bioremediation takes the form of bioaccumulation or conversion of one toxic species to a less toxic form for example Cr(VI) is converted to less toxic (III). Bioremediation is considered an environmentally friendly way for pollution clean-up. Microbial clean up can be applied in situ (in place of contamination) or ex situ (off the site of contamination). In situ remediation in the natural environment is deemed slow and often times difficult to control and optimize the different parameters affecting the bioremediation. To this end, use of engineered bioreactors is preferred. Engineered bioreactors providing for optimum conditions for microbial growth and biodegradation have been developed for use in bioremediation processes to achieve the different desired remediation goals. Bioreactors in use range in mode of operation from batch, continuous, and fed batch bioreactors and are designed to optimize microbial processes in relationship to contaminated media and nature of pollutant. Designed bioreactors for bioremediation range from packed, stirred tanks, airlift, slurry phase, and partitioning phase reactors amongst others.

Keywords*: Bioremediation, Bioreactors, Pollution, Microorganisms, Degradation*

INTRODUCTION

Bioremediation is a natural process that relies on microorganisms and plants and/ or their derivatives (enzymes or spent biomass) to degrade or alter environmental contaminants as these organisms carry out their normal life functions [1, 2]. Bioremediation is considered an economical, versatile, efficient and eco-friendly way of dealing with environmental pollutants as compared to the physico-chemical methods [1, 2, 3]. The use of well-designed microbial bioreactors is acknowledged as an efficient way to ensure that microbial growth and processes occur in a controlled environment that provides the necessary optimum conditions [3, 4, 5]. This chapter focuses on microbial remediation in bioreactors so phytoremediation as facilitated by plants is not discussed. Several studies describe microbial remediation in designed bioreactors ranging from batch, continuous, and fed-batch operated mode which can be in different designs such as suspended carrier, slurry and fixed bed, membrane and fluidized bed reactors [4, 5, 6, 7, 8].

The use of microbial bioreactors in remediation is very attractive in that the bioreactors offer the advantages of providing a controlled environment where it is possible to control critical process parameters to optimize the microbial bioremediation process. Another advantage is that there is flexibility in design of the bioreactor (size and configuration) to suit application or intended purpose of the reactor [6, 7, 8, 9]. However, bioremediation in bioreactors if operated *ex situ*, requires relocation of pollutant, a process which can involve excavation for soils and sediments, transportation and possible containment or controlled handling of the contaminated media thus making the process expensive [4, 5, 6, 8,·9]. There is a potential for exposing other environments to the contamination. Also some pretreatment of contaminated media, e.g., drying and crushing, maybe required thus adding on to the process cost [8, 9].

MICROBIAL BIOREMEDIATION

As defined, microbial bioremediation makes use of microorganisms and/or their derivatives (enzymes or spent biomass) to clean-up environmental contaminants [7, 9, 10]. With microorganisms, it is important to note that microorganisms are everywhere and as such pollutants in the different environmental compartments always come into contact with microorganisms [1, 2]. Microbes break down/transform pollutants via their inherent metabolic processes with or without slight pathway modifications to allow the pollutant to be channeled into the normal microbial metabolic pathway for degradation/ and biotransformation. Applied bioremediation methods therefore focus on tapping the naturally occurring microbial catabolic capabilities to degrade, transform or accumulate most of the synthetic compounds such as hydrocarbons (e.g., oil), polychlorinated biphenyls (PCBs), polyaromatic hydrocarbons (PAHs), radionuclides and metals [4, 6, 7, 8]. The natural existence of a large diversity of microbial species expands the variety of chemical pollutants that are degraded or detoxified.

The advantages of microbial bioremediation are that it has public acceptance, as it is a natural process [8]. It is a low cost technology in most cases when compared to other clean-up methods for hazardous waste [2]. It can be done *in situ* and *ex situ*, instead of contaminants being transferred from one form to another or one medium to another, complete destruction of target organic pollutants is possible [8]. Notable disadvantages are that bioremediation takes relatively long to achieve treatment goals, may not be effective on all contaminants, some products of biodegradation maybe more toxic or persistent than the parent compound, specificity of the biological processes with respect to microbial populations, pollutant and environmental limitations is also a drawback and that specialized expertise are required in designing and implementing.

Bioremediation using microbial bioreactors finds application in soil, air and water environments including:

Waste Water and Industrial Effluent Treatment

Microorganisms are the primary agents of any biological wastewater treatment. Microorganisms are already present in waste water systems and feed on complex substances in the wastewater converting them to simpler substances thus assisting in achieving the treatment. Trickling filters, membrane bioreactors, slurry phase reactors and upflow anaerobic sludge blanket bioreactors (UASB) are some of the reactors that are used in waste water and industrial effluent treatment.

Soil and Land Treatment

Contaminants successfully treated include diesel fuel, fuel oils, oily sludge, wood-preserving wastes (PCP, PAHs, and creosote), coke wastes, and certain pesticides [6, 8, 9]. Soil bioremediation has proven most successful in treating petroleum hydrocarbons and other less volatile, biodegradable contaminants. Slurry phase, stirred tanks, biofilters, partitioning phase and packed microbial reactors find application in contaminated soil remediation.

Control of Air Pollution

Microorganisms are used in the bioremediation of organic and inorganic air pollutants in spent gases before release or escape into the atmosphere [5, 9]. Microorganisms oxidize pollutants such as H_2S, SO_2, VOCs, and reduce pollutants such as NOx to nitrate and this assist to prevent likely environmental, health hazards and nuisances [5]. Bioscrubbers and biofilters are some of the bioreactor types often used in control of air pollution.

Solid Waste Management

Microorganisms are chiefly responsible for the biodegradation of organic wastes in nature and they drive the decomposition processes that occur in landfills and composts. Anaerobic digesters are often applied mostly in the biotreatment solid waste.

Factors Affecting Microbial Bioreactor Performance

A number of issues are at play in all bioremediation technologies including when bioreactors are used. These are those that concern the contaminant, microbial community and the design, optimization and monitoring of the process [6, 8, 9]. The microbial science of bioremediation is therefore approached from many scientific frontiers: abiotic interactions (solubility, transport, sorption and photolysis), biotic interactions (taxonomic diversity, physiological, genetic and ecological interactions). In the design and operation of bioreactors in remediation, many of these factors have to be optimized and controlled for best reactor performance [5, 10, 11, 12].

Variables that affect the operation and efficiency of a microbial bioreactor relate to biotic and abiotic factors that affect microbial growth and those factors that relate to the reactor design and configuration. Factors that affect microbial growth and activities in bioreactors include; environmental factors (temperature, pH, moisture), pollutant mix, pollutant concentration, macronutrient [5, 10, 11, 12]. Factors on reactor design include; size, configuration and mode of operation.

Environmental Related Factors

Environmental conditions (temperature, pH, oxygen availability/electron, and salinity) affect growth; the metabolic activities of microorganisms and to some extent the behavior of the pollutant such as solubility and volatility [11]. In any process optimization for biodegradation, it is always necessary to investigate the effects of the environmental conditions and optimize the process in relationship to all the relevant environmental conditions. Tekere et al. [13], established the optimum growth conditions with respect to pH, aeration and nutrients in the growth and degradation of pollutants by white rot fungi and found that optimized conditions result in high enzyme and degradation activities.

Temperature

There is always a temperature range at which microorganisms grow and survive (i.e., minimum, optimum and maximum survival temperature). In addition, there is always a temperature optimum at which biochemical processes take place to achieve required bio treatment by each microorganism [13]. Extremes of temperature (too low or too high) affect both microbial growth and microbial enzyme catalyzed reactions [2]. With an increase in temperature within appropriate range, microbial metabolism increases and thus the rate of the bioremediation processes. Increased temperatures lead to higher solubility of many chemicals, and increased fluidity and diffusion rates. For example with pollutants, such as PAHs and heavy metals, their solubility and in turn bioavailability increases with temperature [2, 7]. Temperature is thus a critical factor in the optimum operating efficiency of bioreactors to achieve best biotreatment results. Often specialized bioreactors are designed with provision for temperature control.

pH

Similar to temperature, pH affects microbial growth and metabolic processes. pH influences microbial cell ionic properties thus microbial growth. Microorganisms have minimum, optimum and maximum pH of growth with most bacteria for example growing optimally at pH 6–7.5, though there are some which thrive best at acidic pHs (acidophiles) or at alkaline pH (alkaliphiles). Fungi generally grow at pHs lower than that of bacteria. Reactor operating pH has to be set to provide the best pH conditions for growth and enzyme activities. Behavior of pollutants is also influenced by pH thus affecting their bioremediation. For example with metals, pH affects the redox and solubility of metals, different forms and valence have different effects on microorganisms [14]. Metal solubility increases with a decrease in medium pH and alkaline pH favor metal ion precipitation. Often lower pH values are required for metal attachment to the microbial cell surface [7, 14]. Microorganisms that produce acids result in increased solubility of the metal ions [10]. To provide for best pH conditions, buffers are used in media formulations, acids and bases can be added during the bioreactor process [13].

Nutrients

Nutrients are required for growth and metabolism of the microorganisms. Several elements are required in biosynthesis and energy production. Carbon is the most basic element of living forms and is needed in greater quantities than other elements. Other elements that are important in ensuring a balanced nutritional bioreactor environment depending on the type of microorganism include hydrogen, oxygen, nitrogen, sulfur, phosphorus, iron, calcium and magnesium [10, 11]. All necessary macro- and micro-nutrients requirements are provided in reactor media. Microorganisms can use the pollutants they are degrading as primary energy sources or a primary source of energy is provided to the microorganism in the case of co metabolism of the pollutants.

Moisture

Water is required to support microbial growth and catalysis. Cellular chemical reactions occur in aqueous conditions and water is required to ensure the correct osmotic pressure is maintained for microbial growth. The amount of water available for microbial growth is called (aW). Most microorganisms grow at water activities of 0.98 or higher, osmotolerant species can however grow at a range of low aW [11].

Electron Acceptors

The presence of electron acceptors, e.g., oxygen in aerobic microbes and NO_3^{1-}, SO_4^{2-} and Fe (III) oxides in case of anaerobic microbes, also affects the biodegradation processes.

Reactor Design Related Factors

Bioreactors have to provide for the best conditions for microbial growth and biochemical process to occur. The reactor size, configuration and mode of operation are key reactor design factors. The reactor should provide favorable physical, biological and the combined physical-chemical conditions for the best biological remediation processes to be achieved. In designing the bioreactor, favorable physical conditions for transport of gases and liquids and solids over time that ensure that the physical entity of the bioreactor is favorably adapted to the biological system that performs the bioreactions are required [12, 15]. On the other hand there is need to ensure that the biophysical and biochemical events taking operate at optimum levels under real situation application.

Polluted samples for remediation can be fed into the reactor either as dry or slurry matter [9]. Pollutants with hydrophobic properties are often unavailable for microbial degradation, particularly if they are bound to soil matrix [7]. Their degradation is therefore limited by their transfer to liquid [4]. Minimizing mass transfer resistance was found to be a key factor in the degradation of hexachlorocyclohexane (HCH) in slurry batch bioreactors [4].

Despite the rapid development of bioreactors due to their widespread use in biotechnology, the aspects of maintaining stability and rates of bioprocesses are still areas to be addressed. Poor bioreactor construction and design, leading to inadequate mixing, may jeopardize the stability and performance of the process [15]. Mixing prevents thermal stratification, help maintain uniform conditions in the reactor, ensure good contact between microbial culture and media reactants. The importance of mixing in bioreactor cannot be over emphasized, poor mixing affect microbial process efficiency.

Hydraulic retention times (HRT) required to achieve the necessary remediation goals in the bioreactor have to be determined and optimized. Longer HRTs result in poor substrate loading which diminishes the microbial population, whereas shorter ones do not allow microorganisms to effectively degrade the pollutant and can result in microbial wash out from the system [16].

Organism Related Factors

Organism related factors include population density, composition, inter and intraspecific interaction. Microbes are the most diverse forms of life and have developed a wide range of metabolic pathways that enable them to cope under the varying ecological conditions including exposure to xenobiotics. A whole range of environments ranging from aerobic, anaerobic, acidic, alkaline, and low to high temperature have been utilized as sources of microorganisms for bioremediation [13]. Only certain species of bacteria and fungi have proven their ability as potent pollutant degraders [13]. In the natural environment degradation of pollutants is often achieved through complex microbial population interactions. Single or mixed microbial cultures are used for pollutant remediation in bioreactors. In the event where bioagumentation is applied the introduced organisms need to be able to co-exist with indigenous residents.

Different microorganisms often have different metabolic capabilities, to this extend the evaluation of several strains of different microbial players have to be investigated in order to come up with the best degraders [13]. In screening and comparison of the bio-degradation of PAHs by white rot fungi [17], found out that newly screened white rot fungi strains had higher or comparable degradation capacity to the model well applauded *P. chrysosporium*, and these strains did not accumulate the metabolite quinone which accumulates as a dead end metabolite in *P. chrysosporium.*

Polluted environments provide sources of microorganisms resistant or acclimatized to the pollutant [18]. However microorganisms that are known to have certain inherent physiological characteristic, e.g., metabolism of known substrate with structural similarity to xenobiotics of interest and/or adaptation to certain environmental conditions can be selected. This is the case in several studies that used microorganisms for pollutant degradation [11, 17, 18, 19].

Pollutant Related Factors

Factors that affect bioremediation in bioreactors that are related to the pollutant include: nature of pollutant, i.e., the physical and chemical properties including solubility, volatility, molecular complexity, concentration and toxicity. Investigations for most pollutant biodegradation have centered on how different concentrations, mixed pollutants, solubility and molecular structure can affect microbial bioremediation [17, 20]. In the case of PAHs, degradation decreases in the order alkane> branched chain alkanes>low molecular weight aromatics> cycloalkanes [17]. It should be noted however that some pollutants are resistant to biodegradation (recalcitrant, i.e., resistant to degradation) they are degraded at very low pace even if the right microbial population and conditions are present.

MICROBIAL BIOREACTORS IN BIOREMEDIATION

Several laboratory, and pilot bioremediation studies have been done using microbial (fungi and bacteria) bioreactors [6, 8, 17, 18, 20]. Bioreactor technologies may offer effective means for treatment of many contaminants in groundwater, soil and air [4, 5, 7, 12]. The bioreactor type of choice for any application should be easy to operate and maintain for the selected purpose and application. Table 1 presents some of the studies that involved the use of bioreactors in bioremediation. Flexibility to design bioreactor tailor made for different processes and remediation applications makes the use of bioreactors in bioremediation attractive [9]. The design should accommodate high biomass from cell growth, supply of necessary nutrients and also removal of waste components from the system. A description of some bioreactor types and their application.

Slurry Phase Bioreactors

Slurry phase bioreactors, as the name implies treats polluted media that is within a slurry phase. Alternative names are bio-slurry reactors and slurry phase biological treatment. Slurry bioreactors offer an *ex situ* environmentally friendly way for remediating mostly soils and sediments from petrochemical hydrocarbons, tars, creosotes, chlorinated solvents, herbicides, pesticides and explosives or when a solid substrate that is formulated into a slurry is used [4, 6, 25, 26]. Hydrophobic nature of most persistent chemicals makes them sorb to soil or sediments and not easily accessible for biodegradation.

Operation of the slurry reactor can be in batch, semi-continuous and continuous mode, with the batch process being the most common one [6, 26]. Figure 1 shows an illustration of a simplified slurry reactor. Water is mixed with the contaminated solid matrix in suitable ratios and this enhances contact between microorganisms, pollutant, media and oxygen. Pollutants that are solubilized become more bioavailable. Table 2 shows some of the studies that have involved the use of slurry phase bioreactors in bioremediation.

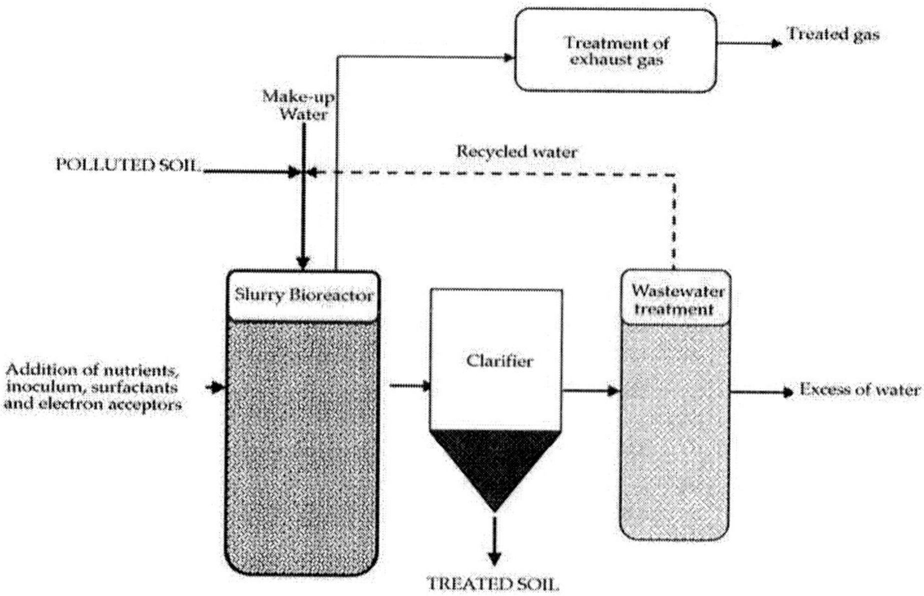

Figure 1. Simplified slurry reactor [26].

Table 1. Studies that involved the use of bioreactors in bioremediation

Bioreactor type	**Application details**	**Reference(s)**
Packed bed	Different fungi and bacteria used for remediation of organochlorine pesticides, PAHs, pharmaceuticals, amines, and textile dyes. Packing material varied from organic material (sawdust, wood chips) to inert solid materials (polyurethane foam, poraver stones); chlorinated aliphatic compounds	[14, 17, 21, 22, 23]
Fluidised bed	Treatment of pharmaceuticals using fungi	[20, 22]
Two-phase partitioning	Benzene biodegradation by cow dung microflora	[24]
Slurry phase	Bacterial and fungal remediation of soil from VOC, organochlorines, PAHs, 2,4-dichlorophenoxyacetic acid	[4, 6, 25, 26]
Suspended carrier	Fungi used for remediation of organochlorine pesticides, PAHs, textile dyes.	[21]

Up-flow anaerobic stage reactor (UASR)	Bacterial degradation of tylosin	[16]
Membrane bioreactor	Textile dye in waste water; pharmaceuticals, 1,2-dichloroethane, 1,2-dichlorobenzene and 2-chlorophenol groundwater; metal recovery	[27, 28, 29, 30, 31]
Air lift	Textile dye effluent decolorization by fungi, olive mill effluent, cellulose industry bleaching effluent	[15, 32, 33]
Biotrickling filter	Municipal waste water, brewery waste, olive oil mill waste water, VOC contaminated air	[32, 34]
Upflow Anaerobic Sludge Blanket	Potato waste water, BTEX	[9, 35]
Sequence batch reactor	Nanosilver, Nanofullerenes	[36]
Continuous flow Bioreactor	PCP and creosote by some Pseudomonas species	[37]
Nonisothermal bioreactors	Degradation of phenol by fungal laccase	[38]
Continuously stirred tank bioreactor (CSTR)	For hydrocarbon-rich industrial wastewater effluents by mixed microbial cultures, petroleum hydrocarbon	[7, 8]

Table 2. Some examples of remediation studies in slurry phase bioreactor

Pollutant	**Microorganism(s)**	**Bioremediation details**	**Reference(s)**
Petroleum hydrocarbons in oil sludge	Indigenous microbial consortium	24% biodegradation of Total Petroleum Hydrocarbon in oily waste	[39]
2,4,6-trinitrotoluene (TNT)	Mixed soil bacteria under anoxic/microaerophilic conditions	99% of 10,000 mg kg^{-1} was degraded in 82 days under co-metabolism with molasses	[40]
PAHs in creosote	Degradation by *Pseudomonas fluorescens, Pseudomonas stutzeri,* and an *Alcaligenes* species	93.4% of creosote degraded in 12 weeks	[41]
Explosives 2,4,6-trinitrotoluene (TNT) and 2,4,6-trinitrobenzene (TNB)	Selected Gram positive bacterial isolates	Complete removal of the explosive after 80 days	[42]

Hexachlorocyclohexane (HCH)	White rot fungi *Bjerkandera adusta*	Maximal degradations of 94.5, 78.5 and 66.1% were attained after 30 days for the-HCH isomers, respectively	[4]
High molecular weight PAH in soil	PAH-degrading consortium	Pyrene degraded at 19 mg L^{-1} day^{-1}, chrysene and benzo[*a*]pyrene respectively at 3.5 and 0.94 mg L^{-1} day^{-1}.	[43]
Chlorpyrifos	Enriched indigenous soil microorganism	Degradation of 48% in aerobic and 31% in anaerobic soil slurries	[44]

Partitioning Bioreactors

Partitioning bioreactors are used in bioremediation when two phases need to be achieved, e.g., such as for organic solvents or water immiscible compounds in aqueous solutions. Reactors are designed with the aqueous and organic phase, and can be single or multiphased [24]. With toxic hazardous waste, toxicity to degrading microorganisms is a problem. In partitioning bioreactors, there is a two-phase system where a water immiscible and biocompatible organic solvent is allowed to float on the surface of a cell containing aqueous phase [45].

This means that high amounts of hazardous waste dissolved in a solvent can be added to the reactor without the microorganism experiencing inhibitory concentrations of the pollutant [24, 45, 46]. A rigorous process involving selection of the solvent, taking into consideration the biological, physical, operational, environmental and economic factors is necessary in developing an efficient partitioning biotreatment system. Partitioning reactors find application in the remediation of toxic compounds from petrochemical industry such as benzene as well as VOC in waste gases of many industrial processes [45, 47, 48]. Angelucci et al. [49], successfully tested a continuous two-phase-partitioning reactor in the treatment of tannery wastewater. Several other studies involving phase partitioning bioreactors are described [24, 45, 46, 47, 48, 49, 50].

Stirred Tank Bioreactors

A continuous stirred tank bioreactor consists of a cylindrical vessel with motor driven central shaft that supports one or more agitators (impellers). Stirred tank bioreactors are the predominantly used design for submerged cultures. Stirred tank bioreactors are mechanically agitated where the stirrers are the main gas-dispersing tools and provide high values of mass transfer rates coupled with excellent mixing. Advantages of the STR include the efficient gas transfer to growing cells, good mixing of the contents and flexible operating conditions, besides the commercial availability of the bioreactors. The main shortcoming of the stirred tank bioreactor is its mechanical agitation which requires energy and stirring can cause shear strain on microbial cells.

Gargouri et al. [7] evaluated the use of a continuously stirred tank bioreactor (CSTR) in the treatment of hydrocarbon-rich industrial wastewaters and achieved successful bioremediation using an acclimatized microbial consortium. The residual total petroleum hydrocarbon (TPH) decreased from 320 $^{-8}$ mg TPH l^{-1}. The reactor used is shown in Figure 2. Bi [51], applied a continuously stirred tank reactor for bioremediation of ethanol, toluene and benzyl alcohol by *P. putida*.

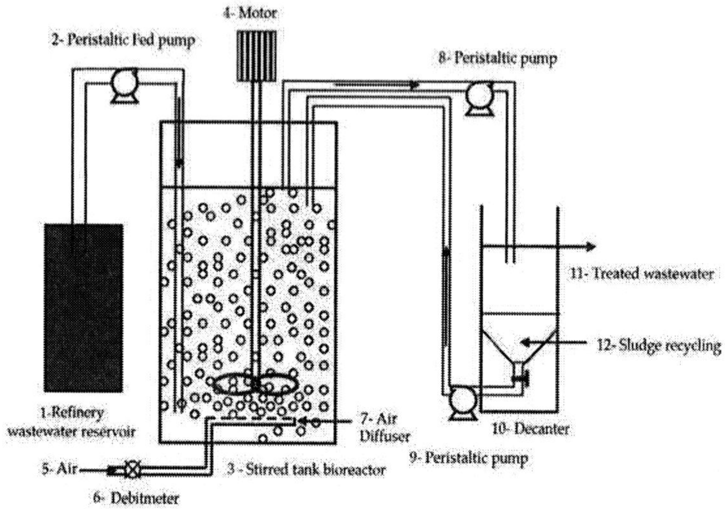

Figure 2. Schematic diagram of the aerobic continuously stirred tank bioreactor (CSTR) used for continuous experiments [7].

Biofilters

A basic biofilter bioreactor consist of a large media bed where pollutants are passed through and get degraded by the microorganisms. Biofilters are amongst the oldest environmental bioremediation techniques. Biofilters are used mostly in waste water treatment as well as in the control of air pollution [34, 52, 53]. A number of materials are used for bed media such as peat, composted yard waste, bark, coarse soil, gravel or plastic shapes. A typical example of a biofilter is the trickling filter which finds extensive application in the treatment of different liquid effluents or waste waters or waste that is constituted into liquid. A trickling filter is usually a round, vertical tank that contains a support rack and is filled with aggregate, ceramic or plastic media and in the middle of the tank is a vertical pipe that has a rotary connection with spray nozzles on the top end [34]. A spray arm is attached to the rotary connection and has spray nozzles installed along its length for distribution of the waste water. Microorganisms grow in biofilm forms on the packing material surface and are responsible for the degradation of the pollutants from the effluent. Schmidt and Anderson [34] described the use of a trickling biofilter in the removal of high concentrations of 1-butanol from contaminated air. The potential application of the biotrickling filter in industrial off gas treatment was evaluated in the removal of high concentrations of 1-butanol from contaminated air with efficiency exceeding 80% for butanol concentrations of 0.4–1.2 g m^{-3} [34]. The laboratory-scale perlite-packed biotrickling filter was operated for 60 days and demonstrated effective and efficient removal of butanol concentrations up to 4.65 g m^{-3} with a maximum elimination capacity of 100 g m^{-3} h^{-1} [34].

Packed Bed Bioreactors

Packed bed bioreactor systems provide for microbial growth on fixed film substrata. In order to obtain compact reactors and ensure greater treatment reliability, fixed film reactors are used. They offer the advantage that dilute aqueous solutions can be remediated at high biomass without the need to separate biomass and the treated effluent [13, 54]. In packed bed biofilm biotreatment processes, unlike suspension cultures there is no need to incorporate special measures such as centrifugation and membrane filters to retain the biomass. This feature makes the use of packed bed reactors particularly appropriate in bioreactors systems where large substrate—flow through is required. The concentration of cells in a given volume may be increased, a factor that leads to enhanced efficiency/productivity of the bioreactor and decreased volume of bioreactors [55]. While high biomass concentrations can be easily maintained, the medium to biofilm mass transfer of substrate is the rate limiting process in packed bed bioreactors [54, 56]. Within the biofilm there are considerable differences in the microorganisms' microenvironment, depending on the distance from the surface of the biofilm [54]. Substrates such as oxygen, carbon and nitrogen sources have to cross the biofilm—liquid interface by diffusion, thus a diffusion gradient occurs. To calculate the kinetics of conversion in the biofilm processes, two important processes that occur in the system are considered and these are (i) transport of solutes over the biofilm and (ii) combined reactions and diffusion inside the biofilm [54]. In the packed bed reactors, development of excess microbial biomass also occurs leading to hydraulic channeling or loss of interstitial fluid volume. To overcome the severe constraints of hydraulic hold up within the interior of the reactor extra-capillary space transverse flow bioreactors were developed [57].

Selection of suitable substances as packing materials is an important consideration. Materials that have been used include nylon web, polyurethane foam, silicone tubing, sintered glass, porous ceramics, propylene, stainless steel, agarose and agar gel beads [58, 59, 60, 61, 62, 63, 64, 65, 66, 67]. The ideal support should be chemically inert in physiological growth medium, rigid and porous to facilitate mycelial attachment and re-usable after removal of the fungus. Figure 4 shows a Simplified diagram of a laboratory based packed bed bioreactor. Examples of remediation studies in packed bed reactors are given in Table 3.

Table 3. Some examples of remediation studies in packed bed reactors

Support	Experimental study details	References
Polyurethane foam	Anaerobic fixed film horizontal flow bench scale reactor. Benzene, toluene, ethylbenzene, and xylene, BTEX removal with efficiency of 75–99% in 11.4 hrs	[58]
Laterite stones	Microbial consortium anaerobic degradation of textile azo dyes, 61.7% degradation of 55 μg mL^{-1} of simulated effluent dye.	[59]

Coconut shell bio-char	Congo red dye degradation in batch and continuous packed bed bioreactors by *Brevibacillus parabrevis*. A 95.71% removal of in 6 days of 150 ppm dye.	[60]
Polyurethane foam	Bacterial degradation of malathion in batch and continuous packed bed bioreactors, removal at 89% for up to 145.4 mg L^{-1} day^{-1}	[61]
Wire Mesh	Fungal degradation of textile effluent	[62]
Wood chips	Chlorophenol degradation by *Phanerochaete chrysosporium*	[63]
Sugarcane bagasse	Degradation of dyes and industrial effluents by *Garnoderma weberianum* B-18 immobilized in a lab-scale packed-bed bioreactor. 55–98% for different dyes tested	[64]
Celite	Perchlorate-Contaminated groundwater 800 µg L^{-1} reduced to less than 4 μ^{-1} at 0.3 h retention time	[66]
Polyurethane foam	Biodegradation of an actual petroleum wastewater by an immobilized biomass of *Bacillus cereus*	[66]
Polyurethane foam and alginate beads	Benzene biodegradation Bacillus sp. M3 at 84 in alginate beads and 90% on polyurethane foam within 9 days	[67]

Airlift Bioreactors

Airlift bioreactors can provide an attractive treatment alternative for treatment of gaseous or volatile air pollutants. Frequently, the most limiting factor in the performance of these reactors is that they are susceptible to being limited by gas-liquid mass transfer and by poor mixing of the liquid phase, particularly when they are operating at high cell densities [68, 69]. The bioreactor performance is dependent on the pumping (injection) of air and the liquid circulation. The airlift bioreactor can have a forced flow in an internal or external loop as shown in Figure 5. Specific volatile organic chemicals may be completely degraded by a microorganism at normal temperature and pressure without producing a second polluted byproduct [70]. Nikakhtari and Hill [68], applied and External Loop Airlift Bioreactor with a small amount (99% porosity) of a stainless steel mesh packing inserted in the riser section for bioremediation of a phenol polluted air stream. Phenol removal of 100% was achieved using the bacterium *Pseudomonas putida*, and at a phenol loading rate of 22,160 mg h^{-1} m^{-3}, thus demonstrating the novelty and potential VOCs bioremediation application of the reactor at high loading rates. Figure 5 presents a schematic diagram of airlift bioreactor. Several other studies involving the use of airlift bioreactors [19, 69, 70, 71].

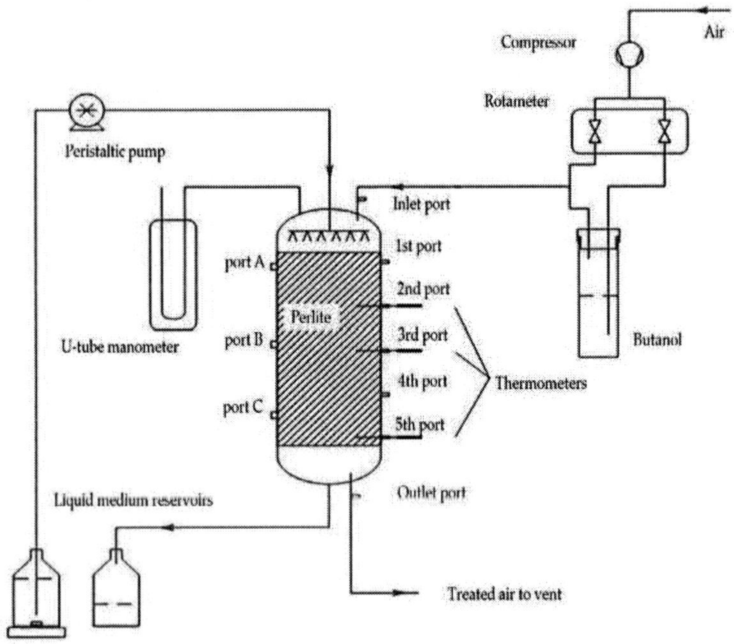

Figure 3. Schematic diagram of biotrickling filter [34].

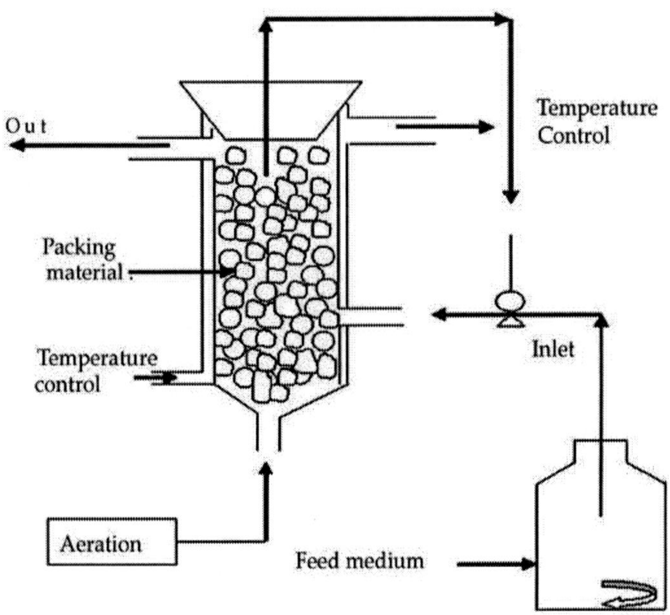

Figure 4. Simplified diagram of a laboratory based packed bed bioreactor [21].

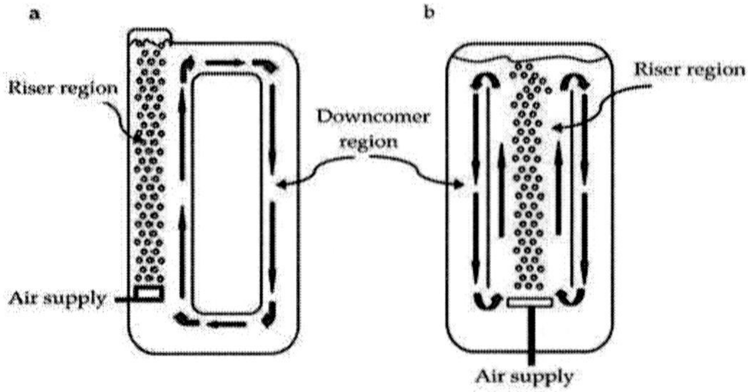

Figure 5. Schematic diagram of airlift bioreactor with (a) external recirculation and (b) internal recirculation [15].

Membrane Bioreactor

Membrane bioreactors (MBR) combine the use of a membrane that forms a filtration system and the biological process. The membrane provides a physical barrier that separates the liquid from the solid and ensures retention of the solids and good quality effluent. The quality of the treated effluent from the membrane bioreactor is of high quality than that achieved by employing other techniques, enabling optimal functioning of the secondary treatment system [72, 73]. MBR offer the advantages that often smaller tank size is used and filtration function of the membrane ensures that solids are separated from treated effluent. Membrane fouling has been recognized however as a major drawback in the application of membrane bioreactors in bioremediation. Also membranes are often expensive thus making the process costly. Development of low cost membrane filters is an ongoing feature in the science of MBR [72]. MBR reactors have been used in the biological treatment of domestic and industrial waste water. MBR have been evaluated in the remediation of pentachlorophenol in concentration ranges that occur in waste water [73], textile waste water [27], 1,2-dichloroethane, 1,2-dichlorobenzene and 2-chlorophenol [30].

Other Bioreactors in Bioremediation

Due to flexibility in bioreactor designs, the configuration of reactors is numerous. While an effort has been made here to describe some of the common bioreactors used for different bioremediation applications, several other bioreactor types have not been discussed. These include the UASB which find major application in anaerobic digestion of waste waters as well as solid wastes, bio-scrubbers which are applied in off gas air pollution control, continuous stirred tank reactors as well as rotating contactor reactors.

CONCLUSIONS

It is evident that a wide range of microbial bioreactors have been developed and evaluated in the bioremediation of a wide range of pollutants in water, air and soil. Also a wide range of pollutants in physical and chemical properties are amenable to microbial degradation. Very diverse microbial species have the capability of pollutant degradation naturally and the use of well-developed optimized microbial bioreactors ensure improved rates of degradation when compared to degradation that happens *in situ* in the environment under natural environmental conditions.

REFERENCES

1. Kumar A, Bisht BS, Joshi VD, Dhewa T. Review on bioremediation of polluted environment: A management tool. International Journal of Environmental Sciences. 2011;1(6):1079
2. Sharma S. Bioremediation: Features, strategies and applications. Asian Journal of Pharmacy and Life Science. 2012;2231:4423
3. Jeon CO, Madsen EL. In situ microbial metabolism of aromatic-hydrocarbon environmental pollutants. Current Opinion in Biotechnology. 2013;24(3):474-481
4. Quintero JC, Lu-Chau TA, Moreira MT, Feijoo G, Lema JM. Bioremediation of HCH present in soil by the white-rot fungus Bjerkandera adusta in a slurry batch bioreactor. International Biodeterioration & Biodegradation. 2007;60(4):319-326
5. U.S. Environmental Protection Agency. Using bioreactors to control air pollution—U.S. Environmental Protection Agency, EPA-456/R-03-003. 2003. Available from: http://www.epa.gov/ttn/catc [Accessed: Nov 23, 2018]
6. Pino-Herrera DO, Pechaud Y, Huguenot D, Esposito G, Van Hullebusch ED, Oturan MA. Removal mechanisms in aerobic slurry bioreactors for remediation of soils and sediments polluted with hydrophobic organic compounds: An overview. Journal of Hazardous Materials. 2017;339:427-449
7. Gargouri B, Karray F, Mhiri N, Aloui F, Sayadi S. Application of a continuously stirred tank bioreactor (CSTR) for bioremediation of hydrocarbon-rich industrial wastewater effluents. Journal of Hazardous Materials. 2011;189(1-2):427-434
8. Chikere CB, Chikere BO, Okpokwasili GC. Bioreactor-based bioremediation of hydrocarbon-polluted Niger Delta marine sediment, Nigeria. 3 Biotech. 2012;2(1):53-66
9. Azubuike CC, Chikere CB, Okpokwasili GC. Bioremediation techniques–classification based on site of application: Principles, advantages, limitations and prospects. World Journal of Microbiology and Biotechnology. 2016;32(11):180
10. Srivastava J, Naraian R, Kalra SJ, Chandra H. Advances in microbial bioremediation and the factors influencing the process. International Journal of Environmental Science and Technology. 2014;11(6):1787-1800
11. Naik MG, Duraphe MD. Review paper on-parameters affecting bioremediation. International Journal of Life Science and Pharma Research. 2012;2(3):L77-L80
12. Mandenius CF. Bioreactors: Design, Operation and Novel Applications. Germany: John Wiley & Sons; 2016
13. Tekere M, Mswaka AY, Zvauya R, Read JS. Growth, dye degradation and ligninolytic activity studies on Zimbabwean white rot fungi. Enzyme and Microbial Technology. 2001;28(4-5):420-426
14. Liu SH, Zeng GM, Niu QY, Liu Y, Zhou L, Jiang LH, et al. Bioremediation mechanisms of combined pollution of PAHs and heavy metals by bacteria and fungi: A mini review. Bioresource Technology. 2017;224:25-33
15. Mahmood KA, Wilkinson SJ, Zimmerman WB. Airlift bioreactor for biological applications with microbubble mediated transport processes. Chemical Engineering Science. 2015;137:243-253
16. Chelliapan S, Wilby T, Yuzir A, Sallis PJ. Influence of organic loading on the performance and microbial community structure of an anaerobic stage reactor treating pharmaceutical wastewater. Desalination. 2011;271(1-3):257-264
17. Tekere M, Read JS, Mattiasson B. Polycyclic aromatic hydrocarbon biodegradation in extracellular fluids and static batch cultures of selected sub-tropical white rot fungi. Journal of Biotechnology. 2005;115(4):367-377

18. Lladó S, Gràcia E, Solanas AM, Viñas M. Fungal and bacterial microbial community assessment during bioremediation assays in an aged creosote-polluted soil. Soil Biology and Biochemistry. 2013;67:114-123

19. Ryan DR, Leukes WD, Burton SG. Fungal bioremediation of phenolic wastewaters in an airlift reactor. Biotechnology Progress. 2005;21(4):1068-1074

20. Gros M, Cruz-Morato C, Marco-Urrea E, Longrée P, Singer H, Sarrà M, et al. Biodegradation of the X-ray contrast agent iopromide and the fluoroquinolone antibiotic ofloxacin by the white rot fungus Trametes versicolor in hospital wastewaters and identification of degradation products. Water Research. 2014;60:228-241

21. Tekere M, Read JS, Mattiasson B. Polycyclic aromatic hydrocarbon biodegradation by a subtropical white rot fungus in packed bed and suspended carrier bioreactor systems. Environmental technology. 2007;28(6):683-691

22. Svobodová K, Petráčková D, Kozická B, Halada P, Novotný Č. Mutual interactions of Pleurotus ostreatus with bacteria of activated sludge in solid-bed bioreactors. World Journal of Microbiology and Biotechnology. 2016;32(6):94

23. Juarez-Ramirez C, Galíndez-Mayer J, Ruiz-Ordaz N, Ramos-Monroy O, Santoyo-Tepole F, Poggi-Varaldo H. Steady-state inhibition model for the biodegradation of sulfonated amines in a packed bed reactor. New Biotechnology. 2015;32(3):379-386

24. Singh D, Fulekar MH. Benzene bioremediation using cow dung microflora in two phase partitioning bioreactor. Journal of Hazardous Materials. 2010;175(1-3):336-343

25. Plangklang P, Reungsang A. Bioaugmentation of carbofuran by Burkholderia cepacia PCL3 in a bioslurry phase sequencing batch reactor. Process Biochemistry. 2010;45(2):230-238

26. Robles-González IV, Fava F, Poggi-Varaldo HM. A review on slurry bioreactors for bioremediation of soils and sediments. Microbial Cell Factories. 2008;7(1):5

27. Hossain K, Ismail N. Bioremediation and detoxification of pulp and paper mill effluent: A review. Research Journal of Environmental Toxicology. 2015;9(3):113

28. Couto CF, Lange LC, Amaral MC. A critical review on membrane separation processes applied to remove pharmaceutically active compounds from water and wastewater. Journal of Water Process Engineering. 2018;26:156-175

29. Jegatheesan V, Pramanik BK, Chen J, Navaratna D, Chang CY, Shu L. Treatment of textile wastewater with membrane bioreactor: A critical review. Bioresource Technology. 2016;204:202-212

30. Carucci A, Manconi I, Manigas L. Use of membrane bioreactors for the bioremediation of chlorinated compounds polluted groundwater. Water Science and Technology. 2007;55(10):209-216

31. Mack C, Burgess JE, Duncan JR. Membrane bioreactors for metal recovery from wastewater: A review. Water SA. 2004;30(4):521-532

32. Olivieri G, Russo ME, Giardina P, Marzocchella A, Sannia G, Salatino P. Strategies for dephenolization of raw olive mill wastewater by means of Pleurotus ostreatus. Journal of Industrial Microbiology & Biotechnology. 2012;39(5):719-729

33. Souza ÉS, Souza JV, Silva FT, Paiva TC. Treatment of an ECF bleaching effluent with white-rot fungi in an air-lift bioreactor. Environmental Earth Sciences. 2014;72(4):1289-1294

34. Schmidt T, Anderson WA.Biotrickling filtration of air contaminated with 1-butanol. Environments. 2017;4(3):57

35. Manhokwe S, Parawira W, Tekere M. An evaluation of a mesophilic reactor for treating wastewater from a Zimbabwean potato-processing plant. African Journal of Environmental Science and Technology. 2009;3(4):091-096

36. Yang Y, Wang Y, Hristovski K, Westerhoff P. Simultaneous removal of nanosilver and fullerene in sequencing batch reactors for biological wastewater treatment. Chemosphere. 2015;125:115-121

37. Mueller JG, Lantz SE, Ross D, Colvin RJ, Middaugh DP, Pritchard PH. Strategy using bioreactors and specially selected microorganisms for bioremediation of groundwater contaminated with creosote and pentachlorophenol. Environmental Science & Technology. 1993;27(4):691-698

38. Georgieva S, Godjevargova T, Portaccio M, Lepore M, Mita DG. Advantages in using non-isothermal bioreactors in bioremediation of water polluted by phenol by means of immobilized laccase from Rhus vernicifera. Journal of Molecular Catalysis B: Enzymatic. 2008;55(3-4):177-184

39. Machin-Ramirez C, Okoh AI, Morales D, Mayolo-Deloisa K, Quintero R, Trejo-Hernández MR. Slurry-phase biodegradation of weathered oily sludge waste. Chemosphere. 2008;70(4):737-744

40. Clark B, Boopathy R. Evaluation of bioremediation methods for the treatment of soil contaminated with explosives in Louisiana Army Ammunition Plant, Minden, Louisiana. Journal of Hazardous Materials. 2007;143(3):643-648

41. Lewis RF. Site demonstration of slurry-phase biodegradation of PAH contaminated soil. Air & Waste. 1993;43(4):503-508

42. Fuller ME, Manning JF Jr. Microbiological changes during bioremediation of explosives-contaminated soils in laboratory and pilot-scale bioslurry reactors. Bioresource Technology. 2004;91(2):123-133

43. Villemur R, Deziel E, Benachenhou A, Marcoux J, Gauthier E, Lépine F, et al. Two-liquid-phase slurry bioreactors to enhance the degradation of high-molecular-weight polycyclic aromatic hydrocarbons in soil. Biotechnology Progress. 2000;16(6):966-972

44. Tiwari MK, Guha S. Kinetics of biotransformation of chlorpyrifos in aqueous and soil slurry environments. Water Research. 2014;51:73-85

45. Daugulis AJ. Two-phase partitioning bioreactors: A new technology platform for destroying xenobiotics. Trends in Biotechnology. 2001;19(11):457-462

46. Davidson CT, Daugulis AJ. Addressing biofilter limitations: A two-phase partitioning bioreactor process for the treatment of benzene and toluene contaminated gas streams. Biodegradation. 2003;14(6):415-421

47. Dorado AD, Dumont E, Muñoz R, Quijano G. A novel mathematical approach for the understanding and optimization of two-phase partitioning bioreactors devoted to air pollution control. Chemical Engineering Journal. 2015;263:239-248

48. Muñoz R, Daugulis AJ, Hernández M, Quijano G. Recent advances in two-phase partitioning bioreactors for the treatment of volatile organic compounds. Biotechnology Advances. 2012;30(6):1707-1720

49. Angelucci DM, Stazi V, Daugulis AJ, Tomei MC. Treatment of synthetic tannery wastewater in a continuous two-phase partitioning bioreactor: Biodegradation of the organic fraction and chromium separation. Journal of Cleaner Production. 2017;152:321-329

50. Tomei MC, Angelucci DM, Daugulis AJ. Towards a continuous two-phase partitioning bioreactor for xenobiotic removal. Journal of Hazardous Materials. 2016;317:403-415

51. Bi Y. Bioremediation of volatile organic compounds in a continuous stirred tank bioreactor (doctoral dissertation). Saskatoon: University of Saskatchewan; 2005

52. Lebrero R, Gondim AC, Pérez R, García-Encina PA, Muñoz R. Comparative assessment of a biofilter, a biotrickling filter and a hollow fiber membrane bioreactor for odor treatment in wastewater treatment plants. Water Research. 2014;49:339-350

53. Rabbani KA, Charles W, Kayaalp A, Cord-Ruwisch R, Ho G. Pilot-scale biofilter for the simultaneous removal of hydrogen sulphide and ammonia at a wastewater treatment plant. Biochemical Engineering Journal. 2016;107:1-10

54. Van Loosdrecht MC, Heijnen SJ. Biofilm bioreactors for waste-water treatment. Trends in Biotechnology. 1993;11(4):117-121

55. Bisping B, Rehm HJ. Multistep reactions with immobilized microorganisms. Biotechnology and Applied Biochemistry. 1988;10(2):87-98

56. Guieysse B, Bernhoft I, Andersson BE, Henrysson T, Olsson S, Mattiasson B. Degradation of acenaphthene, phenanthrene and pyrene in a packed-bed biofilm reactor. Applied Microbiology and Biotechnology. 2000;54(6):826-831

57. Burton SG, Boshoff A, Edwards W, Jacobs EP, Lfukes WD, Rose PD, et al. Membrane Based Biotechnological System for the Treatment of Organic Pollutants. South Africa: Water Research Commission; 1998

58. de Nardi IR, Ribeiro R, Zaiat M, Foresti E. Anaerobic packed-bed reactor for bioremediation of gasoline-contaminated aquifers. Process Biochemistry. 2005;40(2):587-592

59. Senan RC, Shaffiqu TS, Roy JJ, Abraham TE. Aerobic degradation of a mixture of Azo dyes in a packed bed reactor having bacteria-coated laterite pebbles. Biotechnology Progress. 2003;19(2):647-651

60. Talha MA, Goswami M, Giri BS, Sharma A, Rai BN, Singh RS. Bioremediation of Congo red dye in immobilized batch and continuous packed bed bioreactor by Brevibacillus parabrevis using coconut shell bio-char. Bioresource Technology. 2018;252:37-43

61. Geed SR, Kureel MK, Giri BS, Singh RS, Rai BN. Performance evaluation of malathion biodegradation in batch and continuous packed bed bioreactor (PBBR). Bioresource Technology. 2017;227:56-65

62. Kapdan IK, Kargi F, McMullan G, Marchant R. Biological decolorization of textile dyestuff by Coriolus versicolor in a packed column reactor. Environmental Technology. 2000;21(2):231-236

63. Yum KJ, Peirce JJ. Biodegradation kinetics of chlorophenols in immobilized-cell reactors using a white-rot fungus on wood chips. Water Environment Research. 1998;70(2):205-213

64. Torres-Farradá G, Manzano AM, Ramos-Leal M, Domínguez O, Sánchez MI, Vangronsveld J, Guerra G. Biodegradation and detoxification of dyes and industrial effluents by Ganoderma weberianum B-18 immobilized in a lab-scale packed-bed bioreactor. Bioremediation Journal. 2018;22:1(1-2):20-27

65. Losi ME, Giblin T, Hosangadi V, Frankenberger WT Jr. Bioremediation of perchlorate-contaminated groundwater using a packed bed biological reactor. Bioremediation Journal. 2002;6(2):97-103

66. Banerjee A, Ghoshal AK. Biodegradation of an actual petroleum wastewater in a packed bed reactor by an immobilized biomass of Bacillus cereus. Journal of Environmental Chemical Engineering. 2017;5(2):1696-1702

67. Kureel MK, Geed SR, Giri BS, Rai BN, Singh RS. Biodegradation and kinetic study of benzene in bioreactor packed with PUF and alginate beads and immobilized with bacillus sp. M3. Bioresource Technology. 2017;242:92-100

68. Nikakhtari H, Hill GA. Hydrodynamic and oxygen mass transfer in an external loop airlift bioreactor with a packed bed. Biochemical Engineering Journal. 2005;27(2):138-145

69. Patel BP, Kumar A. Biodegradation of 4-chlorophenol in an airlift inner loop bioreactor with mixed consortium: Effect of HRT, loading rate and biogenic substrate. 3 Biotech. 2016;6(2):117

70. Bertollo FB, Lopes GC, Silva EL. Phenol biodegradation by Pseudomonas putida in an airlift reactor: Assessment of kinetic, hydrodynamic, and mass transfer parameters. Water, Air, & Soil Pollution. 2017;228(10):398

71. Azeez TO, Onukwuli OD, Araromi DO, Arinkoola AO, Salam KK, Iwuji SC, et al. Optimization of bioremediation of cheese whey with the activity of Klebsiella pneumonia using response surface methodology. International Journal for Science and Engineering Technologies with Latest Trends. 2013;11(1):10-21

72. Meng F, Chae SR, Drews A, Kraume M, Shin HS, Yang F. Recent advances in membrane bioreactors (MBRs): Membrane fouling and membrane material. Water Research. 2009;43(6):1489-1512

73. Visvanathan C, Thu LN, Jegatheesan V, Anotai J. Biodegradation of pentachlorophenol in a membrane bioreactor. Desalination. 2005;183(1-3):455-464

3

Contamination of Water Resources by Pathogenic Bacteria

Pramod K Pandey[1], Philip H Kass[1], Michelle L Soupir[2], Sagor Biswas[1] and Vijay P Singh[3]

[1]Department of Population Health and Reproduction, University of California, Davis, California, USA

[2]Department of Agricultural and Biosystems Engineering, Iowa State University, Ames, Iowa, USA

[3]Department of Biological and Agricultural Engineering & Zachry Department of Civil Engineering, Texas A & M University, College Station, Texas, USA

ABSTRACT

Water-borne pathogen contamination in water resources and related diseases are a major water quality concern throughout the world. Increasing interest in controlling water-borne pathogens in water resources evidenced by a large number of recent publications clearly attests to the need for studies that synthesize knowledge from multiple fields covering comparative aspects of pathogen contamination, and unify them in a single place in order to present and address the problem as a whole. Providing a broader perceptive of pathogen contamination in freshwater (rivers, lakes, reservoirs, groundwater) and saline water (estuaries and coastal waters) resources, this review paper attempts to develop the first comprehensive single source of existing information on pathogen contamination in multiple types of water resources. In addition, a comprehensive discussion describes the challenges associated with using indicator organisms. Potential impacts of water resources development on pathogen contamination as well as challenges that lie ahead for addressing pathogen contamination are also discussed.

Keywords: *Pathogens, Contamination, Water resources, Watershed, Pathogens transport*

INTRODUCTION

Water-borne pathogen contamination in ambient water bodies and related diseases are a major water quality concern throughout the world. Pathogen contamination is a serious issue for almost all types of ambient water bodies, making its recognition and understanding essential (U.S. EPA [2012a]). The United Nations identified improving water quality as one of the eight Millennium Development Goals (MDGs). Its target is to reduce the number of people without access to safe water by 50% by 2015 (WHO [2011]). Because of the overwhelming scientific evidence for climate change (IPCC [2007]), it is also important to understand how perturbations in weather patterns can potentially impact pathogen levels in water resources. To meet future demands of water for food, energy, and ecosystems, increasing water storage structures (i.e., dams) must be a component of long-range planning (World Bank [2010]). However, such new structures can potentially degrade water quality and exacerbate public health risk.

While several review papers are currently available (Bradford et al. [2013]; Pachepsky and Shelton [2011]; Pang [2009]; Jin and Flury [2002]; John and Rose [2005]; Jamieson et al. [2004]; Jamieson et al. [2002]; Arnone and Walling [2007]; Kay et al. [2007]), there is a manifest need for additional transdisciplinary studies that assimilate knowledge gained from multi-research endeavors studying pathogen contamination, and provide a comprehensive synopsis in order to comprehend the entirety of the problem. Therefore, the goal of this review is to present a broad research scope assessment of pathogen contamination of water resources and the associated challenges it presents. We synthesize the potential health risks imposed by pathogens in water resources by providing existing knowledge that covers surface water, groundwater, fresh water, and saline water. Further, the impact of water resources development on pathogen contamination, future challenges, and recommendations are summarized. In addition, we provide a brief discussion describing water-borne pathogen footprints and potential challenges associated with the use of indicator organisms for assessing water quality.

Health Risk

Water-borne diseases (i.e., diarrhea, gastrointestinal illness) caused by various bacteria, viruses, and protozoa have been the causes of many outbreaks (Craun et al. [2006]). In developing countries, such as those in Africa, water-borne diseases infect millions (Fenwick [2006]). According to World Health Organization (WHO), each year 3.4 million people, mostly children, die from water-related diseases (WHO [2014]). According to United Nations Children's Fund (UNICEF) assessment, 4000 children die each day as a result of contaminated water (UNICEF [2014]). WHO ([2010]) reports that over 2.6 billion people lack access to clean water, which is responsible for about 2.2 million deaths annually, of which 1.4 million are in children. Improving water quality can reduce the global disease burden by approximately 4% (WHO [2010]).

Although water-associated diseases in developing countries are prevalent, they are also a serious challenge in developed countries. A study by Arnone and Walling ([2007]), who compiled data of outbreaks in the U.S. (1986 – 2000), reported 5,905 cases and 95 outbreaks associated with recreational water. Gastrointestinal Illness (GI) caused by variety of different microbes and germs, which causes symptoms, such as diarrhea, nausea, vomiting, fever, abdominal pain, was responsible for about 29.53% cases. More than 27% of cases were caused by *Shigella spp*. In addition, 10.99%, 10.08%, and 6.59% of the cases were caused by *Cryptosporidium parvum*, Adenovirus 3, and Leptospira, respectively. Nearly 23% and 21% of the outbreaks were caused by GI and *Shigella spp*, respectively. In addition, 16.84%, 12.63%, and 7.37% of the outbreaks were caused by *Naegleria fowleri*, *E. coli* 0157:H7, and *Schistosoma spp.*, respectively. Besides acute gastroenteritis, major etiological agents such as *Giarida*, *Cryptosporadium*, *E. coli* 0157:H7, *V. cholera*, and *Salmonella* were the agents responsible for many outbreaks (Craun et al. [2006]). During the same period 437,082 cases and 48 outbreaks were caused by contaminated drinking water, of which about 95.89% of the cases were caused by *Cryptosporidium parvum*. Nearly 42% and 31% of the outbreaks were caused by *Giardia lamblia* and GI, respectively. Reporting statistics on water-borne outbreaks in the U.S., Craun et al.

([2006]) found that at least 1870 outbreaks (23 per year) occurred between 1920 and 2002. These reported outbreaks and their reported incidence of illnesses are likely to be an underestimation of actual numbers because of nonreported cases and missing exposure information. To protect public health, the U.S. EPA's National Primary Drinking Water Regulations (NPDWRs) contain standards describing the Maximum Contaminant Level (MCL) – the highest level of a contaminate allowable in drinking water. The U.S. EPA has defined the MCL of various microorganisms, such as *Cryptosporidium*, *Giardia lamblia*, *Legionella*, and Total Coliforms (including fecal coliform and *E. coli*), and viruses (U.S. EPA [2012b]). The Maximum Contaminant Level Goal (MCLG) – the level of a contaminant in drinking water below which there is no known risk to public health, has also been proposed by the U.S. EPA. The MCLC levels for *Cryptosporidium*, *Giardia lamblia*, *Legionella*, and Total Coliforms are zero. The EPA requires 99% removal of *Cryptosporidium* in drinking water, and the removal percentages of *Giardia lamblia* and viruses are 99.9 and 99.99%, respectively. Although there is no limit for *Legionella*, EPA believes that if *Giardia lamblia* and viruses are removed/inactivated, then drinking water likely to be free of *Legionella.* The U.S. EPA requires routine sampling of drinking water for testing total coliform and *E. coli*, and if a routine sample is positive, then repeat samples are required. If, in any repeat sample, total coliform or *E. coli* is detected then the drinking water has an acute MCL violation. For a drinking water system that collects fewer than 40 routine samples per month, no more than one sample can be total coliform-positive per month. For a system that collects more than 40 routine samples, no more than 5% of samples total coliform-positive in a month is allowed (U.S. EPA [2012b]).

Each year approximately 42,000 cases of salmonellosis are reported in the U.S. (CDC [2014]). Schistosomiasis is not reported in the U.S. because it is not endemic; however, 200 million people are infected worldwide. In 2011, about 1,060 cases of Guinea worm disease, caused by the parasite *Dracunculus medinensis*, were reported in many remote parts of Africa that do not have safe drinking water. Malaria, a protozoal disease of the Genus Plasmodium transmitted by mosquitos breeding in contaminated water, affects 300–500 million people, and causes over one million deaths each year (more than 90% of deaths in Africa). Overall the morbidity and mortality caused by contaminated water are enormous and need to be controlled by improving the security of safe water (i.e., recreational as well as drinking water) in both developing and developed countries.

Historical Perspective of Water-borne Diseases

Water contamination has a long presence in human history, with descriptions in the Sushruta Samshita about water-borne diseases resembling cholera in an Indian text written in Sanskrit as early as 500–400 B.C. (Colwell [1996]). Although cholera infections have not been reported in recent years in developed countries mainly due to improved sanitation, millions of people each year continue to get infected by *Vibrio cholera* in developing countries (Nelson et al. [2009]). The World Health Organization reports about 3–5 million cholera cases and 10,000 – 120,000 deaths, mainly in developing countries, due to cholera every year. Over time, cholera has caused millions of deaths in developing as well as developed countries (Colwell [1996]; Okun [1996]). For instance, a major outbreak of cholera was reported in London in 1849. Dr. John Snow, a physician to Queen Victoria, showed a relationship between people infected by cholera and contaminated water (Snow [1854]; Colwell [1996]). Jordan et al. ([1904]), Ruediger ([1911]), Simons et al. ([1922]), and Rudolfs et al. ([1950]) provide excellent reviews on incidents during the early 19th century. Colwell ([1996]) reported that in the mid and late 18th century, cholera infected millions of people all over the world. The worst outbreak in recent memory occurred in Haiti following the devastating earthquake affecting the capital and surrounding regions, with almost a half a million cases, killing thousands of people (CDC [2011]).

Water-borne Pathogen Footprints and Challenges

Indicator organisms are commonly used to assess the levels of pathogens in water resources; i.e., water-borne pathogen footprints of water resources. Monitoring the levels of indicator organisms (such as fecal coliforms, *E. coli*) (Figure 1) is a common approach for quantifying the potential pathogen loads in ambient water bodies. For decades, public health officials/scientists have evaluated water quality by enumerating fecal coliforms and *E. coli* levels in rivers, lakes, estuaries, and coastal waters (Malakoff [2002]; Pandey et al. [2012a]; Pandey et al. [2012b]; Pandey and Soupir [2013]). There is, however, much debate regarding current indicator organisms and their ability to represent the potential presence of pathogenic bacteria. In addition, identifying the source of pathogens (e.g., human waste, animal waste, wildlife excreta, and waterfowl droppings) (Figure 2) is challenging (Malakoff [2002]; Dickerson et al. [2007]). There is potential to use a relatively new approach such as microbial source tracking (MST) to trace the origin of fecal coliform (Scott et al. [2002]; Grave et al. [2007]; Dickerson et al. [2007]; Ibekwe et al. [2011]; Ma et al. [2014]). In the past, the MST method was exploited by antibiotic resistance analysis to assess the impact of cattle on water quality on a watershed scale (Grave et al. [2007]). The authors suggested that host-origin libraries, based on a phenotypic method, are useful for tracking the pathogen sources. Many MST methods, however, rely on the assumption that some strains of bacteria are found only within a single kind or group of animals. This assumption can be debatable when it comes to the common fecal bacteria *E. coli* (Malakoff [2002]). Therefore, caution is needed while using *E. coli* for source tracking (Gordon [2001]). Further, the cost to develop libraries, implement extensive sampling programs needed for verifying the MST method, and calculate uncertainties associated with the method are legitimate issues, which requires attention before exploiting the MST method at watershed scale.

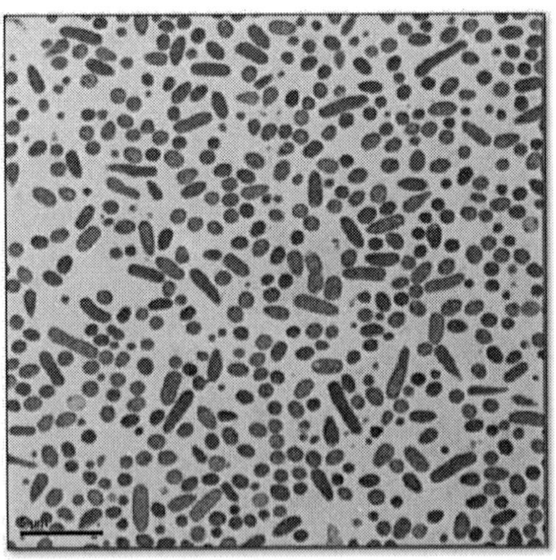

Figure 1. Transmission electron micrograph of *E. coli* (0157:H7; ATCC: 35150).

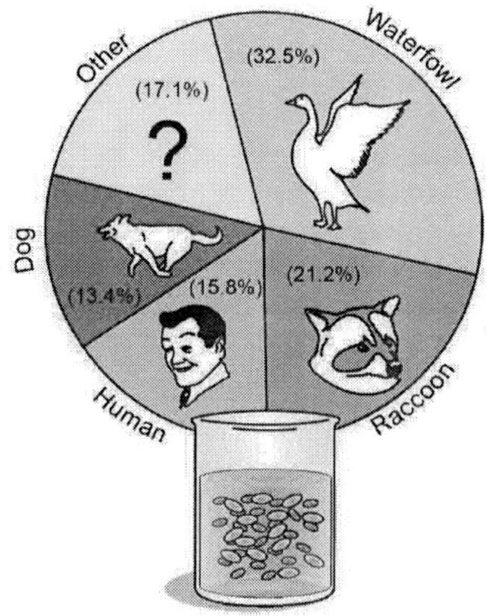

Figure 2. Challenges in identifying enteric pathogen sources (source: Malakoff,[2002]).

Currently, public health officials/scientists rely on exposure limits for assessing pathogen levels in water resources, which have been established to protect human health. The EPA defines acceptable recreational limits as those that will result in eight or fewer swimming-related gastrointestinal (GI) illnesses out of every 1,000 swimmers (U.S. EPA [1986]). The current U.S. EPA fresh water quality criteria for *E. coli* is a geometric mean not exceeding 126 CFU/100 ml, or no samples exceeding a single sample maximum of 235 CFU/100 ml (U.S. EPA [2001]). Criteria were developed based on the U.S. EPA measurements of total and Highly Credible Gastrointestinal Illnesses (HCGI), which correlated with *E. coli* densities (r = 0.804) in fresh recreational waters (Dufour [1984]). Multiple studies have identified trends between indicator organisms in water and GI illness in humans, including vomiting, diarrhea, and fever (Cabelli [1983]; Wade et al. [2006]). Recent work by Edge et al. ([2010]) detected water-borne *E. coli* in 80% of water samples with *E. coli* levels of less than 100 CFU/100 ml. Another study by Wade et al. ([2006]) reported significant positive trends between increased GI illness and indicator organisms at the Lake Michigan beach, and a positive trend with indicators such as *E. coli* at a Lake Erie beach. Recently, the use of indicator organisms (e.g., fecal coliforms, *E. coli*) for assessing pathogen levels has been debated more often than ever; however, the use of indicator organisms is likely to continue for assessing pathogen levels in water resources potentially because of the lack of an alternative reliable solution.

Pathogen Contamination in Water Resources

The U.S. EPA, which monitors water quality of various ambient water bodies, estimated that pathogens impair more than 480,000 km of rivers and shorelines and 2 million ha of lakes in the U.S. (U.S. Environmental Protection Agency [2010a]). According to EPA estimates, pathogens are the leading cause of impairment for 303 (d) listed waters (i.e., list of impaired and threatened waters that the Clean Water Act requires all states to submit for EPA approval) (Figure 3) (U.S. EPA [2014a], [2014b], [2014c]). A total of

71,917 causes of impairment have been reported, and the top five causes of impairment are shown in Figure 3. Pathogen contamination clearly dominates the causes of impairment (U.S. EPA [2014a], [2014b], [2014c]).

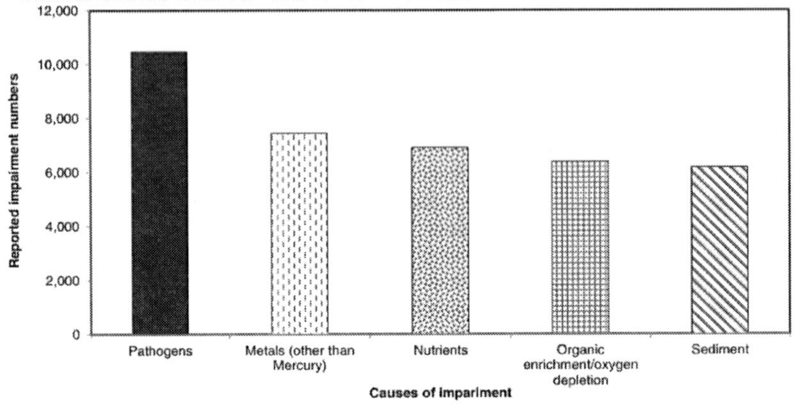

Figure 3. Causes of impairment in the U.S. (data source: U.S. EPA ([2014a],[2014b],[2014c])).

Studies by Diffey ([1991]), Brookes et al. ([2004]), Jamieson et al. ([2004]), Gerba and Smith ([2005]), Gerba and McLeod ([1976]), Hipsey et al. ([2008]), Pachepsky and Shelton ([2011]) reviewed the current studies of water-borne pathogen transport, with particular reference to freshwater and estuarine sediments. In addition, many current reviews focus on specific aspects of water resources, for instance, John and Rose ([2005]) focused on groundwater, Brookes et al. ([2004]) focused on reservoirs and lakes, Jamieson et al. ([2004]) focused on agricultural watersheds, and Kay et al. ([2007]) reviewed catchment microbial dynamics. The review study presented here uses a relatively broader approach for understanding how water-borne pathogens can potentially impact public health and various ambient water bodies. In addition, existing challenges, while assessing pathogen levels in water resources are discussed.

Coastal and Estuarine Environments

In the U.S., elevated pathogen levels are a leading cause of impairments of coastal environments (U.S. EPA [2014a], [2014b], [2014c]). Urban runoff and sewers have been identified as the primary source of coastal water impairments. Rippey ([1994]) reported about 400 outbreaks and 14,000 cases caused by pathogen contaminated coastal water since the late 1800s in the U.S. Impairments of coastal environments have major economic impacts on the U.S. For example, losses caused by pathogen contamination in Massachusetts are more than $75 million each year (Weiskel et al. [1996]). The studies, which elaborate various pathogens in coastal environment and their survival mechanism, are summarized in Table 1.

The sources of coastal water contamination are: point discharges of treated and untreated sewage from shoreline outfalls, and non-point discharges. The non-point sources, such as runoff from naturally vegetated areas, discharge pathogens into coastal waters. Besides runoff from vegetated areas, the storm water runoff from urban, commercial, and industrial lands also discharges pathogens into coastal waters.

Table 1. Studies describing pathogen contamination in saline water (coastal and estuary environments)

Author(s) year	Organisms	Results	Study remarks
Coastal water			
Gerba and McLeod ([1976])	*E. coli*, fecal coliform	Longer survival in the sediment presence in seawater	Sediment influence on pathogen survival
Goyal et al. ([1977])	Total coliform, fecal coliform	Sediments of shallow canal can act as a reservoir	Pathogens distribution in water and sediment
Kapuscinski and Mitchell ([1983])	*E. coli*, bacteriophages	*E. coli* survives longer than bacteriophages	Survival of pathogens in sunlight
Rao et al. ([1984])	Enteroviruses (Polio and Rota)	Abundance viruses were attached with sediment	Viruses distribution in water and sediment
Weiskel et al. ([1996])	Fecal coliform	Waterfowl major source of fecal coliform inputs	Pathogen source and transport pathways
Sinton et al. ([1999])	Bacteria and Fecal bacteriophages	Somatic coliphages shown prolonged survival	Sunlight influence on sewage-polluted seawater
Solo-Gabriele et al. ([2000])	*E. coli*	Riverbanks as the primary pathogen source	Sources of pathogens on subtropical environment
Nasser et al. ([2003])	*Cryptosporidium, viruses, E. coli*	*E. coli* die-off was faster than other pathogens	Comparative survival of various pathogens
Schriewer et al. ([2010])	*Bacteroidales,* fecal indicator, protozoa, bacteria	*Bacteroidales* have shown higher predictive skill than fecal indicators	*Bacteroidales* as a predictor of pathogens in coastal water
Estuaries			
Ketchum et al. ([1952])	Coliform, zooplankton	Sactericidal and predation caused coliform die-off	Processes responsible for pathogens decrease
Smith et al. ([1978])	Echovirus 1, coxsackieviruses	Sediment prolonged viruses survival	Persistence of pathogen viruses
Rhodes and Kator ([1990])	*E. coli*	Mortality rises in sunlight	Indigenous microbiota and sunlight influence
White et al. ([1998])	*Perkinsus marinus*	Use of Kriging analysis for disease prevalence	Use of GIS in pathogen distribution analysis
Lipp et al. ([2001])	*Vibrio vulnificus*	Salinity controls the distribution of pathogens	Distribution of human pathogens
Desmarais et al. ([2002])	*E. coli, C. perfringens*	Pathogens re-grown with tides and sterile sediment	Influence of soil on fecal indicator in tidally influenced environment
Frias-Lopez et al. ([2002])	*Clostridium, Campylobacter, Arobacter*	Pathogen partitioning was found in surface and overlying water	Bacterial communities partitioning between sea water, dead coral surface
Chandran and Hatha ([2005])	*E. coli, Salmonella*	*E. coli* shows better survival capacity than *Salmonella*	Relative survival in microcosm studies
Baker-Austin et al. ([2009])	*Vibrio vulnificus*	Prevalence of antibiotic resistance in a human pathogen	Multi-site analysis shows widespread antibiotic resistance in pathogens

In addition, other sources, such as malfunctioning or poorly sited septic systems, can also introduce significant amounts of pathogens (Sayler et al. [1975]; Howe et al. [2002]). Weiskel et al. ([1996]) reported that direct deposition of waterfowl feces was a considerable source of pathogens. Fayer and Trout ([2005]) summarized the transport of various pathogens, such as *Giardia*, *Toxoplasma*, and *Cryptosporidium* (zoonotic parasites) in the coastal environment. Moreover, the presence of sediment in seawater can also increase the survival chance of fecal coliforms, such as *E. coli* (Gerba nd McLeod [1976]; Goyal et al. [1977]). Solo-Gabriele et al. ([2000]) showed that the location and timing of storms of the coastal area in tropical and subtropical environments are also important factors that can potentially influence coastal water quality.

Previous studies have shown that the direct discharge of storm water runoff into coastal waters through storm drain systems can cause pathogen contamination, even where separate storm and sanitary sewer systems are in place. For instance, Weiskel et al. ([1996]) found that about 16% of the total fecal coliform inputs were caused by storm water entering Buttermilk Bay in Massachusetts. In addition, coastal rivers draining largely undeveloped watersheds with extensive riparian wetlands can be a natural source of fecal pathogens to coastal waters (Viau et al. [2011]; Staley et al. [2014]; Roberts et al. [2013]; Liang et al. [2013]; Wilkes et al. [2014]). On-site septic systems can also contribute significant amounts of fecal pathogens to coastal waters in low-lying fine-grained geological settings where saturated soils enhance pathogen growth. Weiskel et al. ([1996]) reported that shoreline wrack deposits could act as a reservoir of fecal bacteria, and the removal of wrack deposits from inter-tidal zones can improve the water quality of adjacent coastal waters.

Similar to the coastal environment, increasing water-borne pathogen levels in estuaries are a serious threat to public health. Human activities can impact estuary pathogen levels when they are adjacent to populated areas, and often provide a means of transportation and substantial recreation (Schriewer et al. [2010]; Pachepsky and Shelton [2011]). The most common pathogens, previously identified in estuaries by Rhodes and Kator ([1990]), were *Vibrio cholerae*, *Giardia*, *Cryptosporidium*, *Salmonella*, and *Campylobacter* spp. As shown in Table 1, the presence of various pathogens (e.g., *E. coli, C. perfringens, Clostridium, Salmonella*) has been reported in many previous studies. Municipal point sources are the primary cause of pathogen contamination in estuaries. Urban water disposed through combined sewer outflows is the cause of approximately 12% of estuary impairments in the U.S. (Arnone and Walling [2007]). Pathogens, including *Vibrio vulnificus* which carries the highest fatality rate of any food-borne pathogen in the U.S., were detected in the Gulf of Mexico Estuary (Lipp et al. [2001]; Baker-Austin et al. [2009]). Several studies discovered that bed sediment plays a vital role (i.e., with the release of particle-attached pathogens from bed sediment to a water column through a resuspension process) for the persistence and transport of pathogens in the estuaries (Smith et al. [1978]; Desmarais et al. [2002]). Previous studies have shown that pathogen growth and decay are influenced by environmental conditions. For instance, a study by Chandran and Hatha ([2005]) revealed that sunlight is a major factor that influences survival of pathogens like *E. coli* and *S. typhimurium* in the estuarine water.

Groundwater

Groundwater is heavily used all over the world as the primary source of domestic drinking water supplies, and contaminated groundwater certainly enhances risk to public health. Nationally, 40% of the U.S. domestic water supply originates from groundwater, and over 40 million people use groundwater as their drinking water via private wells (Alley et al. [1999]). Groundwater pathogen contamination has led to numerous disease outbreaks in the U.S.; for example, at least 46 outbreaks of disease occurred between 1992 and 1999, resulting in 2,739 cases of illness and several deaths (John and Rose [2005]). These are reported cases; due to underdiagnosis and underreporting, the actual morbidity is almost certainly higher.

Several studies have shown that microbial pathogens, such as *Salmonella*, *E. coli*, *S. faecalis*, and enteroviruses are relatively stable in groundwater (Bittion et al. 1983; Schijven and Hassanizadeh [2000]; Pang et al. [2004]) (Table 2). Controlling groundwater pathogen contamination has recently been emphasized in many countries, as pathogens can survive up to 400 days depending on the soil temperature (Nevecherya et al. [2005]; Filip and Demnerova [2009]). For example, identifying sources of groundwater pathogen contamination has received significant attention in France (Grisey et al. [2010]). Many studies reported that health risks caused by chlorine-resistant protozoans, such as *Cryptosporidium* spp. (Ferguson et al. [2003]; Kay et al. [2007]; Kay et al. [2008]), are considerable. One of the major concerns is that wetlands without lining might cause pathogen contamination of groundwater (Kay et al. [2007]). Similar concerns have been expressed in the United Kingdom by water regulators. The European Union (EU) has also emphasized protecting groundwater from pathogen contamination. Pathogen-contaminated groundwater can cause pollution in coastal environments. For example, a study of Buttermilk Bay has shown that groundwater is capable of transporting a large quantity of pathogens from surface to sub-surface water either by direct discharge or by discharge to rivers flowing into the bay (Moog [1987]; Weiskel et al. [1996]). The risk of contaminating groundwater particularly increases in areas where shallow aquifers exist. In these situations it is more likely that contaminated surface water or water from septic tanks can reach groundwater (Weiskel et al. [1996]). Precipitation events are likely to increase groundwater pathogen contamination because of contaminated ground water recharge.

Table 2. Pathogen contamination in freshwater environment (ground water, rivers and lakes and reservoirs)

Author(s) year	**Organisms**	**Results**	**Study remarks**
Groundwater			
Bitton et al. ([1983])	*Salmonella, E. coli, S. faecalis, enteroviruses*	*S. faecalis* **decay rate was similar to viruses**	Survival of pathogens in groundwater
Schijven and Hassanizadeh ([2000])	Viruses	Viruses attachment with soil was influenced by pH, and favorable sites	Soil passage impacts on virus removal at field-scale
Pang et al. ([2004])	*E. coli* **and F-RNA phages**	Pathogens were sorbed in aquifer material	Transport of *E. coli* **and F-RNA phages**
Nevecherya et al. ([2005])	*Salmonella*, viruses, *E. coli*, shigellos	Mathematical model was derived for temperature depends inactivation rate	Pathogenic bacteria and viruses survival in groundwater

Filip and Demnerova ([2009])	*Bacillus megaterium* **and** *Staphylococcus*	Pathogens survived 10 to 100 days	Pathogens survival in groundwater; FT-IR characterization
Grisey et al. ([2010])	Total coliforms, *E. coli, Enterococci, Pseudomonas aeruginosa, Salmonella and Staphylococcus aureus*	Bacterial density monitoring coupled with artificial trace experiments proved useful in locating pathogens sources	Pathogens survival in groundwater and landfill leachate
Rivers			
Chin ([2010])	Fecal coliform	Summer and rainfall raises pathogens	Urban areas impacts on stream pathogens
Smith et al. ([1973])	*Salmonella*, fecal coliforms, streptococci	*Salmonella* **decline was close to fecal coliform**	Usefulness of indicators organisms
Burton et al. ([1987])	*Pseudomonas aeruginosa, Salmonella newport, E. coli*	Clay in sediments improves *E. coli* **survival**	Survival of pathogens in fresh water sediments
Smith et al. ([1987])	*E. coli*, Fecal bacteria	U.S. rivers shows decline in fecal indicator	Water quality assessment from 1974 to 1981
Terzieva and McFeters ([1991])	*E. coli, Campylobacter jejuni, Yersinia enterocolitica*	Temperate zone surface water serve as a rersisitent verhicle in transimsision of bacteria between animals and humans	Survival and injury study of bacteria in agricultural surface water
Terzieva and McFeters ([1991])	*Yersinia enterocolitica* **and** *E. coli*	Experimental design and environmental play major role in pathogens survival	Survival in stream water, comparison between field and lab studies
Fraser et al. ([1998])	Fecal coliform	Model predicted pathogens	Modelling non-point source pollution
Lakes and reservoirs			
Beaver and Crisman ([1989])	Ciliates	Grazing habits of ciliates are discussed	Predators roles in fresh water
Rubentschik et al. ([1936])	*Serratia marcescens*	Adsorption of bacteria could be questionable	Adsorption of bacteria in salt lakes
Mac Kenzie et al. ([1994])	*Cryptosporidium*	*C. oocysts* **study passes through the filtration system of water supply**	Contaminated water from Milwaukee lake caused outbreak
Wcislo and Chrost ([2000])	*E. coli*	Predators controlled pathogen levels	Survival of pathogens in man-made reservoir

Kistemann et al. ([2002])	*E. coli*, coliform, fecal streptococcal, and *Clostridium perfringens*	Most of the pathogens increases during extreme runoff events	Microbial load in drinking water reservoir during rainfall events
Howe et al. ([2002])	*Cryptosporidium oocysts*	Animal feces was a major source of pathogens	Water supply's oocysts caused outbreak in northern England
Ishii et al. ([2006])	*E. coli*	***E. coli* survived longer in soil**	Presence and growth of *E. coli* **in Lake superior watershed**

Pathogen contamination (e.g., bacteria, protozoa, and viruses) poses a serious risk in water resources. The transport of pathogens from surface water to groundwater increases the vulnerability of groundwater (Jin and Flury [2002]). These authors reported that 70% of the water-borne microbial illness outbreaks in the United States have been associated with ground water. Pathogens such as viruses are much smaller than bacteria and protozoa, and many can potentially reach groundwater through porous soil matrices. Jin and Flury ([2002]) reviewed the fate and transport of viruses in porous media to understand mechanisms and modeling of virus sorption, and concluded that factors such as solution chemistry, virus properties, soil properties, temperature, and association with solid particle influences virus survival, transport, and sorption in porous media. Pang ([2009]) studied microbial removal rates in subsurface media, and reported that soil types considerably influence microbial removal rates. For instance, volcanic soils, pumice sand, fine sand, and highly weathered aquifer rocks showed high removal rates. The author found that microbial removal rates were inversely correlated with infiltration rates and transport velocity.

Considerable work recently has been done towards understanding pathogen transport in the vadose zone (Wang et al. [2014a]; [2014b]; Unc and Goss [2004]; Darnault et al. [2004]). Groundwater can be contaminated by seepage and percolation of contaminated water from the vadose zone (Darnault et al. [2004]). The macropores of agricultural land are also known to play a considerable role in polluting groundwater, particularly from fields where manure is applied (Jamieson et al. [2002]). Unc and Goss ([2004]) evaluated the influence of manure on the transport of bacteria from land receiving manure to water resources. These authors reported that manure application in the land influences pathogen transport in the vadose zone. The presence of straw and coarse organic matter influences the persistence of bacteria, and manure application changes the physical configuration of soil, the soil chemistry, and the properties of the microbial cells, which control the survival and persistence of bacteria in soils. Another recent study by Wang et al. ([2014]) assessed the transport of *E. coli* in soils with preferential flow. The authors reported that a decrease in macropore length resulted in a decreased apparent saturated hydraulic conductivity of the macropore and an increase in the mass transfer. Wang et al. ([2014a]; [2014b]) concluded that macropore length has a considerable influence on preferential transport of *E. coli*.

Reservoirs and Lakes

Previous studies have shown the presence of many pathogens in lakes and reservoirs (Table 2), and that these pathogens can pose risks to human health. In many countries surface reservoirs serve as the main source of drinking water, and these surface water bodies are often vulnerable to pathogen contamination (Kistemann et al. [2002]). In the developed world, although there is increased awareness of water treatment for pathogen contamination and water quality, outbreaks of water-borne disease via public water supplies continue to be reported (Gibson et al. [1998]; Howe et al. [2002]; Brookes et al. [2004]).

In the past, more than 403,000 residents of the greater Milwaukee, Wisconsin area experienced gastrointestinal illnesses due to infection with the parasite *Cryptosporidium parvum* following contamination of the city's water supply, which was associated with inadequate filtration of contaminated water from Lake Michigan (Mac Kenzie et al. [1994]; Cicirello et al. [1997]). In the 1990s, *Cryptosporidiosis* became the most common cause of outbreaks associated with public drinking water supplies in the United Kingdom (Howe et al. [2002]). In developing countries, diseases such as diarrhea and cholera are the leading cause of morbidity (Nelson et al. [2009]). Overall, diarrhea associated with drinking contaminated water is responsible for 2 to 2.5 million deaths annually (Fenwick [2006]). In lakes and reservoirs, increased pathogens are often associated with storm events, and the stream inflow is considered to be the major source of pathogens during storm events. Elevated flows in rivers most likely agitate bed sediment, which causes enhancement of pathogen levels of the water column (Jamieson et al. [2005a]; Jamieson et al. [2005b]; Pandey and Soupir [2013]; Bai and Lung [2005]). During the rainy season, the influx of contaminated water from rivers to lakes and reservoirs can substantially increase pathogen levels (Kistemann et al. [2002]). The quantity of pathogen influxes from tributaries of lakes and reservoirs during the rainy season is of particular importance in determining pathogen transport and distribution (Brookes et al. [2004]).

Rivers

Pathogen contamination is a major cause of stream impairments. The sources of impairment and health risks induced by water-borne pathogens are extensively reported (Table 2). In the U.S. pathogen contamination is the leading cause of stream water pollution. The EPA's National Water Quality Inventory Report suggests that about 53% of the assessed rivers are impaired, and a majority of them are contaminated by pathogens (U.S. EPA [2012a]). The cost to implement the total maximum daily load (TMDL) plans to improve stream water is estimated as \$0.9 to \$4.3 billion per year (U.S. EPA [2010b]).

Pathogen influxes into rivers from agricultural lands (Figure 4) are the main cause of stream impairments (Chin [2010]; U.S. EPA [2012a]). A weak understanding of pathogen transport from agricultural lands to rivers is considered to be a major challenge in implementing and deriving suitable land management practices capable of improving stream water quality. For instance, despite common knowledge that agricultural land's non-point source pollution is a leading cause of stream impairment, it is difficult to identify points of origin of pathogens and the pathways by which they enter streams. As an example, pathogens are likely to enter rivers from many potential sources, including lateral inputs from pastures and riparian zones, influx of pathogen-contaminated groundwater, direct deposit of fecal matter from livestock and wildlife, discharge of contaminated sanitary sewer flows, and wastewater treatment plant effluents. In rainy events, pathogens in rivers are influenced by fresh input from watersheds as well as sub-surface flow. In addition, the resuspension of legacy pathogens from bed sediments can considerably increase pathogen levels (Cho et al. [2010]; Droppo et al. [2009]; Jamieson et al. [2005b]; Kiefer et al. [2012]; Nagels et al. [2002]; Muirhead et al. [2004]; Kim et al. [2010]; Smith et al. [2008]).

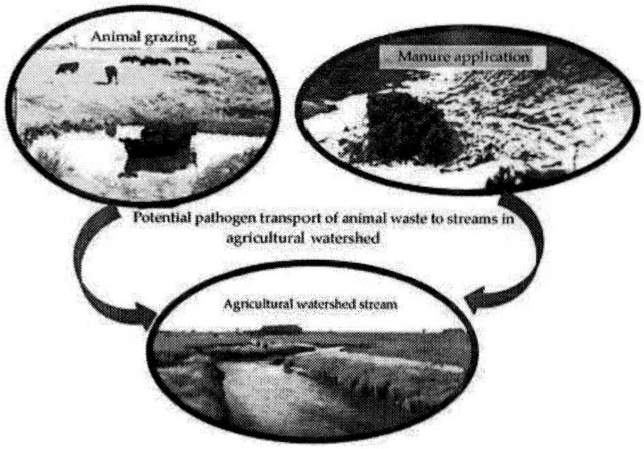

Figure 4. Simplified path of animal waste pathogen transport from agricultural land to rivers.

Controlling pathogen contamination from livestock/wildlife to streams is challenging (Terzieva and McFeters [1991]). For example, it is doubtful that pathogen contamination can be prevented by fencing off riparian buffers, and even if buffers are useful in controlling stream water pathogens, it is not certain what their width must be (Nagels et al. [2002]). There are review studies that elaborate on stream water pathogen contamination (Fraser et al. [1998]; Jamieson et al. [2004]; Pachepsky et al. [2006]).

Many studies have emphasized the use of mathematical models to understand pathogen transport from agricultural land to rivers (Kim et al. [2010]; Muirhead et al. [2004]; Jamieson et al. [2005a]; Jamieson et al. [2005b]). Previous studies (Gerba and Smith [2005]; Pandey et al. [2012b]; Pandey and Soupir [2013]; Pachepsky and Shelton [2011]; Martinez et al. [2014]) have emphasized the need to improve existing models for calculating the fate and transport of pathogens at the watershed scale. Currently, empirical as well as mechanistic models are being used to calculate microbial fate and transport (Muirhead and Monaghan [2012]). Numerous studies are available for exploiting watershed scale models such as WATFLOOD (Dorner et al. [2006]), the Soil and Water Assessment Tool (SWAT) (Neitsch et al. [2005]), the Spatially Explicit Deliver Model (SEDMOD) (Fraser [1999]), and KINEROS/STWIR (Guber et al. [2011]) for predicting pathogen transport. Though numerous watershed scale models are available, which can be exploited for calculating pathogen transport at watershed scale, considerable difficulties exist while using the models (Pandey et al. [2012b]; Pandey and Soupir [2013]). For instance, correctly identifying the model input parameter values is a daunting task. Recently, considerable emphasis has been given to understand the sensitivity of the input parameters to the model output (Martinez et al. [2014]; Parajuli et al. [2009]).

When implementing watershed scale models for predicting pathogen transport, difficulties related to the selection of model input parameters are common (Martinez et al. [2014]). A study by Parajuli et al. ([2009]) evaluated the sensitivity of fecal coliform bacteria loads modeled with SWAT, and the authors reported that many of the parameters (e.g., bacterial die-off rates, the temperature adjustment factor) were insensitive to the model output. Similarly, Coffey et al. ([2010]) reported that initial concentration of *E. coli* and the bacterial partition coefficient parameters of the SWAT model were overly sensitive in affecting the model's output. Another recent study by Martinez et al. ([2014]) evaluated the KINEROS/STWIF model input parameter sensitivities to the output. These authors reported that environmental controls such as soil saturation, rainfall duration, and rainfall intensity had the most sensitivity, while parameters such as soil and manure properties were the least sensitive in affecting model output. Many previous studies (Pandey and Soupir [2012a], [2012b]; Kim et al. [2010]; Martinez et al. [2014]; Parajuli et al. [2009]) reported that identification and selection of model input parameters are major challenges when implementing the model for predicting fate and transport of pathogens at the watershed scale.

Blooming of Cyanobacteria

While water-borne pathogens are a serious concern, excessive algal bloom (Figure 5) in water resources can potentially limit their uses for recreation activities as well as for drinking water. Cyanobacteria (blue-green algae) have unique roles in oxygenation of the atmosphere (Hofer [2013]); however, their excessive growth or dense algal bloom in water resources diminishes the quality and quantity of light in the water column ([U.S. EPA 2014b]). When blooms are excessive, the risk of toxin contamination (released by harmful algal bloom (HABs)) is likely to be elevated. The HAB includes many types of algal taxa such as dinoflagellates, diatoms, and cyanobacteria. Eutrophication caused by excessive algal bloom can cause fish kills and reduce the diversity of aquatic life ([U.S. EPA 2014b]). In hypoxic water, dissolved oxygen levels can be less than 2 – 3 ppm (U.S. EPA [2014c]). For example, in the hypoxic zone in the northern Gulf of Mexico, an area along the Louisiana-Texas coast, less than 2 ppm of dissolved oxygen concentration has been reported. This is believed to be caused by excess nutrients delivered from the Mississippi River, in combination with seasonal stratification of Gulf waters (U.S.G.S., [2014]). The largest U.S. hypoxic zone, which occurred in 2002 in the Gulf of Mexico, was about 13,518 square kilometers (U.S.G.S. [2012]).

Figure 5. Algal bloom in Squaw Creek, Iowa, U.S.

Freshwater cyanobacterial blooms produce highly potent cyanotoxins and cyanobacterial HABs, which can affect the liver, nervous system, and skin (U.S. EPA [2014b]). Cyanobacterial blooms can be potentially detrimental to human and animal health, aquatic habitats, and aquaculture industries (Kaloudis et al. [2013]; Carmichael [2001]; Falconer [2005]; Codd et al. [1999]). Previous studies (Mackintosh et al. [1990]; Yoshizawa et al. [1990]) have shown that microcystins (i.e., cynotoxins) are hepatotoxic and act as tumor promoters through the inhibition of protein phosphatases, which play a key role in cellular regulation. Eutrophic water conditions combined with warm surface water temperatures (15 – 30°C) can potentially enhance cyanobacterial blooms in water (Oikonomou et al. [2012]; Vareli et al. [2009]). Currently more than 400 hypoxic zones exist in the world affecting 245,000 square kilometers (Diaz and Rosenberg [2008]). These dead zones in coastal waters have spread exponentially since the 1960s and have considerably impacted ecosystems. The increase in these dead zones is likely to be influenced by climate change. Various factors such as how climate change affects water-column stratification and how nutrient runoff affects organic matter production will determine further expansion of the dead zones (Diaz and Rosenberg [2008]). For instance, climate predictions of the Mississippi River basin indicate a 20% increase in river discharge, which will enhance nutrient loading and result in expansion of the oxygen depleted area (IPCC [2007]). Considering the importance of fresh water, estuarine, and marine environment to public health and aquatic life, identifying approaches capable of controlling excessive algal blooms is required before these dead zones spread globally.

Impact of Water Resources Development

Water resources development involves altering the natural flow path of rivers and lakes, as well as designing irrigation schemes and dams. These activities have been alleged to be responsible for causing new diseases and enhancing health risks (Fenwick [2006]; Steinmann et al. [2006]).

The influence of water resources development in spreading diseases, such as schistosomiasis, a parasitic disease which is ranked second only to malaria with regard to the number of people infected, has been reported extensively; one estimate says that about 103 million out of 779 million infected people live in close proximity to large reservoirs and irrigation schemes (Steinmann et al. [2006]).

Designing dams and irrigation schemes in tropical and subtropical climate zones has often resulted in disease outbreaks caused by water-borne pathogens. Consider, for example, the Sennar Dam on the Blue Nile River and Sudan's Gezira Scheme, the world's largest irrigation project. Because of the dam's commercial success, irrigation in the region has doubled from the 1940s and 1950s. After the 1950s, infections from malaria and schistosomiasis increased significantly, becoming the subject of the first integrated disease-control program, the Blue Nile Health Project, implemented from 1978 to 1990. The project failed to have any impact in controlling the prevalence of schistosomiasis (Eltoum et al. [1993]; Fenwick [2006]; Steinmann et al. [2006]). Another example is China's Three Gorges Dam, built across the Yangtze River and completed in 2009, which created a 50,700 km^2 reservoir and submerged more than 220 counties. Hotez et al. ([1997]) reported that the reservoir would produce environmental changes that could lead to the transmission of schistosomiasis in the area served by the dam. A recent study by Schrader et al. ([2013]) found major high risk areas for schistosomiasis occurrence in the large lakes and flood plain regions of the Yangtze River. Another study by Gray et al. ([2012]) reported that the Three Gorges Dam will likely to impact the transmission of schistosomiasis in China.

In the U.S., because of increasing concern for produce safety, pathogen-free irrigation water is attracting considerable attention (Martinez et al. [2014]). Painter et al. ([2013]) reported that produce accounted for nearly half of food-borne illnesses in the U.S. between 1998 and 2008. Growing concern about the safety of food and water will likely help in developing improved strategies while planning and designing large dams for irrigation purposes.

Challenges and Recommendations

Infectious diseases caused by pathogens are the third leading cause of death in the United States, and the leading cause in the world (Binder et al. [1999]). The past two decades have seen the emergence of many new pathogenic infectious diseases (Daszak et al. [2000]). Many of these are caused by anthropogenic changes, such as water resources development, climate warming, and interactions between humans and animals, both domestic and wild (Krause [1994]; Epstein [2001]; Woolhouse [2002]; Fenwick [2006]; Schriewer et al. [2010]).

Multidisciplinary knowledge about how ambient water bodies, wildlife, domestic animals, and human populations interact with and impact each other are crucial in dealing with future challenges. Generally, domestic animals, wildlife, and humans are considered to be major sources of water-borne pathogens; however, finding the specific culprit—the primary pathogen source—is challenging (Malakoff [2002]). A watershed, for example, can have many pathogen sources, such as agricultural land, riparian areas, agricultural feeding operations, livestock, wildlife, and humans.

Developing models that are reliable in predicting pathogen survival and transport at the watershed scale can be helpful in implementing/evaluating the strategies for mitigating ambient water body pathogen levels. Evaluating the impacts of various environmental factors on pathogen survival in water resources is crucial. Various publications (i.e., Dorner et al. [2006]; Kim et al. [2010]; Rehmann and Soupir [2009]; Droppo et al., [2011]; Cho et al. [2010]; Pandey et al. [2012b]; Pandey and Soupir [2013]) are available describing models capable of predicting pathogen contamination levels in ambient water bodies; however, further work is required to improve model predictions. The evaluation of predictions by existing models clearly demonstrates the need for improvement. Many pathogen transport models use only temperature-induced mortality and growth, and do not include interactions among other environmental factors (e.g., pH, nutrients, DO, solar radiation); future inclusion of these environmental factors will likely to improve the model predictions.

Typically most studies have relied on *E. coli* and other indicator bacteria to indicate pathogen levels in water. Although widely used in monitoring contamination levels, *E. coli* alone can lead to mercurial and misleading information (Gordon [2001]). Schriewer et al. ([2010]) suggested that with improved pathogen detection technology (i.e., PCR-based detection) an indicator organism, such as *E. coli*, can be sufficiently accurate in most cases. Overall, improving technology to identify causative agents more accurately, creating standard epidemiological data for diseased populations, and enhancing the knowledge of disease dynamics can improve the understanding of risks caused by interactions among various populations (Harvell et al. [1999]; Daszak et al. [2000]; Harvell et al. [2002]).

In the past, a number of studies on pathogen contamination have been conducted on a scale where the conditions of ambient water bodies were simulated in laboratories. These studies are helpful in understanding pathogen behavior only up to a point. For enhancing the understanding of pathogen interactions in the environment, more emphasis should be given to field-scale studies.

CONCLUSIONS

This review examines studies from various disciplines to understand pathogen contamination in ambient water bodies. The worldwide prevalence of pathogen contamination is a serious concern, and enhancing the understanding of major pathogen sources and their significant impacts on water resources is crucial. A considerable number of studies on pathogen contamination have been conducted on a laboratory-scale; more emphasis should be given to field-scale studies for enhancing the understanding of pathogen interactions in the environment. Developing new models, and improving existing modeling approaches commonly used for predicting water-borne pathogen levels will likely to help in assessing pathogen contamination at watershed-scale. Considering the limited ability of existing models to predict pathogen contamination, improvement and development of new models are needed so that pathogen levels can be predicted more accurately. Integrating knowledge from multiple fields (e.g., hydrology, microbiology, and ecology) would increase the understanding of pollution levels and potential causes of pollution, and can also help devise long-term strategies to improve water quality.

Acknowledgment

The authors thank the Division of Agriculture and Natural Resources and Veterinary Medicine Extension, University of California, Davis, and National Science Foundation (award No. CBET-0967845) for supporting this work.

REFERENCES

1. Alley WM, Reilly TE, Franke OL: Sustainability of Groundwater Resources. U.S. Geological Survey (U.S.GS), Denver, CO; 1999.
2. Arnone RD, Walling JP: Waterborne pathogens in urban watersheds. J Water Health 2007, 5(1):149–162.
3. Bai S, Lung WS: Modeling sediment impact on the transport of fecal bacteria. Water Res 2005, 39: 5232–5240.
4. Baker-Austin C, McArthur J, Lindell A, Wright M, Tuckfield R, Gooch J, Warner L, Oliver J, Stepanauskas R: Multi-site analysis reveals widespread antibiotic resistance in the marine pathogen: Vibrio vulnificus . Microb Ecol 2009, 57(1):151–159.
5. Beaver JR, Crisman TL: The role of ciliated protozoa in pelagic freshwater ecosystems. Microb Ecol 1989, 17(2):111–136.
6. Binder S, Levitt AM, Sacks JJ, Hughes JM: Emerging infectious diseases: public health issues for the 21st Century. Science 1999, 284(5418):1311–1313.
7. Bitton G, Farrah SR, Ruskin RH, Butner J, Chou YJ: Survival of pathogenic and indicator organisms. Groundwater 1983, 21(4):405–410.
8. Bradford SA, Morales VL, Zhang W, Harvey RW, Packman AI, Mohanram A, Welty C: Transport and fate of microbial pathogens in agricultural settings. Crit Rev Env Sci Tec 2013, 43: 775–893.
9. Brookes JD, Antenucci J, Hipsey M, Burch MD, Ashbolt NJ, Ferguson C: Fate and transport of pathogens in lakes and reservoirs. Environ Int 2004, 30(5):741–759.
10. Burton GA, Gunnison D, Lanza GR: Survival of pathogenic bacteria in various freshwater sediments. Appl Environ Microbiol 1987, 53(4):633–638.

11. Cabelli VJ: Public health and water quality significance of viral diseases transmitted by drinking water and recreational water. Water Sci Technol 1983, 15(5):1–15.
12. Carmichael WW: Health effects of toxin-producing cyanobacteria: the CyanoHABs. Hum Ecol Risk Assess 2001, 7: 1393–1407.
13. Centers for Disease Control and Prevention (CDC) Cholera in Haiti: One Year Later. 2011. http://www.cdc.gov/haiticholera/haiti_cholera.htm (accessed on5/23/2014)
14. Centers for Disease Control and Prevention (CDC) Salmonella. 2014. http://www.cdc.gov/salmonella/general/ (accessed on 4/28/2014)
15. Chandran A, Mohamed Hatha AAM: Relative survival of Escherichia coli and Salmonella typhimurium in a tropical estuary. Water Res 2005, 39(7):1397–1403.
16. Chin DA: Linking pathogen sources to water quality in small urban streams. J Environ Eng 2010, 136(2):249–253.
17. Cho KH, Pachepsky YA, Kim JH, Guber AK, Shelton DR, Rowland R: Release of Escherichia coli from the bottom sediment in a first-order creek: Experiment and reach-specific modeling. J Hydrol 2010, 391(3–4):322–332.
18. Cicirello HG, Kehl KS, Addiss DG, Chusid MJ, Glass RI, Davis JP, Havens PL: Cryptosporidiosis in children during a massive waterborne outbreak in Milwaukee, Wisconsin: clinical, laboratory and epidemiologic findings. Epidemiol Infect 1997, 119(1):53–60.
19. Codd G, Bell S, Kaya K, Ward C, Beattie K, Metcalf J: Cyanobacterial toxins, exposure routes and human health. Eur J Phycol 1999, 34: 405–415.
20. Coffey R, Cummins EO, Flaherty V, Cormican M: Pathogen sources estimation and scenario analysis using the Soil and Water Assessment Tool (SWAT). Hum Ecol Risk Assess 2010, 16(4):913–933.
21. Colwell RR: Global climate and infectious disease: The Cholera Paradigm. Science 1996, 274(5295):2025–2031.
22. Craun GF, Fraun MF, Calderon RL, Beach MJ: Waterborne outbreaks reported in the United States. J Water Health 2006, 4: 19–30.
23. Darnault CJD, Steenhuis TS, Garnier P, Kim YJ, Jenkins MB, Ghiorse WC, Baveye PC, Parlange JY: Preferential flow and transport of Cryptosporidium parvum oocysts through the vadose zone: Experiments and modeling. Vadose Zone J 2004, 3(2):262–270.
24. Daszak P, Cunningham AA, Hyatt AD: Emerging infectious diseases of wildlife – threats to biodiversity and human health. Science 2000, 287: 443–449.
25. Desmarais TR, Solo-Gabriele HM, Palmer CJ: Influence of soil on fecal indicator organisms in a tidally influenced subtropical environment. Appl Environ Microbiol 2002, 68(3):1165–1172.
26. Diaz RJ, Rosenberg R: Spreading dead zones and consequences for marine ecosystems. Science 2008, 321: 926–929.
27. Dickerson JW, Crozier JB, Hagedorn G, Hassall A: Assessment of 16 s-23srDNA interagenic spacer regions in Eterococcus spp. for microbial source tracking. J Environ Qual 2007, 36: 1661–1669.
28. Diffey BL: Solar ultraviolet-radiation effects on biological-systems. Phys Med Biol 1991, 36(3):299–328.
29. Dorner SM, Anderson WB, Slawson RM, Kouwen N, Huck PM: Hydrologic modeling of pathogen fate and transport. Environ Sci Technol 2006, 40(15):4746–4753.
30. Droppo IG, Liss SN, Williams D, Nelson T, Jaskot C, Trapp B: Dynamic existence of waterborne pathogens within river sediment compartments: Implications for water quality regulatory affairs. Environ Sci Technol 2009, 43(6):1737–1743.

31. Droppo IG, Krishnappan BG, Liss SN, Marvin C, Biberhofer : Modeling sediment-microbial dynamics in the South Nation River, Ontario, Canada: Towards the prediction of aquatic and human health risk. Water Res 2011, 45: 3797–3809.
32. Dufour A (1984) Health Effects Criteria for Fresh Recreational Waters. Toxicology and Microbiology Division, U.S. Environmental Protection Agency Report EPA- 600–1-84–2004. Cincinnati, OH
33. Edge TA, Hill S, Seto P, Marsalek J: Library-dependent and library independent microbial source tracking to identify spatial variation in faecal contamination sources along a Lake Ontario beach (Ontario, Canada). Water Sci Technol 2010, 62: 719–727.
34. Eltoum IA, Sulaiman SM, Elturabi H, Mahgoub E, Homeida MMA: Infection with Schistosoma-Mansoni in 2 different endemic areas – a comparative population – based study in Elzidab and Gezira-Managil irrigation schemes, Sudan. J Trop Med Hyg 1993, 96(2):100–106.
35. Epstein PR: Climate change and emerging infectious diseases. Microbes Infect 2001, 3(9):747–754.
36. Falconer IR: Is there a human health hazard from microcystins in the drinking water supply? Acta Hydrochim Hydrobiol 2005, 33: 64–71.
37. Fayer R, Trout JM: Zoonotic protists in the marine environment. In: Belkin S and Colwell RR (ed) Oceans and Health:. Pathogens in the Marine Environment, Springer, New York, U.S; 2005.
38. Fenwick A: Waterborne Infectious Diseases-Could they be consigned to History? Science 2006, 313: 1077–1081.
39. Ferguson C, Husman AMD, Altavilla N, Deere D, Ashbolt N: Fate and transport of surface water pathogens in watersheds. Crit Rev Environ Sci Technol 2003, 33(3):299–361.
40. Filip Z, Demnerova K: Survival in groundwater and FT-IR characterization of some pathogenic and indicator bacteria. In: Jones JAA, Vardanian TG, Hakopian C (ed). Threats to Global Water Security, Springer, Dordrecht, The Netherlands; 2009.
41. Fraser RH: SEDMOD: A GIS-based delivery model for diffuse source pollutants. Yale University, PhD dissertation, School of Forestry and Environmental Studies; 1999.
42. Fraser RH, Barten PK, Pinney DAK: Predicting stream pathogen loading from livestock using a geographical information system-based delivery model. J Environ Qual 1998, 27(4):935–945.
43. Frias-Lopez J, Zerkle AL, Bonheyo GT, Fouke BW: Partitioning of bacterial communities between seawater and healthy, black band diseased, and dead coral surfaces. Appl Environ Microbiol 2002, 68(5):2214–2228.
44. Gerba CP, McLeod JS: Effect of sediments on the survival of Escherichia coli in marine waters. Appl Environ Microbiol 1976, 32(1):114–120.
45. Gerba CP, Smith J: Sources of pathogenic microorganisms and their fate during land application of wastes. J Environ Qual 2005, 34: 42–48.
46. Gibson CJ, Haas CN, Rose JB: Risk assessment of waterborne protozoa: current status and future trends. Parasitology 1998, 117: S205-S212.
47. Gordon DM: Geographical structure and host specificity in bacteria and the implications for tracing the source of coliform contamination. Microbiology 2001, 147(5):1079–1085.
48. Goyal SM, Gerba CP, Melnick JL: Occurrence and distribution of bacterial indicators and pathogens in canal communities along Texas Coast. Appl Environ Microbiol 1977, 34(2):139–149.

49. Grave AK, Hagedorn C, Brooks A, Hagedorn RL, Martin E: Microbial source tracking in a rural watershed dominated by cattle. Water Res 2007, 41: 3729–3739.

50. Gray DJ, Thrift AP, Williams GM, Zheng F, Li Y-S, Guo J, Chen H, Wang T, Xu XJ, Zhu R, Zhu H, Cao CL, Lin DD, Zhao ZY, Li RS, Davis GM, McManus DP: Five-year longitudinal assessment of the downstream impact on schistosomiasis transmission following closure of the Three Gorges Dam. PLoS Negl Trop Dis 2012, 6(4):e 1588. doi:10.1371/journal.pntd.0001588

51. Grisey E, Belle E, Dat J, Mudry J, Aleya L: Survival of pathogenic and indicator organisms in groundwater and landfill leachate through coupling bacterial enumeration with tracer tests. Desalination 2010, 261(1–2):162–168.

52. Guber AK, Pachepsky YA, Yakirevich AM, Shelton DR, Sadeghi AM, Goodrich DC, Unkrich CL: Uncertainty in modelling of faecal coliform overland transport associated with manure application in Maryland. Hydrolical Process 2011, 25(15):2393–2404.

53. Harvell CD, Kim K, Burkholder JM, Colwell RR, Epstein PR, Grimes DJ, Hofmann EE, Lipp EK, Osterhaus AD, Overstreet RM, Porter JW, Smith GW, Vasta GR: Emerging marine diseases-climate links and anthropogenic factors. Science 1999, 285(5433):1505–1510.

54. Harvell CD, Mitchell CE, Ward JR, Altizer S, Dobson AP, Ostfeld RS, Samuel MD: Climate warming and disease risks for terrestrial and marine biota. Science 2002, 296: 2158–2162.

55. Hipsey MR, Antenucci JP, Brookes JD: A generic, process-based model of microbial pollution in aquatic systems. Water Resour Res 2008., 44(7):

56. Hofer U: Getting to the bottom of Cyanobacteria. Nat Rev Microbiol 2013, 11: 818–819.

57. Hotez PJ, Feng Z, Xu LQ, Chen MG, Xiao SH, Liu SX, Blair D, McManus DP, Davis GM: Emerging and reemerging helminthiases and the public health of China. Emerg Infect Dis 1997, 3(3):303–310.

58. Howe AD, Forster S, Morton S, Marshall R, Osborn KS, Wright P, Hunter PR: Cryptosporidium oocysts in a water supply associated with a cryptosporidiosis outbreak. Emerg Infect Dis 2002, 8(6):619–624.

59. Ibekwe AM, Murinda SE, Graves AK: Genetic diversity and antimicrobial resistance of Escherichia coli from human and animal sources uncovers multiple resistances from human sources. PLoS One 2011, 6: e20819. doi:10.1371/journal.pone.0020819

60. IPCC Fourth Assessment Report, Summary for Policymakers. 2007.

61. Ishii S, Ksoll WB, Hicks RE, Sadowsky MJ: Presence and growth of naturalized Escherichia coli in temperate soils from Lake Superior watersheds. Appl Environ Microbiol 2006, 72(1):612–621.

62. Jamieson R, Gordon R, Sharples K, Stratton G, Madani A: Movement and persistence of fecal bacteria in agricultural soils and subsurface drainage water: A review. Can Biosyst Eng 2002, 44: 1.1–1.90.

63. Jamieson R, Gordon R, Joy D, Lee H: Assessing microbial pollution of rural surface waters: A review of current watershed scale modeling approaches. Agric Water Manag 2004, 70(1):1–17.

64. Jamieson R, Joy DM, Lee H, Kostaschuk R, Gordon R: Transport and deposition of sediment-associated Escherichia coli in natural streams. Water Res 2005, 39(12):2665–2675.

65. Jamieson RC, Joy DM, Lee H, Kostaschuk R, Gordon RJ: Resuspension of sediment-associated Escherichia coli in a natural stream. J Environ Qual 2005, 34(2):581–589.

66. Jin Y, Flury M: Fate and transport of viruses in porous media. Adv Agron 2002, 77: 39–102.

67. John DE, Rose JB: Review of factors affecting microbial survival in groundwater. Environ Sci Tech 2005, 39(19):7345–7356.

68. Jordan EO, Russell HL, Zeit FR: The longevity of the typhoid bacillus in water. J Infect Dis 1904, 1(4):641–689.

69. Kaloudis T, Zervou S, Tsimeli K, Triantis TM, Fotiou T, Hiskia A: Determination of microcystins and nodularin (cyanobacterial toxins) in water by LC-MS/MS. Monitoring of Lake Marathonas, a water reservoir of Athens, Greece. J Hazard Mater 2013, 263: 105–115.

70. Kapuscinski RB, Mitchell R: Sunlight-induced mortality of viruses and Escherichia coli in coastal seawater. Environ Sci Technol 1983, 17(1):1–6.

71. Kay D, Edwards AC, Ferrier RC, Francis C, Kay C, Rushby L, Watkins J, McDonald AT, Wyer M, Crowther J, Wilkinson J: Catchment microbial dynamics: the emergence of a research agenda. Prog Phys Geogr 2007, 31(1):59–76.

72. Kay D, Crowther J, Stampleton CM, Wyer MD, Fewtrell L, Anthony S, Bradford M, Edwards A, Francis CA, Hopkins M, Kay C, McDonald AT, Watkins J, Wilkinson J: Faecal indicator organism concentrations and catchment export coefficients in the UK. Water Res 2008, 42: 2649–2661.

73. Ketchum BH, Ayers JC, Vaccaro RF: Processes contributing to the decrease of coliform bacteria in a tidal estuary. Ecology 1952, 33(2):247–258.

74. Kiefer LA, Shelton DR, Pachepsky Y, Blaustein R, Santin-Duran M: Persistence of E. coli introduced into streabe dsedient with goose, deer and bovine animal waste. Lett Appl Microbiol 2012, 55(5):345–353.

75. Kim JW, Pachepsky YA, Shelton DR, Coppock C: Effect of streambed bacteria release on E. coli concentrations: Monitoring and modeling with the modified SWAT. Ecol Model 2010, 221(12):1592–1604.

76. Kistemann T, Classen T, Koch C, Dangendorf F, Fischeder R, Gebel J, Vacata V, Exner M: Microbial load of drinking water reservoir tributaries during extreme rainfall and runoff. Appl Environ Microbiol 2002, 68(5):2188–2197.

77. Krause RM: Dynamics of emergence. J Infect Dis 1994, 170(2):265–271.

78. Liang Z, He Z, Zhou X, Powell C, Yang Y, He LM, Stoffella PJ: Impact of mixed land-use practices on the microbial water quality in a subtropical coastal watershed. Sci Total Environ 2013, 449: 426–433.

79. Lipp EK, Rodriguez-Palacios C, Rose JB: Occurrence and distribution of the human pathogen Vibrio vulnificus in a subtropical Gulf of Mexico estuary. Hydrobiologia 2001, 460(1):165–173.

80. Ma LP, Li B, Zhang T: Abundant rifampin resistance genes and significant correlations of antibiotic resistance genes and plasmids in various environments revealed by metagenomic analysis. Appl Microbiol Biotechnol 2014, 98: 5195–5204. doi:10.1007/s00253–014–5511–3

81. Mac Kenzie WR, Hoxie NJ, Proctor ME, Gradus MS, Blair KA, Peterson DE, Kazmierczak JJ, Addiss DG, Fox KR, Rose JB, Davis JP: A massive outbreak in Milwaukee of Cryptosporidium infection transmitted through the public water supply. N Engl J Med 1994, 331(3):161–167.

82. MacKintosh C, Beattie KA, Klumpp S, Cohen P, Codd GA: Cyanobacterial microcystin-LR is a potent and specific inhibitor of protein phosphatases 1 and 2A from both mammals and higher plants. FEBS Lett 1990, 264: 187–192.

83. Malakoff D: Water quality: microbiologists on the trail of polluting bacteria. Science 2002, 295(5564):2352–2353.

84. Martinez G, Pachepsky YA, Whelan G, Yakirevich AM, Guper A, Gish T: Rainfall-induced fecal indicator organisms transport from manured fields: Model sensitivity analysis. Environ Int 2014, 63: 121–129.

85. Moog PL: The hydrogeology and freshwater influx of Buttermilk Bay, Massachusetts, with regard to the circulation of coliforms and pollutants: a model study and development of methods for general application. Boston University, Boston, MA; 1987.

86. Muirhead RW, Monaghan RM: A two reservoir model to predict Escherichia coli losses to water from pastures grazed by dairy cows. Environ Int 2012, 40: 8–14.

87. Muirhead RW, Davies-Colley RJ, Donnison AM, Nagels JW: Faecal bacteria yields in artificial flood events: quantifying in-stream stores. Water Res 2004, 38(5):1215–1224.

88. Nagels JW, Davies-Colley RJ, Donnison AM, Muirhead RW: Faecal contamination over flood events in a pastoral agricultural stream in New Zealand. Water Sci Technol 2002, 45(12):45–52.

89. Nasser AM, Zaruk N, Tenenbaum L, Netzan Y: Comparative survival of Cryptosporidium , coxsackievirus A9 and Escherichia coli in stream, brackish-and sea waters. Water Sci Technol 2003, 47(3):91–96.

90. Neitsch SL, Arnold JG, Kiniry JR, Williams JR, King KW: Soil and water assessment tool: theoretical documentation, version 2005. Texas, U.S.A, Elsevier; 2005.

91. Nelson EJ, Harris JB, Glenn Morris J, Calderwood SB, Camilli A: Cholera transmission: the host, pathogen and bacteriophage dynamic. Nat Rev Microbiol 2009, 7(10):693–702.

92. Nevecherya IK, Shestakov VM, Mazaev VT, Shlepnina TG: Survival rate of pathogenic bacteria and viruses in groundwater. Water Resources 2005, 32(2):209–214.

93. Oikonomou A, Katsiapi M, Karayanni H, Moustaka-Gouni M, Kormas KA: Plankton microorganisms coinciding with two consecutive mass fish kills in a newly reconstructed lake. Sci World J 2012, 2012: 1–14. doi:10.1100/2012/504135

94. Okun DA: From cholera to cancer to cryptosporidiosis. J Environ Eng 1996, 122(6):453–458.

95. Pachepsky YA, Shelton DR: Escherichia coli and fecal coliforms in freshwater and estuarine sediments. Crit Rev Env Sci Tec 2011, 41(12):1067–1110.

96. Pachepsky YA, Sadeghi AM, Bradford SA, Shelton DR, Guber AK, Dao T: Transport and fate of manure-borne pathogens: Modeling perspective. Agric Water Manag 2006, 86(1–2):81–92.

97. Painter JA, Hoekstra RM, Ayers T, Tauxe RV, Braden CR, Angulo FJ, Griffin PM: Attribution of foodborne illnesses, hospitalizations, and deaths to food commodities by using outbreak data, United States, 1998–2008. Emerg Infect Dis 2013, 19(3):407–415.

98. Pandey PK, Soupir ML: Non-point Source Pollution. Berkshire Encyclopedia of Sustainability: Ecosystem Management and Sustainability. Berkshire Publishing Group, LLC, Great Barrington, MA, U.S; 2012a.

99. Pandey PK, Soupir ML: Assessing the impacts of E. coli laden streambed sediment on E. coli loads over a range of flows and sediment characteristics. J Am Water Resour Assoc 2013, 49(6):1261–1269.

100. Pandey PK, Soupir ML, Rehmann CR: A model for predicting resuspension of Escherichia coli from streambed sediments. Water Res 2012b, 46: 115–126.

101. Pang L: Microbial removal rates in subsurface media estimated from published studies of field experiments and large intact soil cores. J Environ Qual 2009, 38: 1531–1559. doi:10.2134/jeq2008.0379

102. Pang L, Close M, Goltz M, Sinton L, Davies H, Hall C, Stanton G: Estimation of septic tank setback distances based on transport of E. coli and F-RNA phages. Environ Int 2004, 29(7):907–921.

103. Parajuli PB, Douglas-Mankin KR, Barnes PL, Rossi CG: Fecal bacteria source characterization and sensitivity analysis of SWAT 2005. Trans ASAE 2009, 52: 1847–1858.

104. Rao VC, Seidel KM, Goyal SM, Metcalf TG, Melnick JL: Isolation of enteroviruses from water, suspended solids, and sediments from Galveston Bay: survival of poliovirus and rotavirus adsorbed to sediments. Appl Environ Microb 1984, 48(2):404–409.

105. Rehmann CR, Soupir ML: Importance of interactions between the water column and the sediment for microbial concentrations in streams. Water Res 2009, 43(18):4579–4589.

106. Rhodes MW, Kator HI: Effects of sunlight and autochthonous microbiota on Escherichia coli survival in an estuarine environment. Curr Microbiol 1990, 21(1):65–73.

107. Rippey SR: Infectious-diseases associated with molluscan shellfish consumption. Clin Microbiol Rev 1994, 7(4):419–425.

108. Roberts MC, Soge OO, No D: Comparison of multi-drug resistant environmental methicillin-resistant Staphylococcus aureus isolated from recreational beaches and high touch surfaces in built environment. Front Microbiol 2013, 4(74):1–8. doi:10.3389/fmicb.2013.00074

109. Rubentschik L, Roisin MB, Bieljansky FM: Adsorption of bacteria in Salt Lakes. J Bacteriol 1936, 32(1):11–31.

110. Rudolfs W, Falk LL, Ragotzkie RA: Literature review on the occurrence and survival of enteric, pathogenic, and relative organisms in soil, water, sewage, and sludge, and on vegetation. Sewage Ind Wastes 1950, 22(10):1261–1281.

111. Ruediger GF: Studies on the self-purification of streams. Am J Public Health Assoc 1911, 1(6):411–415.

112. Sayler GS, Nelson JD, Justice A, Colwell RR: Distribution and significance of fecal indicator organisms in the Upper Chesapeake Bay. Appl Environ Microb 1975, 30(4):625–638.

113. Schijven JF, Hassanizadeh SM: Removal of viruses by soil passage: overview of modeling, processes, and parameters. Crit Rev Env Sci Tec 2000, 30(1):49–127.

114. Schrader M, Hauffe T, Zhang Z, Davis GM, Jopp F, Remais JV, Wilke T: Spatially explicit modeling of Schistosomiasis risk in eastern China based on a synthesis of epidemiological, environmental, and intermediate host genetic data. PLoS Negl Trop Dis 2013, 7(7):e2327.

115. Schriewer A, Miller WA, Byrne BA, Miller MA, Oates S, Conrad PA, Hardin D, Yang HH, Chouicha N, Melli A, Jessup D, Dominik C, Wuertz S: Presence of bacteroidales as a predictor of pathogens in surface waters of the Central California coast. Appl Environ Microbiol 2010, 76(17):5802–5814.

116. Scott TW, Takken W, Knols BGJ, Boete C: The ecology of genetically modified mosquitoes. Science 2002, 298(5591):117–119.

117. Simons GW, Hilscher R, Ferguson HF, Gage SDM: Report of the committee of bathing places. Am J Public Health 1922, 12(1):121–123.

118. Sinton LW, Finlay RK, Lynch PA: Sunlight inactivation of fecal bacteriophages and bacteria in sewage-polluted seawater. Appl Environ Microb 1999, 65(8):3605–3613.

119. Smith RJ, Twedt RM, Flanigan LK: Relationships of indicator and pathogenic bacteria in stream waters. Journal (Water Pollution Control Federation) 1973, 45(8):1736–1745.

120. Smith EM, Gerba CP, Melnick JL: Role of sediment in the persistence of enteroviruses in the estuarine environment. Appl Environ Microb 1978, 35(4):685–689.

121. Smith RA, Alexander RB, Wolman MG: Water-quality trends in the Nation's rivers. Science 1987, 235(4796):1607–1615.

122. Smith J, Edwards J, Hilger H, Steck RTR: Sediment can be a reservoir for coliform bacteria released into streams. J Gen Appl Microbiol 2008, 54: 173–179.

123. Snow J (1854) A Map of Cholera Deaths in London, 1840's. York University

124. Solo-Gabriele HM, Wolfert MA, Desmarais TR, Palmer CJ: Sources of Escherichia coli in a coastal subtropical environment. Appl Environ Microb 2000, 66(1):230–237.

125. Staley ZR, Rohr JR, Senkbeil JK, Harwood VJ (2014) Agrochemicals indirectly increase survival of E.coli O157:H7 and indicator bacteria by reducing ecosystem services. Ecol Appl, [http://dx.doi.org/10.1890/13–1242.1]

126. Steinmann P, Keiser J, Bos R, Tanner M, Utzinger J: Schistosomiasis and water resources development: systematic review, meta-analysis, and estimates of people at risk. Lancet Infect Dis 2006, 6(7):411–425.

127. Terzieva SI, McFeters GA: Survival and injury of E. coli , Campylobacter jejuni , and Yersinia Enterocolitica in stream water. Can J Microbiol 1991, 37(10):785–790.

128. U.S. Environmental Protection Agency (2010a) WATERS (Watershed Assessment, Tracking & Environmental Results). Washington, DC, . Accessed May 8 2014, [http://water.epa.gov/scitech/datait/tools/waters/index.cfm]

129. Environmental Protection Agency (U.S. EPA) Ambient Water Quality Criteria for Bacteria. EPA 44015–84–002. Office of Regulations and Stand, Washington, DC; 1986. Accessed May 8 2014

130. U.S. Environmental Protection Agency (U.S. EPA) Protocol for Developing Pathogen TMDLs. National Summary of Impaired Waters and TMDL Information Washington, DC. 2001. Accessed May 8 2014

131. U.S. Environmental Protection Agency (U.S. EPA) Protocol for Developing Pathogen TMDLs. National Summary of Impaired Waters and TMDL Information. Washington, DC; 2010b. http://iaspub.epa.gov/waters10/attains_nation_cy.control? p_report_type=T. Accessed May 8 2014

132. U.S. Environmental Protection Agency (U.S. EPA) Impaired Waters and Total Maximum Daily Loads. 2012a. Accessed May 8 2014

133. U.S. Environmental Protection Agency (U.S. EPA) Drinking Water Contaminants. National Primary Drinking Water Regulations. 2012b. Accessed May 18 2014

134. U.S. Environmental Protection Agency (U.S. EPA) Protocol for Developing Pathogen TMDLs. National Summary of Impaired Waters and TMDL Information, Washington, DC; 2014. http://iaspub.epa.gov/waters10/attains_nation_cy.control?p_report_type=T. Accessed May 8 2014

135. U.S. Environmental Protection Agency (U.S. EPA) Cyanobacterial Harmful Algal Blooms. 2014. Accessed May 8 2014

136. U.S. Environmental Protection Agency (U.S. EPA) Hypoxia. 2014. http://water.epa.gov/type/watersheds/named/msbasin/hypoxia101.cfm. Accessed May 8 2014

137. U.S. Geological Survey (U.S.G. S.) Dead Zone: the Source of the Gulf of Mexico's Hypoxia. 2012. http://www.usgs.gov/blogs/features/usgs_top_story/deadzone-the-source-of-the-gulf-of-mexicos-hypoxia/. Accessed Apr 28 2014

138. U.S. Geological Survey (U.S.G. S.) The Gulf of Mexico Hypoxic Zone. 2014. http://toxics.usgs.gov/hypoxia/hypoxic_zone.html. Accessed May 8 2014

139. Unc A, Goss MJ: Transport of bacteria from manure and protection of water resources. Appl Soil Ecol 2004, 25: 1–18.

140. World Water Day 2025: 4,000 children die each day from a lack of safe water. 2014.

141. Vareli K, Briasoulis E, Pilidis G, Sainis I: Molecular confirmation of Planktothrix rubescens as the cause of intense, microcystin—synthesizing cyanobacterial bloom in Lake Ziros, Greece. Harmful Algae 2009, 8: 447–453.

142. Viau EJ, Goodwin KD, Yamahara KM, Layton BA, Sassoubre LM, Burns SL, Tong HI, Wong SHC, Lu Y, Boehm AB: Bacterial pathogens in Hawaiian coastal streams — associations with fecal indicators, land cover, and water quality. Water Res 2011, 45: 3279–3290.

143. Wade TJ, Calderon RL, Sams E, Beach M, Brenner KP, Williams AH, Dufour AP: Rapidly measured indicators of recreational water quality are predictive of swimming-associated gastrointestinal illness. Environ Health Perspect 2006, 114: 24–28.

144. Wang Y, Bradford SA, Simunek J: Estimation and upscaling of dual-permeability model parameters for the transport of Ecoli D21g in soils with preferential flow. J Contam Hydrol 2014a, 159: 57–66.

145. Wang Y, Bradford SA, Simunek J (2014b) Physicochemical factors influencing the preferential transport of Escherichia coli in soils. Vadose Zone J 13(1) doi:, [10.2136/vzj2013.07.0120]

146. Wcislo R, Chrost RJ: Survival of Escherichia coli in freshwater. Pol J Environ Stud 2000, 9(3):215–222.

147. Weiskel PK, Howes BL, Heufelder GR: Coliform contamination of a coastal embayment: Sources and transport pathways. Environ Sci Technol 1996, 30(6):1872–1881.

148. White DL, Bushek D, Porter DE, Edwards D: Geographic information systems (GIS) and kriging: analysis of the spatial and temporal distributions of the oyster pathogen Perkinsus marinus in a developed and an undeveloped estuary. J Shellfish Res 1998, 17(5):1473–1476.

149. Millennium Development Goals: progress towards the health-related Millennium Development Goals. 2011.

150. Wilkes G, Brassard J, Edge TA, Gannon V, Jokinen CC, Jones TH, Lapen DR: Coherence among different microbial source tracking markers in a small agricultural stream with or without livestock exclusion practices. Appl Environ Microbiol 2014, 79(20):6207–6219.

151. Woolhouse MEJ: Population biology of emerging and re-emerging pathogens. Trends Microbiol 2002, 10(10):s3-s7.

152. World Bank (2010) Water Resource Management. Washington, D. C, . Accessed 26 Apr 2012, [http://www.worldbank.org/en/topic/waterresourcesmanagement]

153. World Health Organization (WHO) Water Sanitation and Health. 2010. http://www.who.int/water_sanitation_health/diseases/en/. Accessed 20 Apr 2012

154. World Health Organization (WHO) Water Quality and Health. Drinking water chlorination – A review of disinfection practices and issues. 2014. http://www.waterandhealth.org/drinkingwater/wp.html. Accessed 28 Apr 2014

155. Yoshizawa S, Matsushima R, Watanabe MF, Harada K, Ichihara A, Carmichael WW, Fujiki H: Inhibition of protein phosphatases by microcystis and nodularin associated with hepatotoxicity. J Cancer Res Clin Oncol 1990, 116: 609–614.

4 Engineering Bacteria for Bioremediation

Elen Aquino Perpetuo, Cleide Barbieri Souza and Claudio Augusto Oller Nascimento

CEPEMA-University of São Paulo, Brazil

INTRODUCTION

Bioremediation is a process that uses microorganisms or their enzymes to promote degradation and/or removal of contaminants from the environment. The use of microbial metabolic ability for degradation/removal of environmental pollutants provides an economic and safe alternative compared to other physicochemical methodologies. However, although highly diverse and specialized microbial communities present in the environment do efficiently remove many pollutants, this process is usually quite slow, which leads to a tendency for pollutants to accumulate in the environment and this accumulation can potentially be hazardous. This is especially true for heavy metals. Heavy metal contamination is one of the most significant environmental issues, since metals are highly toxic to biota, as they decrease metabolic activity and diversity, and they affect the qualitative and quantitative structure of microbial communities. For treating heavy metal contaminated tailings and soils, bioremediation is still the most cost-effective method, although various heavy metals are beyond the bioaccumulation capabilities of microorganisms. Perhaps, because of the toxicity of these compounds, microorganisms have not evolved appropriate pathways to bioaccumulate them; populations of microorganisms responsible for this bioaccumulation are not large or active enough to remove these compounds completely, or complex mixtures of pollutants resist removal by existing pathways. The pathway used to accumulate these compounds is adsorption, where metals are taken up by microbial cells (biosorption). Biosorption mechanisms are numerous and are not yet fully understood. However, biosorption capacity often varies with test conditions, such as initial metal concentration, solution pH, contact time, biomass dosage, processing method, and so on. Accordingly, populations of microorganisms that are able to promote metal adsorption and accumulate them are not large or active enough to support these compounds by existing pathways. Furthermore, there are several strategies that optimize the bioremediation process of pollutants. One approach to enhance populations of microorganisms capable of pollutant removal is the addition of exogenous microorganisms in order to expand indigenous populations. This process, commonly known as bioaugmentation, can be performed either by adding microorganisms that naturally contain catabolic genes or those that have been genetically modified (GMOs). This strategy can also result in the transfer of plasmids containing the necessary genetic material between the different populations. Recent advances in the molecular biology field have been applied to microorganisms in order to produce novel strains with desirable properties for the bioremediation processes. These include the construction or adaptation of catabolic pathways; redirection of carbon flux to prevent the formation of harmful intermediates; modification of catabolic enzyme affinity and specificity; improvement of the genetic stability of catabolic activities; increasing the bioavailability of pollutants; and enhancement of the monitoring, yield, control, and efficiency of processes. Despite the many advantages of GMOs with regards to bioremediation, their use is still limited in the environment because of the instability of the inserted genetic material. There are two major reasons for this: first, the efficiency of GMOs is dependent on their ability to carry the genetic material in a stable manner; second, the transfer of genetic material to the indigenous organisms is perceived to be a negative attribute, despite the fact that this transfer is a common phenomenon among native organisms. These factors have incentivized the study of survival, competition and persistence of GMOs in the environment, as well as the potential risks involved in their use. Besides the significant advances that have already been made with regards to the development and utilization of GMOs for bioremediation of contaminants in the environment, many more challenges still remain. In this chapter, we will detail how genetic engineering may improve bioremediation through the engineering of bacteria. Several genetic approaches have been developed and used to optimize enzymes, metabolic pathways and organisms that are relevant to biodegradation. New information on metabolic routes is still being accumulated, thus the available toolbox is continuously being expanded. With molecular methods enabling the characterization of microbial community structure, metabolic pathways and enzyme activities, the performance of microorganisms under *in situ* conditions can be improved by making heavy metal bioremediation a much more efficient process. The present review also highlights the current situation pertaining to biosorbents, their mechanisms and advantages and disadvantages. Thus, this article reviews the achievements and current status of biosorption technology, which exploits natural biodiversity and molecular tools, in order to engineer microorganisms and provide new information about this research frontier.

Heavy Metals and Toxicicity

Heavy metals are considered to be chemical elements with an atomic mass greater than 22 and a density greater than 5g/mL. This definition includes 69 elements, of which 16 are synthetic. Some of these elements are extremely toxic to human beings, even at very low concentrations (Roane & Pepper, 2000; Wang & Chen, 2006). The main heavy metals associated with environmental contamination, and which offer potential danger to the ecosystem, are copper (Cu), zinc (Zn), silver (Ag), lead (Pb), mercury (Hg), arsenic (As), cadmium (Cd), chromium (Cr), strontium (Sr), cesium (Cs), cobalt (Co), nickel (Ni), thallium (Tl), tin (Sn) and vanadium (V) (Wang & Chen, 2006). In general, metal ions can be classified as: 1) Essential and important for metabolism (Na, K, Mg, Ca, V, Mn, Fe, Co, Ni, Cu, Zn, Mo and W); 2) Toxic heavy metals (Hg, Cr, Pb, Cd, As, Sr, Ag, Si, Al, Tl), which have no biological function (in ecotoxicology terms, hexavalent forms of Hg, Cr, Pb and Cd ions are the most dangerous); 3) Radionuclides (U, Rn, Th, Ra, Am, Tc), which are radioactive isotopes and, although toxic to cells, they are nonetheless important in nuclear medicine procedures; 4) Semi-metals or metalloids (B, Si, Ge, As,

Sb, Te, Po, At, Se), which exert distinct biological effects on metals. However, metals are predominantly present in the environment in cationic and anionic forms in semimetals, and As is often classified as heavy metal (Roane & Pepper, 2000; Ahluwalia & Goyal, 2007). In the environment, metals can be divided into two categories: 1) bioavailable (soluble, non-absorbed, mobile); and 2) non-bioavailable (precipited, complexed, sorbed, non-mobile). The ionic form (speciation) of a metal determines its bioavailability and its destination. Most heavy metals are cations and this determines their sorption to negatively charged functional groups that are present in: cell surfaces, which are generally anionic at a pH of between 4 and 8; surfaces with residual hydroxides (OH^-) or thiol (SH^-) and anionic salts, such as PO^{4-} and SO^{4-}, humic acid, and clay minerals (Roane & Pepper, 2000). Heavy metal ions possess great electrostatic attraction and high binding affinities to the same sites that essential metal ions normally bind to various cellular structures, causing destabilization of the structures and biomolecules (cell-wall enzymes, DNA and RNA), thus inducing replication defects and consequent mutagenesis, hereditary genetic disorders and cancer. This occurs, for example, with arsenate, which competes with phosphate, and cadmium, which competes with zinc. By employing microarray technology, Kawata et. al. (2007), found that six heavy metals (arsenic, cadmium, nickel, antimony, mercury and chromium) induce gene expression patterns that are very similar to the pattern induced by DMNQ (2.3-dimethoxy-1, 4-naphthoquinone), the reactive oxygen species (ROS) chemical generating agent, which causes "oxidative stress", leading to deleterious effects (membrane damage or other cellular lipid structures, modification of proteins, fragmentation and cross-links, changes in DNA that can induce mutations or be repaired by repair mechanisms). Therefore, the ions of heavy metals cause oxidative damage, both directly, by producing ROS, and indirectly, by inactivating the cellular antioxidant system, thus leading to cell damage (Mannazzu et. al., 2000; Liu et. al., 2005).

Heavy Metals and the Environment

Among the different contaminants, heavy metals have received special attention due to their strength and persistence in accumulating in ecosystems, where they cause damage by moving up the food chain to finally accrue in human beings, who are at the top of this chain (Figure 1) (Volesky, 2001; Ahluwalia & Goyal, 2007; Machado et. al., 2008).

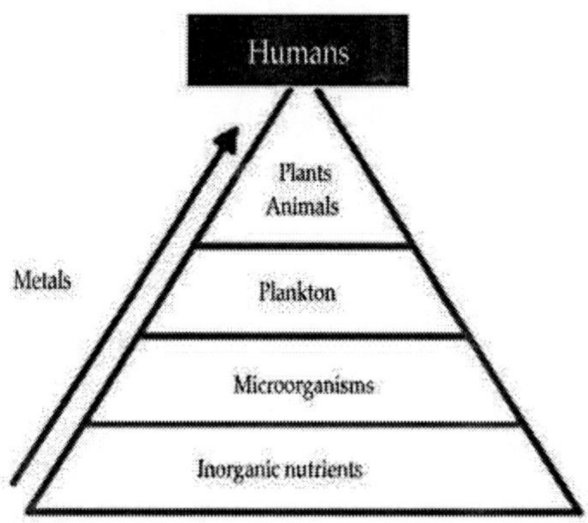

Figure 1. The destiny of heavy metals released into the environment and their accumulation throughout the chain food. Adapted from Volesky (2001).

\The toxic potential of heavy metals with regards to the human body is diverse and, because of their toxicity and persistence in nature, the levels of heavy metals in the environment need to be controlled by mandating waste treatment at the sources of pollution. The development of new treatment technologies is required at these sources; however, even though there is awareness of this problem, sustainable solutions are not easily accessible. In general, the conventional treatment methods used to remove metals from wastewater are inefficient and cost-prohibitive.

Conventional Technologies for Treating Environments Contaminated by Heavy Metals

Environments contaminated by heavy metals are treated by means of conventional technologies based on physicochemical principles, which are considered inefficient and uneconomic. One method often employed to remove metals from aqueous solutions involves the addition of reagents that increase pH, thus converting metals from a soluble form into an insoluble form (hydroxides), which results in their precipitation. This procedure produces large quantities of mud in the final wastewater with concentrations of metals in the order of mg/L, which is difficult to dispose of. More complex processes of this type can involve single or multiple steps: 1) precipitation with hydroxides, carbonates or sulfides; 2) redox chemistry; 3) sorption (adsorption with activated carbon/ion exchange); 4) use of membranes (ultrafiltration, electrodialysis and reverse osmosis-RO); 5) electrolytic recovery; 6) evaporation; 7) liquid-liquid extraction; 8) electrodeposition. On the other hand, bioremediation is increasingly gaining importance as an alternative technology, due the advantages it offers: simplicity, efficiency and low cost (Goyal et. al., 2003; Tabak et. al., 2005; Hameed, 2006; Machado et. al., 2008; Wang & Chen, 2009).

Types of Bioremediation

Bioremediation involves the use of plants or microorganisms, viable or not, natural or genetically engineered to treat environments contaminated with organic molecules that are difficult to break down (xenobiotics) and to mitigate toxic heavy metals, by transforming them into substances with little or no toxicity, hence forming innocuous products (Dobson & Burgess, 2007; Li & Li, 2011). With the objective of improving the process of bioremediation, different strategies can be employed, depending of the state of the contaminated environment. One of these strategies, biostimulation, involves promoting the growth of autochthonous microorganisms at the contaminated site, in order to introduce pH-correction substances, nutrients, surfactants and oxygen. As a consequence, the rate of biodegradation/bioremediation can be increased. Another strategy, bioaugmentation or bioaddition, is the addition of microbial populations to indigenous, alien or genetically modified organisms (GMO), in places where there is an insufficiency of indigenous microorganisms with ecophysiological characteristics compatible with the habitat conditions that are conducive to the promotion of bioremediation (Vidali, 2001; Silva et. al., 2004; Gaylard *et. al.*, 2005; Li & Li, 2011). Bioremediation is a versatile process that can be applied *in-situ*, at the contaminated site, or *ex-situ*, involving removal of contaminated material to be treated elsewhere. *In-situ* bioremediation technologies are more economical and release fewer pollutants into the environment; however, they may require longer treatment timeframes than the *ex-situ* techniques (Vidali, 2001; Tabak et. al., 2005; Costa *et. al.*, 2007). Currently, there is wide variety of microorganisms (bacteria, fungi, yeasts and algae) that are being studied for use in bioremediation processes, and some of these have already been employed as biosorbents of heavy metals (Roane & Pepper, 2000; Machado et. al., 2008; Bogacka, 2011). The main advantages of biosorption over conventional treatment methods include: low cost; high efficiency; minimization of chemical and biological sludge; selectivity to specific metals; no additional nutrient requirement; regeneration of the biosorbent; and the possibility of metal recovery (Kratochvil & Volesky, 1998). Most studies on the bioremediation of heavy metals present the following as a biphasic biosorption process: 1) rapid initial phase (adsorption), not dependent on metabolism or temperature, which is generally reversible; and, 2) slower phase (intracellular accumulation) metabolism-dependent, influenced by environmental factors such: temperature, which decreases the biosorption capacity due to damage to the target sites (in general, the temperature considered "ideal" is between 25-35°C); and metabolic inhibitors (Roane & Pepper, 2000; Malik, 2004; Tabak, 2005). Desorption is a very important process in the success of the applicability of bioremediation for the treatment of wastewater, because it allows for the recovery of adsorbed metal ions, as well as the recycling and reuse of biomass for a new cycle of metal recovery. There is obviously great interest in the development of a procedure that enables the recovery of removed metal ions, as well as for the cellular integrity of the biosorbents to be maintained, thus allowing for their regeneration and reuse in successive cycles of sorption-desorption. This results in the simultaneous acquisition of two valuable products: treated water and low-cost recovery of metal (Aldor *et. al.,* 1995; Volesky, 2001; Yu & Kaewsarn, 2001).

EXPLOITATION OF THE NATURAL BIODIVERSITY

Microorganisms as Biosorbents of Heavy Metals

Several studies have shown that many organisms, prokaryotes and eukaryotes, have different natural capacities to biosorb toxic heavy metal ions (Table 1), giving them different degrees of intrinsic resistance, particularly in diluted solutions (between 10 to 20 mg/L^{-1}), due to their mobility, as well as the solubility and bioavailability capacities of these metal ions (Malik, 2004; Tabak et. al., 2005; Kim et. al., 2007; Chen & Wang, 2008).

The manner in which microorganisms interact with heavy metal ions depends partly on whether they are eukaryotes or prokaryotes. Eukaryotes are more sensitive to metal toxicity than bacteria. In the presence of toxic concentrations, several resistance mechanisms are activated, for example: the production of peptides of the family of metal binding proteins, such as metallothioneins (MTs); the regulation of the intracellular concentration of metals, with expression of protein transporters of ligand-metal complexes from the cytoplasm to the inside of vacuoles, and efflux of metal ions by ion channels present in the cell wall. In bacteria, these tolerance mechanisms are often encoded by plasmids, which facilitate their dispersion from cell to cell (Valls & Lorenzo, 2002). For the bioremediation of heavy metals on an industrial scale, it is important to use low-cost biomaterial, which can be a byproduct or waste material with high removal capacity, since the low cost of this biomass is crucial for the process to be economically viable (Volesky & Holan, 1995; Zouboulis *et. al.*, 2001). Several studies have been conducted with the purpose of improving the resistance and/or the ability of microorganisms to accumulate heavy metal ions, including a number of studies that follow parameters: pH (Naeem et. al., 2006); temperature; different metal concentrations and biomass (Soares et. al., 2003; Kim et. al., 2005), competitiveness of ions of different elements; microorganism-metal contact time (Kotrba & Ruml, 2000), composition of the culture medium (Ghosh et. al., 2006); bioaugmentation/biostimulation (Roane & Pepper, 2001; Silva et. al., 2004), resistance to toxicity of heavy metals of Gram positive/Gram-negative bacteria (Samuelson et. al., 2002); intracellular/extracellular bioaccumulation; viable /non-viable cells, free /immobilized cells, and biological processes by aerobic/anaerobic microorganisms (Dias et. al., 2002; Liu et. al., 2005; Tabak et. al., 2005; Wang & Chen, 2006).

Table 1. Examples of microorganisms studied and strategically treated for bioremediation of heavy metals

Organisms	Genus/species	Reference
Bacteria	*Arthrobacter*	Roanne & Pepper, 2001
	Bacillus sp	Gupta *et. al.*, 2000; Dias *et. al.*, 2002 ; Kim *et. al.*, 2007
	Citrobacter	Renninger *et. al.*, 2001
	Cupriavidus metallidurans	Roanne & Pepper, 2001 ; Grass *et. al.*, 2005
	Cyanobacteria	Gupta *et. al.*, 2000
	Enterobacter cloacae	Hernandes *et. al.*, 1998; Gupta *et. al.*, 2000
	Pseudomonas aeruginosa	Dias *et. al.*, 2002; Zhang *et. al.*, 2005
	Streptomyces sp	Dias *et. al.*, 2002
	Zoogloea ramigera	Gupta *et. al.*, 2000
Archea	Filo *Crenarchaeota*	Sandaa *et. al.*, 1999
	Phanerochaete chrysosporium	Wu & Yu, 2007
Fungi	*Aspergillus tereus*	Kumar *et. al.*, 2008
	Penicillium chrysogenum	Dias *et. al.*, 2002
Yeast	*Candida utilis*	Kujan *et. al.*, 2006
	Hansenula anomala	Breierová *et. al.*, 2002
	Rhodotorula mucilaginosa	Dias *et. al.*, 2002
	Rhodotorula rubra GVa5	Ghosh *et. al.*, 2006
	Saccharomyces cerevisiae	Gupta *et. al.*, 2000; Dias *et. al.*, 2002; Ghosh *et. al.*, 2006

The search for new technologies for the removal of toxic metals from contaminated sites has focused on biosorption, which is based on the metal binding capacities of various biological materials. Biosorption can be defined as the ability of biological materials to accumulate heavy metals from wastewater through metabolically mediated or physicochemical uptake pathways (Fourest & Roux, 1992). Algae, bacteria, fungi and yeasts have all proven to be potential metal biosorbents (Volesky, 1987). Many indigenous organisms isolated from sites contaminated with heavy metals have tolerance to heavy metal toxicity and these microbial activities have always been the natural starting point for all biotechnological applications. It is therefore necessary to isolate bacterial strains with novel metabolic capabilities and to establish degradation pathways both biochemically and genetically. Potent metal biosorbents in the bacteria class include the genus *Bacillus* (Nakajima & Tsuruta, 2004; Tunali et. al., 2006), *Pseudomonas* (Chang et.

al., 1997; Uslu & Tanyol, 2006) and *Streptomyces* (Mameri et. al., 1999; Selatnia et. al., 2004a). The biosorption process involves a solid phase (sorbent or biosorbent; biological material) and a liquid phase (solvent, normally water) containing a dissolved species to be sorbed (sorbate, metal ions). Due to higher affinity of the sorbent for the sorbate species, the latter is attracted and bound there by different mechanisms. The process continues until equilibrium is established between the amount of solid-bound sorbate species and its portion remaining in the solution. The degree of sorbent affinity to the sorbate determines its distribution between solid and liquid phases.

Biosorbent material: Strong biosorbent behaviour of certain microorganisms towards metallic ions is a function of the chemical make-up of the microbial cells. This type of biosorbent consists of dead and metabolically inactive cells. Some types of biosorbents probably have a broad range, binding and collecting the majority of heavy metals with no specific preference, while others are specific to certain metals. Some laboratories have used easily available biomass whereas others have isolated specific strains of microorganisms and some have also processed existing raw biomass to a certain degree to improve its biosorption properties. Recent biosorption experiments have focused attention on waste materials, which are by-products or residues from large-scale industrial operations. E.g., mycelia waste available from fermentation processes, solid waste from olive oil manufacturing plants (Pagnanelli et. al., 2002), activated sludge from sewage treatment plants (Hammaini et. al., 2003), biosolids (Norton et. al., 2004) and aquatic macrophytes (Keskinkan et. al., 2003), etc. The biosorption mechanism is complex, including mainly ion exchange, chelation, adsorption by physical forces, entrapment in intra and interfibrilliar capillaries and spaces of the structural polysaccharide network as a result of the concentration gradient and diffusion through cell walls and membranes. There are several chemical groups that are thought to attract and sequester metals in biomass: acetamido groups of chitin, structural polysaccharides of fungi, amino and phosphate groups in nucleic acids, amido, amino, sulphydryl and carboxyl groups in proteins, hydroxyls in polysaccharide and mainly carboxyls and sulphates in polysaccharides of marine algae that belong to the divisions Phaeophyta, Rhodophyta and Chlorophyta. However, this does not necessarily mean that the presence of a particular functional group guarantees biosorption, perhaps due to steric, conformational or other barriers. The choice of metal for biosorption process: The appropriate selection of metals for biosorption studies is dependent on the angle of interest and the impact of different metals. Accordingly, they can be divided into four major categories: (i) toxic heavy metals (ii) strategic metals (iii) precious metals and (iv) radionuclides. In terms of environmental threats, categories (i) and (iv) are the ones of most concern with regards to their removal from the environment and/or from point source effluent discharges. Apart from toxicological criteria, the interest in specific metals may also be based on how representative their behavior is in terms of an eventual generalization of results regarding their biosorbent uptake. The toxicity and interesting solution chemistry of elements such as chromium, arsenic and selenium make them good candidates for study. Although not environmentally threatening, strategic and precious metals are important to consider from the standpoint of their recovery value. Research activities related to biosorption were initiated in the 1980s (Volesky & Holan, 1995; Volesky, 2001). Previously, research on this topic involved the use of biorremediation involving microorganisms alone to degrade organic compounds (Lovley & Coates, 1997). Since then, there has been an intensive effort to investigate the binding properties of heavy metals to different types of biomass (Chen & Wang, 2008). In general, biosorption is physicochemical interactions of metal ions with specific groups of the cell surface of microorganisms, which may enhance or inhibit intracellular transport or influence the processes of transformation and extracellular precipitation (biomineralization) (Davis et. al., 2003; Gavrilescu, 2004). Biosorption is based on passive (metabolism-independent) or active (metabolism-dependent) accumulation processes (Wang & Chen, 2006), in combinations that differ qualitatively and quantitatively, depending on the type of biomass, its origin, feasibility, and type of processing (Veglio & Beolchini, 1997). A classification of the mechanisms of metal accumulation can be made based on the dependence of cellular metabolism or according to the location of the metal within the cell.

Biosorption Mechanisms

The complex structure of microorganisms implies that there are many ways for the metal to be taken up by the microbial cell. There are various biosorption mechanisms and they are not yet fully understood. They may be classified according to various criteria (Figure 2).

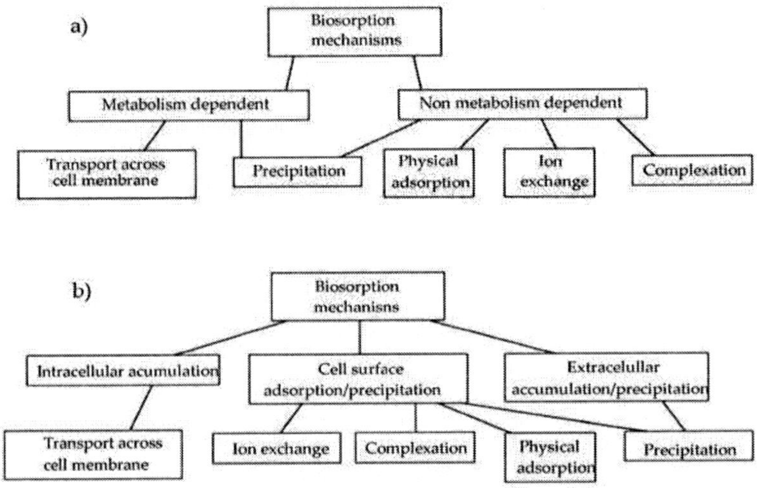

Figure 2. Mechanisms of biosorption, a) classification according to dependence on cell metabolism, b) classification according to the location within the cell and the metal removed (Veglio & Beolchini, 1997).

The transportation of metal across the cell membrane yields intracellular accumulation, which is dependent on the metabolism of the cell. This means that this kind of biosorption may only take place within viable cells. It is often associated with an active defense system of the microorganism, which reacts in the presence of a toxic metal. During non-metabolism dependent biosorption, metal uptake occurs by means of physicochemical interaction between the metal and the functional groups present on the microbial cell surface. This is based on physical adsorption, ion exchange and chemical sorption, which is not dependent on cell metabolism. Cell walls of microbial biomass, which consists mostly of polysaccharides, proteins and lipids, have abundant metal binding groups such as carboxyl, sulphate, phosphate and amino groups. This type of biosorption, i.e., non-metabolism dependent, is relatively rapid and can be reversible (Kuyucak & Volesky, 1988).

In the case of precipitation, metal uptake may take place both in the solution and on the cell surface (Ercole et. al., 1994). Furthermore, it may be dependent on cell metabolism if, in the presence of toxic metals, the microorganism produces compounds that favor the precipitation process. Precipitation may not be dependent on cell metabolism, if it occurs after a chemical interaction between the metal and the cell surface.

Due to the complexity of biomaterial, it is possible for several of these mechanisms to occur simultaneously, in degrees that depend on the biosorbent and environmental conditions (Kefala et. al., 1999; Volesky, 2001; Gavrilescu, 2004). Studies on biosorption by Wang & Chen (2006) have focused on selecting the most promising types of biomass and its future success by sorption will depend on interaction between three knowledge areas: biology, chemistry and engineering (Kefala et. al., 1999). Biosorption capacity is affected mainly by three factors: 1) characteristics of the metal ion (atomic weight, ionic ray, valence), 2) environmental conditions (pH, temperature, ionic strength, contact time, biomass concentration), and 3) the nature of the biosorbent, which may determine differences in selectivity and affinity to metal ions, since the type and species of microorganisms, conditions of growth, physiological state and cell age may all affect the binding mechanism to heavy metals (Wang & Chen, 2006; Chen & Wang, 2008).

Different strategies have been developed using recombinant DNA technology to produce genetically improved strains for use in the biosorption process, and many of these strategies "equip" the bacterial cell wall with metal ion-binding polypeptides to act as anchors. One of these studies was on the fusion protein: the β-domain of IgA protease of N. *gonorrhoeae* with metallothionein (MT) from rats (Valls et. al., 2000), and lpp-ompA-various sizes of peptides (EC20) (Bae et. al., 2000). The following items are the main biosorption mechanisms, which can also be considered mechanisms of resistance or tolerance to heavy metals developed by microorganisms.

Transport across cell membranes: Heavy metal transportation across microbial cell membranes may be mediated by the same mechanism used to convey metabolically important ions such as potassium, magnesium and sodium. The metal transport systems may become confused by the presence of heavy metal ions of the same charge and ionic radius associated with essential ions. This kind of mechanism is not associated with metabolic activity. Basically, biosorption by living organisms comprises of two steps: first, an independent binding metabolism where metals are bound to the cell walls; and second, metabolism-dependent intracellular uptake, whereby metal ions are transported across the cell membrane (Costa *et. al.*, 1990; Gadd et. al., 1988; Huang et. al., 1990; Nourbaksh et. al., 1994).

Physical adsorption: In this category, physical adsorption takes place with the help of van der Waals forces. Kuyucak & Volesky (1988), hypothesized that uranium, cadmium, zinc, copper and cobalt biosorption by dead biomasses of algae, fungi and yeasts takes place through electrostatic interactions between the metal ions in solutions and the cell walls of microbial cells. Electrostatic interactions have been proven to be responsible for copper biosorption by the *Zoogloea ramigera* bacterium and the *Chiarella vulgaris* alga (Asku et. al., 1992), and for chromium biosorption by the *Ganoderma lucidum* and *Aspergillus niger* fungi.

Ion Exchange: Cell walls of microorganisms contain polysaccharides and bivalent metal ions exchange with the counter ions of the polysaccharides. For example, the alginates of marine algae occur as salts of $K+$, $Na+$, $Ca^{2}+$, and $Mg^{2}+$. These ions can exchange with counter ions such as CO^{2+}, Cu^{2+}, Cd^{2+} and Zn^{2+}, resulting in the biosorptive uptake of heavy metals (Kuyucak & Volesky, 1988). The biosorption of copper by *Ganoderma lucidium* (Muraleedharan & Venkobachr, 1990) and *Aspergillus niger* fungi was also taken up by the ion exchange mechanism.

Complexation: An extracellular complexation or coordination is the result of electrostatic attraction between a metallic ion chelating agent and a polymer that can be excreted by a microorganism that is viable or not. It can be caused by: biosurfactants, polysaccharides, proteins and nucleic acids. These chelating agents contain pairs of electrons that present electrostatic attraction and if they cling to the metallic ions, there is no electron transfer. The final structure has the electric charge of the sum of individual charges of the participants of the complex (Veglio & Beolchini, 1997; Davis et. al., 2003). When this detoxification/ complexation system is overloaded, "oxidative stress" of the cell occurs (Gavrilescu, 2004).

Metal removal from the solution may also take place by complex formation on the cell surface after interaction between the metal and the active groups. Asku et. al. (1992) hypothesized that biosorption of copper by C. *vulgaris* and Z. *ramigera* takes place through both adsorption and the formation of coordination bonds between metals and amino and carboxyl groups of cell wall polysaccharides. Complexation was found to be the only mechanism responsible for the accumulation of calcium, magnesium, cadmium, zinc, copper and mercury by *Pseudomonas syringae.* Microorganisms may also produce organic acids (e.g., citric, oxalic, gluonic, fumaric, lactic and malic acids), which may chelate toxic metals, thus resulting in the formation of metallo-organic molecules. These organic acids help in the solubilization of metal compounds and leaching from their surfaces. Metals may be biosorbed or complexed by carboxyl groups found in microbial polysaccharides and other polymers.

Precipitation: Precipitation may be either dependent on the cellular metabolism or independent of it. In the former case, metal removal from solutions is often associated with the active defense system of the microorganisms. They react in the presence of toxic metal-producing compounds, which favor the precipitation process. In the case of precipitation that is not dependent on cellular metabolism, it may be a consequence of the chemical interaction between the metal and the cell surface. The various biosorption mechanisms mentioned above can take place simultaneously.

Adsorption: Physical adsorption is a process where the metal ion in solutions binds onto polyelectrolytes present in microbial cell wall through electrostatic interactions, Van der Waals forces, covalent bonding, redox interaction and biomineralization to achieve electroneutrality. This process is independent of metabolism, and it is reversible and very promising, as it presents many advantages, especially for treating large volumes of wastewater with low concentrations of contaminants (Ahluwalia & Goyal, 2007; Kuroda & Ueda, 2010; Nishitani et. al., 2010). In physical adsorption, the metal ions are attracted by the potential negative of the cell wall, and both are dependent on pH. The influence of pH on metal accumulation by yeasts, algae and bacteria are very similar; for example, in yeast, $pH < 2$ the accumulation of metals is practically zero, because in low pH the active sites of the cell wall are associated with protons, restricting the approach of metal cations, and thus resulting in a repulsive force. Therefore, as the pH increases, an increasing number of sites (acetamide chitin, structural polysaccharides of fungi, phosphate and amino groups of nucleic acids, amino and carboxyl groups of proteins and hydroxyl groups of polysaccharides) are replaced by negative charges, increasing the attraction of metallic cations and adsorption on the cell surface. Accordingly, the solubility of metallic ions decreases and, consequently, their bioavailability is reduced, and precipitation occurs (Esposito et. al., 2002; Chen & Wang, 2008; Nishitani et. al., 2010; Kuroda & Ueda, 2011). Thus, a pH range of between 4 and 8 is generally accepted as "good" for the biosorption of heavy metals for almost all types of biomass (Borroka & Fein, 200; Wang & Chen, 2006; Machado et. al., 2010). Also, has been studied the role of extracellular polymeric substances (EPS) excreted by bacteria in the removal of heavy metal ions by adsorption process (Gupta *et. al.*, 2004).

Siderophores: Like heavy metal chelating agents, some types of microorganisms have low molecular weight, and these are called siderophores. When microorganisms are grown in an iron deficient medium, they produce specific iron chelators, so-called siderophores, in the medium. They play an important role in the complexation of toxic metals and radionuclides, by increasing their solubility. Siderophores have low molecular weights, and have compounds of the catecholate, phenolate or hydroxamate as their binding groups. Many bacteria, such as *Actinomycetes Azotobacter* and those of the genus *Pseudomonas*, synthesize these substances to capture the iron ions they require for their metabolic activity, or for biosorption (Pattus & Abdallah, 2000; Gazsó, 2001).

Biosurfactants: Most surfactants used in bioremediation are produced industrially from petroleum, but they can also be synthesized by microorganisms. Biosurfactants are natural surfactants synthesized by plants: (saponins), microorganisms (glycolipids) and the bodies of organisms (bile salts), and they have several advantages over industrially-produced surfactants, such as lower toxicity to degrading microorganisms and less recalcitrance in the environment, greater diversity of chemical structures; performance over a broader range of conditions at different temperatures and pHs (Bognolo, 1999). Biosurfactants of microbial origin (mainly aerobic) are the result of the metabolic byproducts of bacteria, fungi and yeasts, which are released into the medium. The hydrophilic portion may consist of amino acids, peptides or saccharides, and the hydrophobic portion is usually formed by saturated or unsaturated fatty acids. Biosurfactants are able to form various structures, such as micelles, vesicles and spherical or irregular lamellar structures, among others (Figure 3) (Champion et. al., 1995; Mulligan, 2005; Li & Li, 2011).

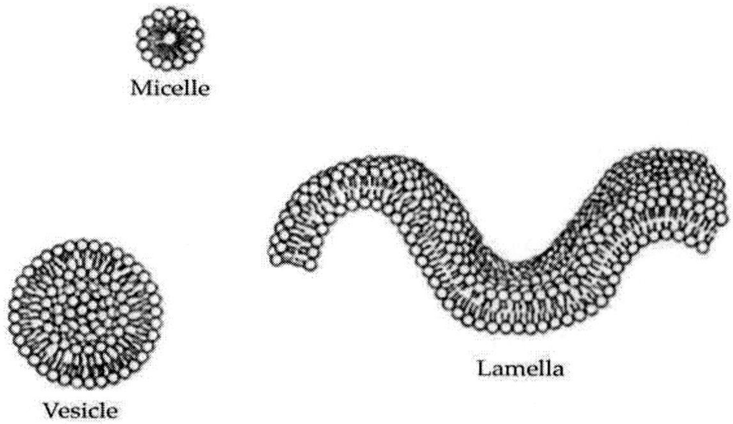

Figure 3. Basic structures formed by biosurfactants (Champion et. al., 1995).

Microorganisms naturally overcome their limitations when faced with insoluble organic and inorganic pollutants (hydrocarbons, oil, pesticides, heavy metals - uranium, cadmium, lead, etc.), performing the excretion of these structures to the culture medium, associated their cell walls. This facilitates the transport and translocation of insoluble substrates, in turn facilitating biosorption. In the process of heavy metal ion bioremediation, a complex non-toxic biosurfactant/metallic ion structure is formed, resulting in emulsification and solubilization of the ions, and, consequently, their physical sequestration. One of the most widely used natural biosurfactants in bioremediation is rhamnolipids, produced by *Pseudomonas aeruginosa* (Bognolo, 1999; Champion et. al., 1995; Mulligan, 2005; Tabak et. al., 2005; Zhang et. al., 2005).

Oxidation-reduction (redox): Microorganisms can mobilize or immobilize metal ions, metalloid and organometal compounds, thus promoting redox processes. Only prokaryotes are capable of oxidizing metals such as Mn^{2+}, Fe^{2+}, Co^{2+}, Cu, AsO^{2-}, Se^0 or SeO_3^{2-}, or reducing Mn^{4+}, Fe^{3+}, Co^{3+}, AsO_4^{2-}, SeO_4^{2-} or SeO_3^{2}, whilst obtaining energy from these reactions (Gavrilescu, 2004). When, for example, the Fe^{3+} ion is reduced to Fe^{2+}, or the Mn^{4+} ion is reduced to Mn^{2+}, there is an increase in the solubility of these metals. Microbial species can efficiently immobilize heavy metals through their ability to reduce heavy metal ions, reducing them to a lower oxidation state, and giving rise to metallic elements (load zero) which are less bioactive (Valls & Lorenzo, 2002; Gadd, 2004).

Biomethylation: Microorganisms can transform metal ions from a more toxic to a less toxic form through the biomethylation mechanism. Hg, As, Cd, Se, Sn, Te and Pb ions can be methylated by a variety of bacteria, filamentous fungi and yeasts, under both aerobic and anaerobic conditions, which results in increased mobility, and also in their suitability for involvement in processes that result in a decrease in their toxicities. This enzymatic mechanism involves a transfer from the methyl group (CH_3) to metals and metalloids. The methylated compounds formed differ in their solubility, volatility and toxicity (Roane & Pepper, 2000; Gadd, 2004). For example, methyl and dimethyl mercury are more toxic than inorganic Hg ions, however, these are intermediate forms of processing for Hg^0. Inorganic forms of As are more toxic than methylated species (acids and methyl-As dimethyl-As), the methylated and inorganic forms of Se and Cd are highly toxic (Roane & Pepper, 2000; Tabak, 2005).

Metal-binding cysteine-rich peptides: When cells are exposed to heavy metals in toxic concentrations an induction of expression of peptides rich in cysteine residues, metallothioneins (MTs), glutathione (GSH) or phytochelatin (PCs) occurs. These are non-enzymatic molecules, with low molecular weight, which are resistant to thermo-coagulation and acid precipitation. The main feature of these peptides is to form complexes with divalent metals and metal-thiols, which consist of important metabolites to combat ROS (Bae et. al., 2000; 2001).

Metallothioneins (MTs): Metallothioneins (MTs) are a group of well-preserved structures of proteins that act as antioxidants, and they are distributed among all living organisms. They have low molecular weight and they are rich in cysteine residues. The presence of thiol groups (SH) in the cysteine chemical structure enables the capture of metal ions such as Cd^{2+}, Fe^{2+}, Hg^{2+}, Cu^{2+} and Zn^{2+}. MTs are composed of two separate domains, the β domain in the N-terminal region, and the α domain in the C-terminal region. The β domain possesses nine cysteine residues linking three divalent ions, the α domain already has eleven cysteine residues and binds four ions, thus a total of seven ions per molecule are bound (Cobbett & Goldsbrough, 2002; Thirumoorthy et. al., 2007). The MTs have several functions, including the detoxification of heavy metals and protection against the presence of ROS. Thus, MTs are responsible for reducing the effect of oxidative stress caused by these ions, but they are also responsible for maintaining homeostatic cellular redox balance. According to these characteristics, protein synthesis is only induced by metals. (Cobbett & Goldsbrough, 2002; Smith et. al., 2007).

Glutathione (GSH): Glutathione (GSH), L-Glutamyl-L-cysteinyl-glycine (Figure 4), is a soluble antioxidant, recognized as the most important non-protein thiol present in all living organisms. It consists of three amino acids (Glu-Cys-Gly), and it is the cysteine thiol group of the active site that is responsible for its biochemical properties (Bae & Mehra, 1997; Penninckx, 2000; 2002; Mendonza-cózatl et. al., 2005).

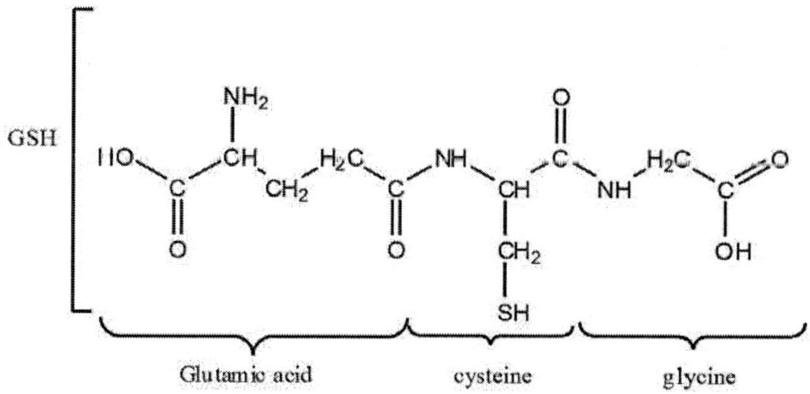

Figure 4. Chemical structure of glutathione (GSH) (Bae & Mehra, 1997).

The GSH controls its own synthesis and participates in multiple processes: regulation of the intracellular redox state, inactivation of ROS, transport of GSH-conjugated amino acid and other molecules, stock of the sulfur and cysteine. In mammals, it is present in greater quantities in the liver. Its biosynthesis is similar in plants, yeast and protists. The mitochondria and the nucleus have their own GSH reservation, which is critical or instrumental in protecting these structures against ROS action (Penninckx, 2002; Inouhe, 2005; Mendoza -Cózatl et. al., 2005). In yeast, the cell protection system against the toxicity of Cd^{2+} occurs through the formation of a GSH- Cd^{2+} complex, because this causes a decrease in the levels of lipid peroxidation of the cell membrane and allows for the transportation of GSH-Cd^{2+} conjugate to the vacuole. This results in a decreased concentration of toxic metals in the cytosol, thus promoting a reduction in the levels of oxidative stress (Penninckx, 2000; Adamis et. al., 2004; Kobayashi *et. al.,* 2005; Preveral et. al., 2006).

Natural phytochelatins (PCs) and synthetic phytochelatin (EC20): PCs are small cysteine-rich peptides with the general structure (Glu-Cys) nGly (n = 2-11) (Figure 5-A) (Grill et. al., 1985; Cobbett, 2000). PCs are synthesized from glutathione (GSH) in steps catalyzed by PC synthase (Grill et. al., 1985; Gupta et. al., 2004). They enable ions to bind to various heavy metal ions through thiol residues and carboxyl (Kobayashi et. al., 2005; Inouhe, 2005). These PCs are present in plants, fungi, nematodes, parasites and algae, including cyanobacteria. Despite being classified as MT-III, the PCs have a greater capacity for binding heavy metal ions (1 atom per cysteine basis) than MTs. The pioneering work that targeted the expression of recombinant PCs in *E.coli* were faced with the difficulty imposed by the chemical bonds of type γ present between Glu-Cys units, which are the result of multi-enzyme processes. These bindings are different for type α among the present amino acid chains of all proteins (Bae et. al., 2001; Cobbett, 2000; Penninckx, 2000; Gupta *et. al.*, 2004; Inouhe, 2005; Hirata, 2005; Mendoza-Cózatl, 2005; Wu et. al., 2006). An alternative was to synthesize an *in vitro* gene that codes for proteins similar to PCs, whose general structure corresponded to (Glu-Cys) nGly (ECs) with all amino acids linked chemically by type α (Figure 5-B). Thus, the synthetic phytochelatin EC20 contains 20 units of repeated Glu-Cys (EC). The synthetic phytochelatin EC20 has greater capacity for binding to heavy metal ions than natural PCs. Recombinant strains of bacteria are currently being constructed (Bae et. al., 2000; 2001; Xu et. al., 2002; Lee *et. al.*, 2006; Wu et. al., 2006), and though few studies have been developed for yeast, we can cite (Schmitt et. al., 2006) expressing EC20 with the aim of identifying microorganisms with increased capacity for binding heavy metal ions for use in bioremediation processes.

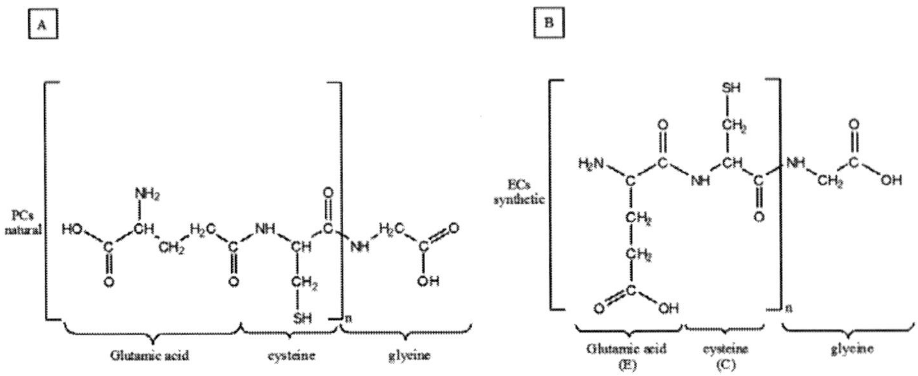

Figure 5. Chemical structures of molecules binding heavy metals: A) natural phytochelatin (PC) and B) synthetic phytochelatin (EC) - glutamic acid (glu-E) and cysteine (Cys-C) (Bae et. al., 2000).

Among these genetic engineering techniques for the construction of new recombinant microbial strains (Deng et. al., 2003; Merle et. al., 2003; Kim et. al., 2005; Nishitani et al., 2010), MTS, PCs and ECs were also explored so that these proteins remain anchored to the outer surface cell ("cell-surface display"). The aim was to increase the capacity these special microorganisms in adsorption processes involving heavy metal ions in comparison with non-recombinant microorganisms (Bae et. al., 2000; 2001; Kuroda et. al., 2002; Kuroda & Ueda, 2003; Jiang et. al., 2007).

The "cell-surface display" system: Cell surface proteins constitute an important class of biomolecules because they are situated at the interface between the cell and the environment. The cells have systems for anchoring specific proteins to the surface and confining them to certain areas. A great many systems are being used in bacteria and in *S. cerevisiae* (Kondo & Ueda, 2004). The expression of heterologous peptides on the cell surface ("cell-surface display ") is a powerful technique widely used in the biotechnology area in the following processes: production of recombinant vaccines, antigens, antibodies, enzymes and library peptides (Kuroda et. al., 2001; Chen & Georgiou, 2002; Samuelson et. al., 2002; Rutherford & Moures, 2006; Wang et. al., 2007; Kuroda & Ueda, 2010; Nishitani et. al., 2010; Kuroda & Ueda, 2011).

Factors Affecting Biosorption

The investigation of the efficacy of metal uptake by microbial biomass is essential for the industrial application of biosorption, as it yields information about the equilibrium of the process that is necessary to design the equipment to be employed.

Metal uptake is usually measured by the parameter 'q', which indicates the milligrams of metal accumulated per gram of biosorbent material, while 'qH' is reported as a function of the metal accumulated, the sorbent material used and the operating conditions.

The following factors affect the biosorption process:

- temperature does not seem to influence biosorption performance in the 20-35° C range (Asku et. al., 1992);
- pH seems to be the most important parameter in the biosorption process: it affects the solution chemistry of the metals, the activity of the functional groups in the biomass and competition between metallic ions (Machado et. al., 2010);
- biomass concentration in solution seems to influence specific uptake: for lower values of biomass concentrations, there is an increase in the specific uptake (Fourest & Roux, 1992; Gadd et. al., 1988). Gadd et. al. (1988) suggested that an increase in biomass concentration leads to interference among the binding sites. Fourest & Roux (1992) invalidated this hypothesis by attributing the responsibility of the decrease of specific uptake to a shortage of metal concentration in the solution. Hence this factor needs to be taken into consideration in any application of microbial biomass as a biosorbent;
- biosorption is mainly used to treat wastewater where more than one type of metal ion are probably present; the removal of one metal ion may be influenced by the presence of other metal ions. For example: Uranium uptake by bacterium, fungus and yeast biomass was not affected by the presence of manganese, cobalt, copper, cadmium, mercury and lead in solution (Sakaguchi & Nakajima, 1991). In contrast, the presence of Fe^{2+} and Zn^{2+} was found to influence uranium uptake by *Rhizopus arrhizus* (Tsezos & Volesky, 1982) and cobalt uptake by different microorganisms seemed to be completely inhibited by the presence of uranium, lead, mercury and copper (Sakaguchi & Nakajima, 1991).

NEW DEVELOPMENTS IN ORGANISMS CAPABLE OF ENHANCED BIOREMEDIATION

The Use of Recombinant Bacteria for Metal Removal

The use of recombinant bacteria to remove specific metals from contaminated water is currently being investigated. For example a genetically engineered *E.coli,* which expresses the Hg^{2+} transport system and metallothionein (a metal binding protein), was able to selectively accumulate 8 μmole Hg^{2+}/g cell dry weight. The presence of the chelating agents Na^{+}, Mg^{2+} and Ca^{2+} did not affect bioaccumulation.

Genetically Modified Biosorbents

Genetic engineering has the potential to improve or redesign microorganisms, where biological metal-sequestering systems will have a higher intrinsic capability as well as specificity and greater resistance to environmental conditions (Bae et. al., 2000; Majare & Bulow, 2001). It is well known that virgin biosorbents usually lack specificity in metal-binding, which may cause difficulties in the recovery and recycling of the desired metal(s).

Genetic modification is a potential solution for enhancing selectivity as well as the accumulating potential of cells (Pazirandeh et. al., 1995). Genetic modification would be feasible, especially when the microbial biomass is produced from fermentation processes where genetically engineered microorganisms are used. Currently, many kinds of amino acids and nucleic acids are being produced on an industrial scale by using genetically engineered microbial cells. Higher organisms respond to the presence of metals, with the production of cysteine-rich peptides, such as glutathione (GSH) (Singhal et. al., 1997), phytochelatins (PCs) and metallothioneins (MTs) (Mehra & Winge, 1991), which can bind and sequester metal ions in biologically inactive forms (Hamer, 1986; Bae et. al., 2000). The overexpression of MTs in bacterial cells will result in enhanced metal accumulation, thus offering a promising strategy for the development of microbial-based biosorbents for the remediation of metal contamination (Pazirandeh et. al., 1995). In addition to the high selectivity and accumulation capacity, Pazirandeh et. al. (1995) demonstrated that uptake by recombinant *E. coli* (expressing the *Neurospora crassa* metallothionein gene within the periplasmic space) was rapid. Greater than 75% Cd uptake occurred within the first 20 min, with maximum uptake achieved in less than 1 h. However, the expression of such cysteine-rich proteins is not devoid of problems, due to the predicted interference with redox pathways in cytosol. More importantly, the intracellular expression of MTs may prevent the recycling of biosorbents, as the accumulated metals cannot easily be released (Gadd & White, 1993). Chen & Georgiou (2002) suggested a solution to bypass this transport problem by expressing MTs on the cell surface. Sousa et. al. (1996) demonstrated the possibility of inserting MTs into permissive site 153 of the *LamB* sequence. The expression of the hybrid proteins on the cell surface dramatically increased the whole-cell accumulation of cadmium.

Also, the expression of proteins on the surface offers an inexpensive alternative for the preparation of affinity adsorbents (Georgiou et. al., 1993). The use of PCs in a similar manner to MTs has also been suggested (Bae et. al., 2000). PCs are short, cysteine-rich peptides, with the general structure (γGlu-Cys)nGly (n=2–11) (Zenk, 1996). PCs offer many advantages over MTs, due to their unique structural characteristics, particularly the continuously-repeating γGlu-Cys units. Also, PCs have been found to exhibit higher metal-binding capacity (on a per cysteine basis) than MTs (Mehra & Mulchandani, 1995). However, the development of overexpressing PC organisms requires a thorough knowledge of the mechanisms involved in the synthesis and chain elongation of these peptides. Several biosorbents, displaying metal-binding peptides on the cell surface, have been successfully engineered. A typical example includes creating a repetitive metal-binding motif, consisting of (Glu-Cys)nGly (Bae et. al., 2000). These peptides emulate the structure of PCs; however, they differ in the fact that the peptide bond between the glutamic acid and cysteine is a standard α peptide bond. Phytochelatin analogs were found to be present on the bacterial surface, which enhanced the accumulation of Cd^{2+} and Hg^{2+} by 12- (Bae et. al., 2000) and 20-fold (Bae et. al., 2001), respectively. Attempts to create recombinant bacteria with improved metal binding capacity have so far been restricted mostly to *E. coli*. This is because *E. coli* greatly facilitates genetic engineering experiments and it is found to have more surface area per unit of cell mass, which potentially should result in higher rates of metal removal from solutions (Chen & Wilson, 1997). Nevertheless, a Gram-positive surface display system also possesses its own merits, compared to Gram-negative bacteria (Malik et. al., 1998; Samuelson et. al., 2000): (a) translocation through only one membrane is required; and (b) Gram-positive bacteria have been shown to be more rigid and, therefore, less sensitive to shear forces (Kelemen & Sharpe, 1979) due to the thick cell wall surrounding the cells, which potentially make them more suitable for field applications, such as bioadsorption. Samuelson et. al. (2000) generated recombinant *Staphylococcus xylosus* and *Staphylococcus carnosus* strains, with surface-exposed chimeric proteins containing polyhistidyl peptides. Both strains of Staphylococcaceae gained improved nickel-binding capacities due to the introduction of the H1 or H2 peptide into their surface proteins. Owing to their high rate of selectivity, genetically engineered biosorbents may prove very competitive in the separation of toxins and other pollutants from diluted contaminated solutions.

Survivability and Stability of GMOs

Although the utilization of GMOs in the field has been limited due to possible risks involved in the horizontal transfer of genetic material, the results that have been obtained are nevertheless important in assessing the benefits and obstacles associated with their applications in bioremediation. Such knowledge is necessary in view of the future possibility of releasing GEMs into contained environments for bioremediation. To be of practical use in the field, a bacterial GMO must be able to survive and grow in such environments. Important parameters in this regard are growth rate, inoculum size, environmental conditions, including spatial distribution, and the presence of competing microorganisms. The spatial distribution of a GMO introduced into the environment is important because it helps define its interactions with the members of the indigenous bacterial community and other components of the ecosystem (Dechesne *et. al.*, 2005). In general, a bacterium that has been recently isolated from a natural environment is more likely to survive when released back into that same environment. A crucial consideration regarding the introduction of engineered bacteria into field sites is their effect on the structure and function of natural ecosystems.

Natural Horizontal Transference of DNA in Bacteria

It is perhaps most useful to consider horizontal transfer of recombinant DNA in the overall context of horizontal gene transfer among bacteria, which is a natural and presumably widespread phenomenon. The role of horizontal gene transfer in bacterial evolution has been demonstrated in many studies (Rensing *et. al.*, 2002; Dennis, 2005). It has been suggested that it is an important process contributing to the development of novel biodegradation capacities of microbial communities when they are exposed to organic pollutants (Rittmann *et. al.*, 1990; Dennis, 2005). The transfer of genes encoding biodegradation functions appears to occur through the action of conjugative plasmids, transposable elements, and "integrative and conjugative transposons" (also known as "genomic islands") (Springael & Top, 2004; Top *et. al.*, 2002; Van Der Meer & Sentchilo, 2003). There is evidence to suggest that the genes in at least some of these elements were assembled in stepwise processes (Springael & Top, 2004). That such horizontal transfer is apparently quite common is suggested by the variety of specific examples. Direct measurement of horizontal transfer has been carried out under both well-defined conditions and in microcosms, the latter serving as models for *in situ* situations. An interesting example of horizontal gene transfer in a completely natural environment is provided by the *pheBA* operon, which originated from the strain EST1001 of *Pseudomonas* sp. It encodes two enzymes involved in phenol catabolism and, like several examples described above, it is carried on a conjugative plasmid with transposable element characteristics. It was transferred by conjugation to *P. putida* PaW85 and this strain has already been released into the field for the large-scale bioremediation of river water contaminated with phenolics, originating from a fire in an oil shale mine (Peters *et. al.*, 1997). Six years later, despite the absence of the PaW85 strain, the operon was once again detected in the watershed, apparently having been transferred to nine *Pseudomonas* strains belonging to four different species (*P. corrugata*, *P. fragi*, *P. stutzeri* and *P. fluorescens* biotypes B, C and F). In eight cases the operon was plasmid-borne, and in one case it had integrated into the host chromosome. The environment in which these bacteria were found was subject to continual pollution with phenolics. This presumably provided positive selection for their perseverance, which appears to have had continual beneficial effects regarding bioremediation in this location. The examples discussed above can be viewed as evidence that horizontal gene transfer of recombinant genes could occur rapidly by the same mechanisms. On the other hand, it may be that any predicted horizontal transfer of DNA from GMOs may occur naturally with the same genes in non-recombinant organisms at rates which make any contribution from GMOs insignificant. As discussed above, there is concern that GMOs introduced into polluted sites to enhance bioremediation may have adverse environmental effects because of horizontal transfer of recombinant DNA (Davison, 1999). In many cases, released GMOs do not survive long, and disappear before they have any effect on biodegradation (Davison, 1999). In other cases, however, transfer of plasmid from an introduced GMO to an indigenous microorganism may occur even though the introduced strain does not survive (Davison, 1999; Peters *et. al.*, 1997). Thus, in general it appears that the potential impact of introduction of GMOs on native microbial populations is not uniform and therefore must be evaluated on a case-by-case basis.

Containment Strategies to Diminish Horizontal Transfer of DNA from GMOs

As mentioned above, one important concern with the use of GMOs bearing recombinant genes on plasmids arises from the instability of the plasmids, which can lead to loss of the desired phenotype. On the other hand, the relative chemical and physical stability of plasmids can contribute to their spreading, along with both the recombinant genes and selective markers (e.g., antibiotic resistance), to other bacteria (Pieper & Reineke, 2000). One solution is to replace antibiotic resistance selective markers with selective markers that do not center on antibiotic resistance (Sanchez-Romero *et. al.*, 1998; Herrero *et. al.*, 1990). One way to obviate the problem of plasmid transfer is to use “mini transposons” for the stable integration of genes into the chromosome of recipient strains (De Lorenzo *et. al.*, 1998; Herrero *et. al.*, 1990). If the chosen GMO recipient proves not to be able to support plasmid maintenance, the transformant bearing gene(s) of interest must undergo transposition of the cloned gene into the host chromosome, where it will remain integrated in a stable manner. Some mini-transposon vectors have also been engineered for use on heavy metals or herbicides, rather than antibiotic resistance, as a selectable marker, to eliminate the problem of horizontal transfer of this characteristic altogether (Herrero *et. al.*, 1990). Other “biological containment strategies” that can minimize this problem are suicide systems, where the GMO dies after it has completed its required task (De Lorenzo *et. al.*, 1998; Molin *et. al.*, 1993; Molina *et. al.*, 1998; Pandey *et. al.*, 2005; Paul et. al., 2005; Ronchel *et. al.*, 1998; Ronchel & Ramos, 2000). Such suicide mechanisms are based on the controlled expression in the gene host that encodes proteins that are lethal to it. A common system induces the “suicide gene(s)” when the pollutant that the host degrades is absent. Expression of these genes, which cause holes to form in the cell membrane, leads to cell death.

Composting is another containment strategy for using GMOs in field applications; this process has recently been reviewed by Singh *et. al.* (2006). The conditions during the composting process include elevated temperatures (as high as 80–90° C), decreases in pH due to organic acid production, and the production of toxic metabolites that can greatly decrease microbial populations. The subsequent lysis of dead microbes releases their DNA into the environment, where it is subject to degradation. These effects presumably minimize horizontal gene transfer from the GMOs, suggesting that composting could be a safe solution for their disposal after they have completed their required functions.

CONCLUSION

The use of genetic engineering to produce microorganisms capable of degrading specific contaminants or to enhance such processes in native organisms with such capabilities has become a popular way of increasing the efficiency of bioremediation in laboratory studies. Techniques used can include engineering with single genes, pathway construction, and alteration of the sequences of existing genes (both coding and controlling sequences). But, before releasing a GMO into the environment, the researchers should emphasize the ethical responsibilities to be considered before using such novel strategies for bioremediation. In this context, several points should be taken into account. The stability of GMOs and their horizontal transfer of engineered DNA are crucial issues regarding the potential impact of their release into the field for bioremediation. In order to determine how released GMOs are affecting the environment, it is necessary to be able to detect and enumerate them in complex samples. Important parameters in this context are survival, number, activity, and dispersion of released GMOs (Widada *et. al.*, 2002). Ideally such methods should be applicable in the field and in real time, and should be simple and inexpensive while also being accurate (Wu *et. al.*, 2001). In addition to the GMO itself, it is useful to track the recombinant DNA with which the GMO has been engineered so as to monitor potential loss of these genes and their possible horizontal transfer to other microorganisms.

In conclusion, a number of important molecular tools have been developed for genetic and metabolic engineering of microorganisms for the degradation of environmental contaminants. These new tools will make the construction of new or improved strains much easier and quicker than in the past. However, these genetic modifications should beunderstood in full and any research must always determine the actual risks and benefits involved.

Acknowledgments

We thank Ingrid Regina Avanzi and Louise Hase Gracioso for helping with the references and Stanley Vasconcelos for drawing the chemical diagrams. INCT-EMA-CNPq (Brasília, DF, Brazil) and FAPESP (São Paulo, SP, Brazil) provided financial support for this study.

REFERENCES

1. Adamis PD, Gomes DS, Pinto ML, Panek AD, Eleutherio EC 2004 The role of glutathione transferases in cadmium stress. Toxicol. Lett., 154 n.1, 281 288 .
2. Adamis PDB, Panek AD, Leite SGF, Eleutherio ECA 2003 Factors involved with cadmium absorption by a wild-type strain of Saccharomyces cerevisiae. J. Microbiol., 34 55 60 .

3. Ahluwalia S. S. Goyal D. 2007 Microbial and plant derived biomass for removal of heavy metals from wastewater. Bioresour. Technol. 98 n.12, 2243 2257 .
4. Asku Z. 1992 The biosorption of Cu (II) by C. vulgaris and Z. ramigera. Environ. Tech. 13 1 579 586 .
5. Bae W. Chen W. Mulchandani A. Mehra R. K. 2000 Enhanced bioaccumulation of heavy metals by bacterial cells displaying synthetic phytochelatins. Biotechnol Bioeng. 70 518 524 .
6. Bae W. Chen W. Mulchandani A. Mehra R. K. 2001 Genetic engineering of Escherichia coli for enhance uptake and bioaccumulation of mercury. Appl. Environ Microbiol., 67 5335 5338 .
7. Bae W. Mehra R. K. 1997 Metal-Binding characteristics of a phytochelatin analog (Glu-Cys)2Gly. Elsevier Sci., 201 210 .
8. Bogacka E K 2011 Surface properties of yeast cells during heavy metal biosorption⁺. Cent. Eur. J. Chem., 9 n.2, 348 351 .
9. Bognolo 1999 (1999) Biosurfactants as emulsifying agents for hydrocarbons Colloids and surfaces A: Physicochemical and Engineering Aspects 152 41 52 .
10. Borro, DM, Fein JB 2005 The impact of ionic strength on the adsorption of protons, Pb, Cd, and Sr onto the surfaces of gram negative bacteria: testing non-eletrostatic, diffuse, and triple-layer models. J. Colloid Interf. Sci., 286 110 126.
11. Breierová E. Vajcziková V. Sasinková V. Styratilová E. Fisera M. Gregor T. Sajbidor J. 2002 Biosorption of cadmium ions by different yeast species. Inst. Chem. Z. Naturforch, 57 634 639 .
12. Bruins M. R. Kapil S. Oehme F. W. 2000 Microbial resistance to metals in the environment. Ecotoxicol and Environ Safety 45 198 207 .
13. Champion J. T. Gilkey C. J. Lamparski H. Retterer J. Miller R. M. 1995 Electrom microscopy of rhamnolipid (biosurfactant) morfphology: Effects of pH, cadmium, and octadecane. J. Colloid and interface science, 170 569 574 .
14. Chang L. Meier J. Smikth M. 1997 Application of plant and earthworm bioassays to evaluate remediation of a lead-contaminated soil. Arch. Environ. Contam. Toxicol, 32 166 171 .
15. Chen C. Wang J. 2008 Removal of Pb2+, Ag +, Cs+, and Sr 2+ from aqueous solution by brewery s waste biomass. J. Hazard. Mater., 151 65 70 .
16. Chen S. Wilson D. B. 1997 Genetic engineering of bacteria and their potential for Hg2+ bioremediation. Biodegradation. 8 n.2, 97 103 .
17. Chen W. Bruhlmann F. Richnis R. D. Mulchandani A. 1999 Engineering of improved microbes and enzymes for bioremediation. Curr Opin Biotechnol, 10 137 141 .
18. Chen W. Georgiou G. 2002 Cell-surface display of heterologous proteins: from high-throughput screening to environmental applications. Biotechnol Bioeng., 79 496 503 .
19. Cobbett C. Goldsbrough P. 2002 Phytochelatins and Metallothioneins: Roles in heavy metal detoxification and homeostasis. Annu. ReVol. Plant Biol., 53 159 182 .
20. Cobbett CS 2000 Phytochelatins and their roles in heavy metal detoxification. Plant Physiol., 123 825 832 , 2000.
21. Costa ACA & Leite SGF 1991 Metals biosorption by sodium alginate immobilized Chiarella homosphaera cells. Biotechnol Left, 13 555 562 .
22. Davis T. A. Volesky B. AA Mucci 2003 Review of the biochemistry of heavy metalbiosorption by brown algae, Water Res., 37 n. 18, 4311 4330 .
23. Dejonghe W. Goris J. El Fantroussi S. Hofte M. De Vos P. Verstraete W. Top E. M. 2000 Effect of dissemination of 2,4-D degradation plasmids on 2,4-D degradation and on bacterial community structure in two different soil horizons. Appl Environ Microbiol., 66 3297 3304 .
24. Deng X. Li Q. B. Lu Y. H. Sun D. H. Huang Y. L. Chen X. R. 2003 Bioaccumulation of nickel from aqueous solutions by genetically engineered E. coli. Water Res., 37 2505 2511 .
25. MA Dias Lacerda. I. C. A. Pimentel P. F. Castro H. F. CA Rosa 2002 Removal of heavy metals by an Aspergillus terreus strain immobilized in a polyurethane matrix. Lett Appl. Microbiol., 34 46 50 .

26. Dobson RS, Burgess, JE 2007 Biological treatment of precious metal refinery wastewater: A review. Miner. Eng. 20 519 532 .
27. Ercole C. Veglio F. Toro L. Ficara G. Lepidi A. 1994 Immobilisation of microbial cells for metal adsorption and desorption. In: Mineral Bioprocessing II. Snowboard. Utah.
28. Esposito A. P. Agnanelli F. E. Veglio F. 2002 pH-related equilibria models for biosorption in single metal systems. Chem. Eng. Sci., 57 n. 3, 307 313 .
29. Fourest E. Roux J. C. 1992 Heavy metal adsorption by fungal mycelial by-products: influence of pH. Appl. Microbiol. Biotechnol, 37 399 403 .
30. Gadd G. M. White C. 1993 Microbial treatment of metal pollution: a working biotechnology? TIBTECH. 11 353 359 .
31. Gadd G M 1988 Heavy metal and radionuclide by fungi and yeasts. In: P.R. Norris and D.P. Kelly (Editors), Biohydrometallurgy. A. Rowe, Chippenham, Wilts, U.K.
32. Gadd GM 2004 Microbial influence on metal mobility and application for bioremediation. Geoderma, 122 n. 2-4, 109 119 .
33. Gadd G. M. De Rome L. 1988 Biosorption of copper by fungal melanine. Appl. Microbiol. Biotech. 29 N.6, 610 617 .
34. Gavrilescu M. 2004 Removal of heavy metals from the environment by biosorption, Eng. Life Sci., 4 n. 3, 219 232 .
35. Gazsó LG 2001 The key microbial processes in the removal of toxic metals and radionuclides from the environment. Mini ReVol. CEJOEM, 7 178 185 .
36. Gentry T. J. Rensing C. Pepper I. L. 2004 New approaches for bioaugmentation as a remediation technology. Crit. Rev. Environ Sci Techn., 34 n. 5, 447 494 .
37. Georgiou G. Poetschke H. L. Stathopoulos C. Francisco J. A. 1993 Practical applications of engineering Gram-negative bacterial cell surfaces. TIBTECH. 11 6 10 .
38. Ghosh S. K. Chaudhuri R. Gachhui R. Mandal A. Ghosh S. 2006 Effect of mercury and organomercurials on cellular glucose utilization: a study using resting mercury-resistant yeast cells. J. Appl. Microbiol., 102 375 383 .
39. Goyal N. Jain S. C. Banerjee U. C. 2003 Comparative studies on the microbial adsorption of heavy metals. AdVol. Environ. Res., 7 n. 2, 311 319 .
40. Grill E. Winnacker E. L. Zenk M. H. 1985 Phytochelatins: the principal heavy-metal complexing peptides of higher plants. Science, 230 674 676 .
41. Gupta D. K. Tohoyama H. Joho M. Inouhe M. 2005 Changes in the levels of phytochelatins and related metal-binding peptides in chickpea seedlings exposed to arsenic and different heavy metal ions. J. Plant Res., 17 253 256 .
42. Gupta R. Ahuja P. Khan S. Saxena R. K. Mohapatra 2000 (2000) Microbial biosorbents: Meeting challenges of heavy metal pollution in aqueous solutions. Curr. Sci., 78 n.8, 967 973 .
43. Hameed MSA 2006 Continuous removal and recovery of lead by alginate beads free and alginate-immobilized Chlorella vulgaris. Afr. J. Biotechnol., 5 n. 19, 1819 1823 .
44. Hamer DH. 1986 Metallothionein. Annu Rev Biochem. 55 913 951 .
45. Hammaini A. 2003 Simultaneous uptake of metals by activated sludge. Minerals Engineering. 16 723 729 .
46. Hernandez A. Mellado R. P. Martinez J. L. 1998 Metal Accumulation and Vanadium-Induced Multidrug Resistance by Environmental Isolates of Escherichia hermannii and Enterobacter cloacae. American. Society for Microbiology Applied and Environmental Microbiology. 64 n. 11, 4317 4320 .
47. Hirata K. Tsuji N. Miyamoto K. 2005 Biosynthetic regulation of phytochelatins, heavy metal-binding peptides. J. Biosc. Bioeng. ReVol., 100 n. 6, 593 599 .
48. Huang C. Huang C. Morehart A. L. 1990 The removal of copper from dilute aqueous solutions by Saccharomyces cerevisiae. Water Res., 24 433 439 .
49. Inouhe M. 2005 Phytochelatins. Braz. J. Plant Physiol., 17 n. 1, 650 678 .
50. Jiang Z. B. Song H. T. Gupta N. Ma Wu L. X. Z. B. 2007 Cell surface display of functionally active lipases from Yarrowia lipolytica in Pichia pastoris. Protein Expr. Purif., 56 35 39 .

51. Kawata K. Yokoo H. Shimazaki R. Okabe S. 2007 Classification of heavy-metal toxicity by human DNA microarray analysis. Environ Sci Technol., 15 n. 41, 3769 3377 .
52. Kefala MI, Zouboulis AIE, Matis KA 1999 Biosorption of cadmium ions by Actinomycetes and separation by flotation. Environ. Pollut., 104 n. 2, 283 293 .
53. Kelemen MV, Sharpe JE 1979 Controlled cell disruption: a comparison of the forces required to disrupt different micro-organisms. J Cell Sci., 35 431 441 .
54. Keskinkan O. Goksu M. Z. L. Yuceer A. Basibuyuk M. Forster C. F. 2003 Heavy metal adsorption characteristics of a submerged aquatic plant (Myriophyllum spicatum). Process Biochemistry, 39 n.2, 179 183 .
55. Kim SU, Cheong YH, Seo DC, Hu JS, Heo JS, Cho JS 2007 Characterisation of heavy metal tolerance and biosorption capacity of bacterium strain CPB4 (Bacillus spp.). Water Sci. Tech., 55 n. 1-2, 105 111 .
56. Kim S. K. BS Lee Wilson. D. B. Kim E. K. 2005 Selective cadmium accumulation using recombinant E. coli. J. Biosci. Bioeng., 99 n. 2, 109 114 .
57. Kobayashi I. Fujiwara S. Saegusa H. Inohe M. Metsumoto H. Tsuzuki M. 2006 Relief of arsenate toxicity by Cd-stimulated phytochelatin synthesis in the green alga Chlamydomonas reinhardtii. Mar. Biotechnol., 8 94 101 .
58. Kondo A. Ueda M. 2004 Yeast cell-surface display-applications of molecular display. Appl. Microbiol. Biotechnol., 64 28 40 .
59. Kotrba P. Ruml T. 2000 Bioremediation of heavy metal pollution exploiting constituents, metabolites and metabolic pathway of livings. Appl. Environ. Microbiol., 65 n. 8, 1205 1247 .
60. Kratochvil D. Volesky B. 1998 Advances in the biosorption of heavy metals. Trends Biotechnol., 16 291 300 .
61. Kujan P. Prell A. Safar H. Sobotka M. Rezanka T. Holler P. P. 2006 Use of the industrial yeast Candida utilis for cadmium sorption. Folia Microbiol., 51 257 260 .
62. Kumar R. Bishnoi N. R. Bishnoi G. K. 2008 Biosorption of chromium (VI) from aqueous solution and electroplating wastewater using fungal biomass. J. Eng. Chem., 135 n. 3, 202 208 .
63. Kuroda K. Shibasaki S. Ueda M. Tanaka A. 2001 Cell surface engineered yeast displaying a histidine oligopeptide (hexa-His) has enhanced adsorption of and tolerance to heavy metal ions. Appl. Microbiol. Biotechnol., 57 697 701 .
64. Kuroda K. Ueda M. Shibasaki A. Tanaka A. 2002 Cell surface-engineered yeast with ability to bind, and self-aggregate in response tom copper ion. Appl. Microbiol. Biotechnol., 59 259 264 .
65. Kuroda K. Ueda M. 2003 Bioadsorption of cadmium ion by cell surface-engineered yeasts displaying metallothionein and hexa-His. Appl. Microbiol. Biotechnol., 63 182 186 .
66. Kuroda K. Ueda M. 2010 Engineering of microorganisms towards recovery of rare metal ions: Mini Review. Appl Microbiol Biotechnol., 87 53 60 .
67. Kuroda K. Ueda M. 2011 Yeast Biosorption and Recycling of Metal Ions by Cell Surface Engineering. Microbial Biosorption of Metals. n. 10, 235 247 , [DOI: 10.1007/978-94-007-0443/5-10].
68. Kuyucak N. Volesky B. Desorption of cobalt-laden algal biosorbent 1988 Biotechnol Bioeng., 33 815 822 .
69. Lee W. Wood T. Chen W. 2002 Engineering TCE-degrading Rhizobacteria for heavy metal accumutation and enhanced TCE degradation. Biotechnol. Bioeng., 399 403 . doi: 10.1002/bit. 20950.
70. Li Y. Li B. 2011 Study on fungi-bacteria consortium bioremediation of petroleum contaminated mangrove sediments amended with mixed biosurfactants. Adv.Mat. Res., Vols. 183-185, 1163 1167 .
71. Liu J. Zhang Y. Huang D. Song G. 2005 Cadmium induced MTs synthesis via oxidative stress in yeast Saccharomyces cerevisiae. Mol. Cell Biochem., 280 n. 1-2, 139 145 .
72. MD Machado Santos. M. S. F. Gouveia C. Soares H. M. V. M. Soares E. V. 2008 Removal of heavy metal using a brewer's yeast strain of Saccharomyces cerevisiae: The flocculation as a

separation process. Bioresour. Technol., 99 2107 2115 .

73. Machado MD, Soares EV, Helena MVM, Soares HMVM 2010 Removal of heavy metals using a brewer's yeast strain of Saccharomyces cerevisiae: Chemical speciation as a tool in the prediction and improving of treatment efficiency of real electroplating effluents. J. Hazard. Mat., 180 347 353 .
74. Majáre M. Bülow L. 2001 Metal-binding proteins and peptides in bioremediation and phytoremediation of heavy metals. TIBTECH. 19 67 73 .
75. Malik A. Metal bioremediation through growing cells. Enkviron. Int., 30 30 n. 2, 261 278 .
76. Malik P. Terry T. D. Bellintani F. RN Perham 1998 Factors limiting display of foreign peptides on the major coat protein of filamentous bacteriophage capsids and a potential role for leader peptidase, FEBS Lett., 436 263 266 .
77. Mameri N. Boudries N. Addour L. Belhocine D. Lounici H. Grib H. Pauss A. 1999 Batch zinc biosorption by a bacterial nonliving Streptomyces rimosus biomass. Water Res., 33 1347 1354 .
78. Mannazzu I. Guerra E. Ferretti R. Pediconi D. Fatichenti F. 2000 Vanadate and copper induce overlapping oxidative stress responses in the vanadate-tolerant yeast Hansenula polymorpha. Biochim. Biophys. Acta, 1475 151 156 .
79. Mehra R. K. Mulchandani P. 1995 Glutathione-mediated transferof Cu(I) into phytochelatins. Biochem. J., 307 697 705 .
80. Mehra RK,Winge DR 1991 Metal ion resistance in fungi-molecular mechanisms and their regulated expression. J Cell Biochem., 45 30 40 .
81. Mendoza-Cózatl D. Tavera H. L. Navarro A. H. Sánchez R. M. 2005 Sulfur assimilation and glutathione metabolism under cadmium stress in yeast, protists and plants. FEMS Microbiol., 29 n. 4, 653 671 .
82. Merle S. S. Cuiné S. Carrier P. Pradines C. L. Luu D. T. Peltier G. 2003 Enhanced toxic metal accumulation in engineered bacterial cells expressing Arabidopsis thaliana phytochelatin synthase. Appl. Environ. Microbiol., 69 n. 1, 490 494 .
83. Mulligan CN 2005 Environmental applications for biosurfactants. Environ. Pollut., 133 n. 2, 183 198 .
84. Murai T. Ueda M. Yamamura M. Atomi H. Shibasaki Y. Kamasawa N. Osumi M. Amachi T. Tanaka A. 1997 Construction of a starch-utilizing yeast by cell surface engineering. Appl. Environ. Microbiol., 63 n. 4, 1362 1366 .
85. Muraleedharan T. R. Venkobachar C. 1990 Mechanism of biosorption of copper (II) by Ganoderma lucidum. Biotechnol. Bioeng., 35 320 325
86. Naeem A. Woertz J. R. Fein J. B. 2006 Experimental measurement of proton, Cd, Pb, Sr, and Zn adsorption onto the fungal species Saccharomyces cerevisiae. Environ. Sci. Technol., 40 n.18, 5724 5729 .
87. Nakajima A. Tsuruta T. 2004 Competitive biosorption of thorium and uranium by Micrococcus luteus. J. Radioanal Nucl. Chem., 260 13 18 .
88. Nishitani T. Shimada M. Kuroda K. Ueda M. 2010 Molecular design of yeast cell surface for adsorption and recovery of molybdenum, one of rare metals. Appl Microbiol Biotechnol., 86 641 648 .
89. Norton L. Baskaran K. Mc Kenzie T. 2004 Biosorption of zinc from aqueous solutions using biosolids. Adv. Environ. Res., 8 n. 3-4, 629 635 .
90. Nourbakhsh M. Sag Y. Ozer D. Aksu Z. Kustal T. Caglar A. 1994 A comparative study of various biosorbents for removal of chromium (VI) ions from industrial waste waters. Process Biochem., 29 1 5 .
91. Pagnanelli F. Esposito A. Vegliò F. 2002 Multi-metallic modelling for biosorption of binary systems. Water Research, 36 4095 4105 .
92. Pagnanelli F. Toro L. Veglio F. 2002 Olive mild solid residues as heavy metal sorbent material: a preliminary study. Waste Management, 22 901 907 .

93. Pattus F. Abdallah M. 2000 Siderophores and iron-transport in microorganisms: Review. J. Chin. Chem. Soc., 47 1 20 .
94. Paul D. Pandey G. Pandey J. Jain R. K. 2005 Acessing microbial diversity for bioremediation and environmental restoration. Trends in Biotechnol, 23 n.3, 135 142 .
95. Pazirandeh M. Chrisey L. A. Mauro J. M. Campbell J. R. Gaber B. P. 1995 Expression of the Neurospora crassa metallothionein gene in Escherichia coli and its effects on heavy-metal uptake. Appl Microbiol Biotechnol., 43 1112 1117 .
96. Penninckx MA 2000 A short review on the role of glutathione in the response of yeasts to nutritional, environment, and oxidative stresses. Enzyme Microbiol. Technol., 26 737 742 .
97. Penninckx MJ 2002 An overview on glutathione in Saccharomyces versus non-conventional yeasts. FEMS Yeast Res., 2 295 305 .
98. Pieper D. H. Reineke W. 2000 Engineering bacteria for bioremediation. Curr. Opin. Biotechnol., 11 262 270 .
99. Preveral S. Ansoborlo E. Mari S. Vavasseur A. Forestier C. 2006 Metal(loid)s and radionuclides cytotoxicity in Saccharomyces cerevisiae. Role of YCF1, glutathione and effect of buthionine sulfoximine. Biochimie, 88 n. 11, 1651 1663 .
100. Renninger N. Mc Mahon K. D. Knop R. Nitsche H. DS Clark Keasling. JD 2001 Uranyl precipitation by biomass from an enhanced biological phosphorus removal reactor. Biodegradation, 12 401 410 .
101. Ríos V. G. Pelegrín Y. F. Robledo D. Mendoza-Cozáti D. Sánchez R. M. Bouchot G. G. 2007 Cell wall composition effects cadmium accumulation and intracellular thiol peptides in marine red algae. Aquat. Toxicol., 81 n. 1, 65 72 .
102. Rittmann B. E. Seagren E. BA Wrenn Valocchi. A. J. Ray C. Raskin L. 1994 In situ bioremediation. Park Ridge, NJ, Noyes Publications.
103. Roane TM, Pepper IL 2001 Environmental Microbiolology In: ROANE, T. M, PEPPER, I. L. (Ed.). Microorganisms and Metal Pollutants. Academic Press, 17 403 423 .
104. Rutherford N. Mourez M. 2006 Surface display of proteins by Gram-negative bacterial autotransporters. Microbiol. Cell Factores, 5 n. 22.
105. Sakaguchi T. Nakajima A. 1991 Accumulation of heavy metals such as uranium and thorium by microorganisms. Smith RW, Misra M. (Eds.), Mineral Bioprocessing. The Minerals, Metals and Materials Society.
106. Samuelson H. Wernérus M. Svedberg Ståhl. S. 2000 Staphylococcal surface display of metal-binding polyhistidyl peptides, Appl Environ Microbiol., 66 1243 1248 .
107. Samuelson P. Gunneriusson E. Nygren P. P. A. Stahl S. 2002 Display of proteins on bacteria. J. Biotechnol., 96 n. 2, 129 154 .
108. Sandaa R. A. Enger O. Torsvik V. 1999 Abundance and Diversity of Archaea in Heavy-Metal-Contaminated Soils. Appl. Environ. Microbiol., 65 n. 8, 3293 3297 .
109. 2000ayler GS & Ripp S (2000) Field application of genetically engineered microorganisms for bioremediation processes. Curr. Opin. Biotechnol., 11 286 289 .
110. Schmitt M. Schwanewilm P. Ludwig J. Fraté L. H. 2006 Use of PMA1 as a housekeeping Biomarker for Assessment of Toxicant- induced Stress in Saccharomyces cerevisiae. Appl. Environ. Microbiol., 72 n. 2, 1515 1522 .
111. Selatnia A. Boukazoula A. Kechid B. N. Bakhti M. Z. Chergui A. Kerchich Y. 2004 Biosorption of lead (II) from aqueous solution by a bacterial dead Streptomyces rimosus biomass. J. Eng. Biochem., 19 n.2, 127 135 .
112. Silva E. Fialho A. M. Sá-Correia I. Burns R. G. Shaw L. J. 2004 Combined bioaugmentation and biostimulation to cleanup soil contamined with high concentrations of atrazine. Environ. Sci. Technol., 15-38 , n. 2, 632 637 .
113. Singhal R. K. ME Andersen Meister. A. 1997 Glutathione, a first line of defense against cadmium toxicity. FASEB J. 1 220 223 .
114. Smets BF, Rittmann BE, Stahl DA 1990 Genetic capabilities of biological processes, Part II. Environ. Sci. Technol., 24 162 170 .

115. Smith MC, Sumner ER, Avery SV 2007 Gluthatione and Gts1p drive beneficial variability in the cadmium resistances of individual yeast cells. Mol. Microbiol., 66 n. 3, 699 712 .
116. Soares E. V. Hebbelinck K. Soares H. M. 2003 Toxic effects caused by heavy metals in the yeast Saccharomyces cerevisiae: a comparative study. J. Microbiol., 49 n. 5, 336 343 .
117. Sousa C. Cebolla A. De Lorenzo V. 1996 Enhanced metalloadsorption of bacterial cells displaying poly-His peptides. Nat. Biotechnol., 14 1017 1020 .
118. Sze K. F. Lu Y. J. Wong P. K. 1996 Removal and recovery of copper ion (Cu2+) from electroplating effluent by a bioreactor containing magnetite-immobilized cells of Pseudomonas putida 5X. Resour. Conserv. Recy., 18 n. 1-4, 175 193 .
119. Tabak H. H. Lens P. Hullebusch E. D. V. Dejonghe W. 2005 Developments in bioremediation of soil and sediments polluted with metals and radionuclides-1. Microbiolal processes and mechanisms affecting bioremediation of metal contamination and influencing meal toxicity. Rev. Environ. Sci. Biotechnol., 4 115 156 .
120. Thirumoorthy N. Kumar K. T. M. AS Sundar Panayappan. L. Chatterjee M. 2007 Metallothionein: An overview. World J. Gastroenterol., 13 n. 7, 993 996 .
121. Timmis KN & Piper DH 1999 Bacteria designed for bioremediation. Trends Biotechnol., 17 201 204 .
122. Travieso L. Cañizares R. O. Borja R. Benítez F. Domínguez A. R. Dupeyrón R. Valiente V. 1999 Heavy metal removal by microalgas. B. Environ. Contam. Tox., 62 n. 2, 144 151 .
123. Tsezos M. Volesky B. 1982 The mechanism of uranium biosorption by Rhizopus arrhizus. Biotech. Bioeng., 24 n.2, 385 401 .
124. Tunali S. Çabuk A. Akar T. 2006 Removal of lead and copper ions from aqueous solutions by bacterial strain isolated from soil. J. Eng. Chem., 115 203 211 .
125. Uslu G. Tanyol 2006 (2006) Equilibrium and thermodynamic parameters of single and binary mixture biosorption of lead(II) and copper(II) ions onto Pseudomonas putida: effect of temperature. J. Hazard. Mater., 135 87 93 .
126. Valls M. Atrian S. Lorenzo V. Fernadéz L. A. 2000 Engineering a mouse metallothionein on the surface of Ralstonia eutropha CH34 for immobilization of heavy metals in soil. Nat. Biotechnol., 18 661 665 .
127. Valls M. Lorenzo V. 2002 Exploiting the genetic and biochemical capacities of bacteria for the remediation of heavy metal pollution. FEMS Microbiol. Rev., 26 n. 4, 327 338 .
128. Veglio F. Beolchini F. 1997 Removal of metals by biosorption: a review. Chem. Hydrometallurgy, 44 301 316 .
129. Velkov VV 2001 Stress-induced evolution and the biosafety of genetically modified microorganisms released into the environment. J. Biosci., 26 667 683 .
130. Vidali M. 2001 Bioremediation. Overview. Pure Appl. Chem., 73 n. 7, 1163 1172 .
131. Volesky B. 2001 Detoxification of metal-bearing effluents: biosorption for the next century. Hydrometallurgy, 59 n. 2-3, 203 216 .
132. Volesky B. Holan Z. R. 1995 Biosorption of heavy metal. Biotechnol. Prog., 11 235 250 .
133. VoleskyB 1987 Biosorbents for metal recovery. Trends in Biotechnology, 5 n. 4, 96 101 .
134. Wang J. Chen C. 2009 Biosorbents for heavy metals removal and their future. Biotechnol. Adv., 27 195 226 .
135. Wang J. Chen C. 2006 Biosorption of heavy metal by Saccharomyces cerevisiae. Biotechnol. Adv., 24 427 451 .
136. Wang Q. Li L. Chen M. Qi Q. Wang P. G. 2007 Construction of a novel system for cell surface display of heterologous proteins on Pichia pastoris. J. Biotechnol. Lett., 29 n. 10, 1561 1566 .
137. Wu C. H. Wood T. K. Mulchandani A. Chen W. 2006 Engineering Plant-microbe symbiosis for rhizoremediation of heavy metal. Appl. Environ. Microbiol., 72 n. 2, 1129 1134 .
138. Wu J. Yu H. Q. 2007 Biosorption of 2,4-dichlorophenol by immobilized white-rot fungus Phanerochaete chrysosporiyum from aqueous solutions. Bioresour. Technol., 98 n. 2, 253 259 .

139. Xu Z. Bae W. Nulchandani A. Mehra R. K. Chen W. 2002 Heavy Metal Removal by Novel CBD-EC20 Sorbents Immobilized on Cellulose. Biomacromolecules, 3 462 465 .

140. Yu Q. Z. Kaewsarn P. 2001 Desorption of Cu2+ from a biosorbent derived from the marine alga Durvillaea potatorum. Separ. Sci. Technol., 36 n. 7, 1495 1507 .

141. Zenk MH 1996 Heavy metal detoxification in higher plants: a review. Gene. 179 21 30 .

142. Zhang G. L. Wu Y. Z. Qian X. P. Meng Q. 2005 Biodegradation of crude oil by Pseudomonas aeruginosa in the presence of rhamnolopids. J. Zhejiang Univ. Sci., 6 n. 8, 725 730 .

143. Zouboulis AI, Matis KA, Lazaridis NK 2001 Removal of metal ions from simulated wastewater by Saccharomyces yeast biomass: Combining biosorption and flotation processes. Separ. Sci. Technol., 36 n. 3, 349 365 . Kobayashi I. Fujiwara S. Saegusa H. Inohe M. Metsumoto H. Tsuzuki M. 2006 Relief of arsenate toxicity by Cd-stimulated phytochelatin synthesis in the green alga Chlamydomonas reinhardtii. Mar. Biotechnol., 8 94 101 .

5

Rapid Reverse Purification DNA Extraction Approaches to Identify Microbial Pathogens in Wastewater

Sarah Schurig[1,2], Rea Kobialka[1], Andy Wende[2], Md Anik Ashfaq Khan[1], Phillip Lübcke[3], Elias Eger[4,5], Katharina Schaufler[3,4,5], Arwid Daugschies[6], Uwe Truyen[1] and Ahmed Abd El Wahed[1]

[1]Institute of Animal Hygiene and Veterinary Public Health, Leipzig University, 04103 Leipzig, Germany
[2]Xpedite Diagnostics GmbH, 80687 Munich, Germany
[3]Institute of Pharmacy, University of Greifswald, 17489 Greifswald, Germany
[4]Institute of Infection Medicine, Christian-Albrecht University Kiel, 24105 Kiel, Germany
[5]University Medical Center Schleswig-Holstein, 24105 Kiel, Germany
[6]Institute of Parasitology, Centre for Infectious Disease, Leipzig University, 04103 Leipzig, Germany

ABSTRACT

Wastewater monitoring became a promising solution in the early detection of outbreaks. Despite the achievements in the identification of pathogens in wastewater using real-time PCR, there is still a lack of reliable rapid nucleic acid extraction protocols. Therefore, in this study, samples were subjected to alkali, proteinase K and/or bead-beating followed by reverse purification magnetic beads-based separation. Wastewater samples spiked with S. aureus, E. coli and C. parvum were used as examples for Gram-positive and -negative bacteria and protozoa, respectively. All results were compared with a spin column technology as a reference method. Proteinase K with bead beating (vortexing with 0.1 mm glass beads for three minutes) was particularly successful for bacterial DNA extraction (three- to five-fold increase). The most useful extraction protocol for protozoa was pre-treatment with proteinase K (eight-fold increase). The selected methods were sensitive as far as detecting one bacterial cell per reaction for S. aureus, ten bacterial cells for E. coli and two oocysts for C. parvum. The extraction reagents are cold chain independent and no centrifuge or other large laboratory equipment is required to perform DNA extraction. A controlled validation trial is needed to test the effectiveness at field levels.

***Keywords**: DNA extraction, Reverse purification, Wastewater, Surveillance*

INTRODUCTION

Classical surveillance methods for the identification of endemic or emerging pathogens have a limited significance with increasing populations [1]. Therefore, the monitoring of wastewater became an important tool to tackle the spread of antimicrobial-resistant bacteria [2], poliovirus [3] and SARS-CoV-2 [4], mostly originating from humans and animals. The

World Health Organization declared that especially zoonotic microorganisms entering the water cycle from animal excreta are an underestimated hazard for humans and animals as well as the environment [5]. Animal waste represents 80% of the global fecal biomass and is expected to increase in the coming years [6]. This huge amount has an influence on the composition of the microbial profile of surface water, leading to an increased risk of waterborne zoonotic diseases. The exact burden of the environment as a reservoir is difficult to determine due to a lack of data and legislation. Wastewater screening has increased the potential for pathogen surveillance to prospectively reduce the risk of (re) infection of humans and animals, including the Gram-positive bacterium *Staphylococcus aureus* (*S. aureus*), the Gram-negative bacterium *Escherichia coli* (*E. coli)* and the protozoan *Cryptosporidium parvum* (*C. parvum*) [5,7,8,9]. *S. aureus* and *E. coli* are, in many cases, commensal but can cause diseases in both humans and animals. Symptoms of *S. aureus* infections in humans and animals include skin lesions, endocarditis, pneumonia and/or septicemia, in addition to mastitis in animals [10,11]. Depending on the *E. coli* subtype, gastrointestinal, urinary tract infections, meningitis and/or septicemia were recorded [12]. *C. parvum* induces gastrointestinal symptoms, such as diarrhea and/or vomiting, mainly in humans and cattle [13,14].

With water scarcity expected to affect half of the world's population by 2025, the use of inadequately treated wastewater, e.g., in agriculture and the community, will be a serious and increasing risk to livestock, wildlife and humans [15]. Routine governmental monitoring for contaminants in water does exist in Europe and North America to prevent waterborne diseases. However, they often cover only a small number of pathogens and are limited to culture-based methods [16,17,18]. Nevertheless, culturing pathogens is time-consuming, and, in addition, not all pathogens are culturable. In contrast, molecular diagnostics such as polymerase chain reaction (PCR) are faster and cover wide ranges of microorganisms with a higher specificity and sensitivity [19,20]. For molecular detection, a suitable DNA extraction method is crucial and can influence the outcomes of the PCR assay [21]. Many extraction methods have been established to assure DNA quality. Most of them are costly, time-consuming and require complex electrical equipment [22]. Moreover, introducing variations in nucleic acid extraction protocols can be deemed necessary due to differences in characteristic cellular features among pathogens. Therefore, rapid and simple extraction procedures with minimum handling will lead to better quality nucleic acids, which improves the final molecular results.

The aim of this study was to evaluate a rapid, portable and reliable extraction method that achieves a high amount of extracted DNA for the subsequent detection of pathogens by real-time PCR. Cell suspensions with *S. aureus*, *E. coli* and *C. parvum* were used as representatives for Gram-positive and -negative bacteria and parasites, respectively.

The extraction and purification of DNA that will be applied here relies on the reverse purification principle utilized by the SwiftX DNA kit. Reverse purification means that cell debris and impurities are bound by magnetic beads during the cell lysis step. The debris- and inhibitor-loaded magnetic beads are then attracted by a magnet, which leads to a clearance of the crude lysate. After magnetic separation, the nucleic acids in the supernatant can be used directly for amplification or for storage.

Different pre-treatment options, such as the addition of proteinase K (PK), alkaline treatment (AT) or bead beating (BB) were evaluated separately or in combination. As a reference, a spin column technique was applied in this study.

MATERIALS AND METHODS

Sample Preparation

Cell suspensions of *Staphylococcus aureus* subsp. *aureus* (DSM 799) and *Escherichia coli* (DSM 682) were obtained from the German Collection of Microorganisms and Cell Cultures in Braunschweig, Germany, and stored at −80 °C. Before use, these samples were cultivated overnight on Columbia Blood Agar with sheep blood (Thermo Fisher Scientific, Waltham, MA, USA) at 37 °C. Bacterial colonies were removed from the agar plate, resuspended in 700 μL phosphate-buffered saline (PBS) and pelleted (6000× *g*, 3 min) using a microcentrifuge (Eppendorf, Hamburg, Germany). Oocysts of *Cryptosporidium parvum* (provided by the Institute of Parasitology, Centre for Infectious Disease, Leipzig University, Leipzig, Germany) were stored in a solution containing 2% of 250 μg/mL Amphotericin B (Biochrom GmbH, Cambridge, UK), 2% of 10,000 U/mL Penicillin-Streptomycin (Thermo Fisher Scientific, Waltham, MA, USA), 1% of 1 mg/mL Gentamycin (Biochrom GmbH, Cambridge, UK) and 95% PBS at 4 °C. The oocyst solution was also pelleted (16,600× *g*, 5 min). The pellets of *S. aureus*, *E. coli* and *C. parvum* were washed in 200 μL PBS and pelleted at 6000× *g* for three minutes and the supernatant was discarded. *S. aureus*, *E. coli* and *C. parvum* were pelleted separately or combined based on the experiment layout.

DNA Extraction

Spin Column-Based Method

A DNeasy Blood and Tissue Kit (Qiagen, Hilden, Germany) was used as the spin column reference method. DNA of *S. aureus* and *E. coli* was extracted following the manufacturer's instructions for Gram-positive and -negative bacteria, respectively. The only modification for *S. aureus* was the inclusion of bead beating as the pellet was resuspended in 400 μL PBS and transferred into a Soil Grinding SK38 Precellys Lysing Tube (Bertin, Montigny-le-Bretonneux, France). The suspension was mixed in Precellys 24 Tissue Homogenizer (Bertin, Montigny-le-Bretonneux, France) at 6500 rpm for one minute. A total of 200 μL of the cell suspension was treated as described in the manufacturer's basic protocol. For *C. parvum*, 100 μL of 1.2% taurocholic acid sodium salt hydrate (Sigma Aldrich, St. Louis, MO, USA) was added to the cell suspension followed by incubation at 37 °C for 120 min. The suspension was pelleted (13,000× *g*, 5 min) and resuspended in 80 μL PBS, 100 μL ATL Buffer (Qiagen, Hilden, Germany) and 20 μL PK. The procedure was continued as the recommendation by the manufacturer's protocol for Gram-negative bacteria. This was considered a "spin column" reference method.

Rapid Principle of DNA Extraction and Pre-Treatment Options

As the main procedure of DNA extraction, the "SwiftX DNA" Kit (Xpedite Diagnostics, Munich, Germany) was used according to the instructions of the manufacturer. Different pre-treatments were applied as follows: None (I), addition of PK (II), AT at room temperature (III) or 95 °C (IV) and BB (V). No pre-treatment included an incubation step at 95 °C for 15 min, as required by the manufacturer's basic protocol. In the case of AT, 200 mM sodium hydroxide was added to the lysis mixture, incubated for 15 min and neutralized with 200 mM hydrochloric acid. An overview of the various procedures can be seen in Table 1. After the selection of the best pre-treatment procedure, a combination of multiple pre-treatments was tested as follows: PK was combined with AT at 95 °C (protocols II + IV) or BB (protocols II + V). In each run, one sample with no extraction procedure, one sample using only BB and one sample extracted by a spin column reference method with and without BB were included as control.

Table 1. Overview of working steps for different extraction protocols

Protocol ID	Extraction Method	Buffer + Magnetic Beads	Proteinase K	Alkali	Bead Beating	10 min 60 °C	15 min RT	15 min 95 °C	Magnetic Separation
I	No pre-treatment	x						x	x
II	Proteinase K	x	x			x		x	x
III	Alkaline treatment RT	x		x			x		x
IV	Alkaline treatment 95 °C	x		x				x	x
V	Bead beating	x			x			x	x

RT = room temperature.

Bead Beating

For the bead beating tests, DNA of *E. coli* and *S. aureus* was extracted with a combination of BB and PK (II + V). The pellets were resuspended in 300 µL DLN Buffer (Xpedite Diagnostics, Munich, Germany) and transferred into a 2 mL microcentrifuge tube containing 250 mg of glass beads (Sigmund Lindner, Warmensteinbach, Germany). Glass bead sizes were Ø 0.1 mm (0.09–0.15 mm), Ø 0.5 mm (0.4–0.6 mm) or Ø 1.0 mm (0.70–1.30 mm). The suspension was mixed at 2000 rpm in the Vortexer (Heathrow Scientific, Vernon Hills, IL, USA) for three minutes or in the Hulamixer (Thermo Fisher Scientific, Waltham, MA, USA) for five minutes. A total of 200 µL of each cell suspension was transferred into a new microcentrifuge tube, mixed with 10 µL PK and treated using protocol II. In the case of *C. parvum*, DNA was extracted either with protocol II or using PK in combination with 0.1 mm or 0.5 mm glass beads in the Vortexer as described before. The performance of BB for *C. parvum* was also evaluated with prefilled tubes containing 0.1 mm zirconium beads (Benchmark Scientific, Sayreville, NJ, USA).

Limit of Detection (LOD)

A total of 10^7 (*S. aureus*) and 10^8 (*E. coli*) bacterial cells and 10^5 oocysts of *C. parvum* were counted with an Olympus BX40 microscope (Microscopy Technologies, Tokyo, Japan), using a Neubauer Chamber—An amount of 200 µL of wastewater, provided as unfiltered influent water retrieved from the sewage treatment plant Greifswald-Ladebow, Greifswald, Germany, was spiked with the bacterial cells and oocysts. A tenfold serial dilution of the spiked wastewater was prepared. For the DNA extraction of *S. aureus* and *E. coli*, 200 µL of each dilution was mixed with 200 µL DLN Buffer and the procedure was continued using 0.1 mm glass beads and the Vortexer for BB. In the case of *C. parvum*, protocol II (Table 1) with DLN buffer was used. Nucleic acids of each dilution after extraction were tested using real-time PCR. For the determination of LOD, this was repeated three times. A layout of the final extraction procedure is illustrated in Figure 1.

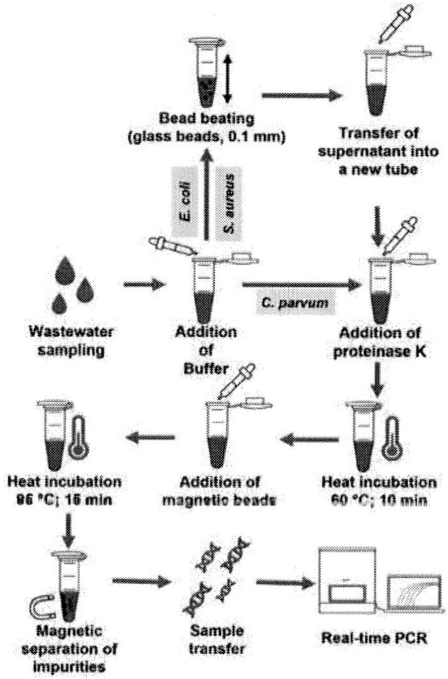

Figure 1. Flowchart of the rapid extraction method selected for determining the limit of detection for *S. aureus*, *E. coli* and *C. parvum*.

Real-Time PCR

All extracted samples were screened in real-time PCR operated in a Stratagene Mx3000P Multiplex Quantitative PCR System (Agilent, Santa Clara, CA, USA) according to the pipetting scheme and thermal profile stated in Table 2. The selection of primers and probes, volumes and thermal profiles was based on the study of Luciani et al. for *S. aureus* [23] and Tillman et al. for *E. coli* [24]. In the case of *C. parvum*, the real-time PCR protocol described by Dresley et al. [25] was employed.

Table 2. Real-time PCR protocols for *S. aureus*, *E. coli* and *C. parvum*

	Mastermix	**Thermal Profile** [2]
S. aureus	10.00 µL QuantiNova Probe Master Mix	Denaturation: 95 °C; 120 s
	(Qiagen, Hilden, Germany)	Amplification (45 cycles):
	0.64 µL Primer/Probe Mix	Denaturation: 95 °C; 5 s
	1.28 µM forward primer StaphF	Annealing and extension: 60 °C; 30 s
	1.28 µM reverse primer StaphR	
	0.64 µM probe StaphP	
	8.36 µL PCR clean water	
	1.00 µL template	

E. coli	10.00 μL QuantiNova Probe Master Mix	Denaturation: 95 °C; 120 s
	(Qiagen, Hilden, Germany)	Amplification (35 cycles) [1]:
	1.00 μL Primer/Probe Mix	Denaturation: 94 °C; 15 s
	0.40 μM forward primer gadE-F	Annealing and extension: 56 °C; 45 s
	0.40 μM reverse primer gadE-R	
	0.20 μM probe gadE-Probe	
	8.00 μL PCR clean water	
	1.00 μL template	
C. parvum	12.50 μL Maxima probe/ROX qPCR Master Mix	Denaturation: 95 °C; 900 s
	(Thermo Fisher Scientific, Waltham, MA, USA)	Amplification (40 cycles):
	0.30 μL forward primer (0.30 μM) CP_hsp70_fwd	Denaturation: 95 °C; 15 s
	0.90 μL forward primer (0.90 μM) CP_hsp70_rvs	Annealing and extension: 60 °C; 60 s
	0.20 μL forward primer (0.20 μM) Hsp70_snd	
	6.10 μL PCR clean water	
	5.00 μL template	

[1] Forty cycles for the determination of limit of detection; [2] Thermal profile of *C. parvum* was used in case of multiplexing with *S. aureus*.

Determination of Nucleic Acid Concentration

Nucleic acid concentration was measured using a Nanodrop 2000c (Thermo Fisher Scientific, Waltham, MA, USA) and a Qubit 2.0 Fluorometer in combination with a Qubit dsDNA BR Assay Kit (Thermo Fisher Scientific, Waltham, MA, USA) according to the instructions of the manufacturers.

Statistical Analysis

The LOD with 95% probability and the probability of detection (POD) were determined by the method of Wilrich and Wilrich recommended in the ISO standard 16140-2:2016 using the PODLOD program version 11 (Freie Universität Berlin, Berlin, Germany) [26]. The correlation between nucleic acid measurement by Qubit, Nanodrop and real-time PCR was determined according to the distribution of data using GraphPad Prism version 9.0 (GraphPad Software Inc., San Diego, CA, USA).

Based on the quantification cycle (C_q), the total amount of extracted DNA was calculated using the following formula making the highest C_q adapted to the reagent volume 100%:

$$DNA_{Norm.ex.} = \frac{1}{200 * 2^{(C_{q1} - Cq_{low})}} * V$$

$$DNA_{Norm.ex.100\%} = \frac{100 * DNA_{Norm.ex.}}{DNA_{Norm.ex.high}}$$

- $DNA_{Norm.ex.}$ = total amount of recovered DNA (%)
- C_{q1} = measured quantification cycle for the sample of interest
- C_{qlow} = lowest quantification cycle of each run
- V = total volume (µL)
- $DNA_{Norm.ex.100\%} = DNA_{Norm.ex.}$ normalized to a maximum amount of 100%
- $DNA_{Norm.ex.high}$ = highest amount of $DNA_{Norm.ex.}$ of each run (%)

RESULTS

Comparison of Various Extraction Procedures

Several pre-treatment options were tested to identify the most efficient DNA extraction procedure for *S. aureus*, *E. coli* and *C. parvum*. All tested protocols are summarized in Table 1. For *S. aureus*, the addition of a BB step to the SwiftX protocol resulted in the highest DNA recovery and was more than two-fold higher than the spin column reference method (Figure 2). The combination of PK or AT with the SwiftX protocol resulted in no significant effect on the DNA yield. The most efficient extraction methods for *E. coli* were SwiftX combined with AT at 95 °C or the addition of PK. Surprisingly, DNA recovery rates using the spin column reference method were five times lower (Figure 2). For the extraction of *C. parvum*, the SwiftX protocols showed a zero- to five-fold better performance than the spin column reference protocol. The AT at 95 °C or preincubation with PK increased the amount of recovered DNA compared to the spin column reference method four- and five-fold, respectively (Figure 2).

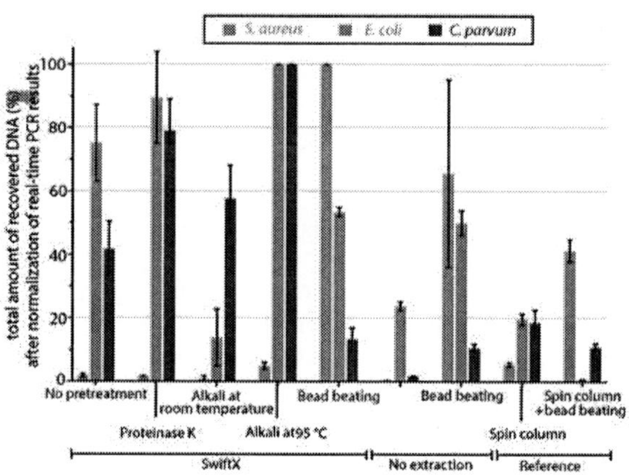

Figure 2. Performance of various extraction protocols with and without pre-treatment. The percentage of recovered DNA for different pre-treatment protocols was measured after the normalization of real-time PCR results. Cell suspension of 10^7 bacterial cells of *S. aureus*, 10^8 bacterial cells of *E. coli* or 10^6 oocysts of *C. parvum* was pelleted and extracted. DNA was measured by real-time PCR. The highest percentage of recovered DNA was achieved using SwiftX with bead beating in the case of *S. aureus*. SwiftX with proteinase K or alkaline treatment for *E. coli* and *C. parvum* revealed the best DNA recovery rate.

Evaluation of Combined Pre-Treatment Protocols

The best single pre-treatment protocols (Figure 2) were combined to determine the most effective mixture with SwiftX. Pre-treatments with none, PK, PK + BB and PK + AT at 95 °C were tested. The results are shown in Figure 3. For *S. aureus*, the highest amount of DNA was obtained in the protocol of SwiftX with PK + BB, which was the only method to outperform the spin column reference technique (an increase of DNA amount by a factor of three). In contrast, all combinations of pre-treatment and SwiftX for the extraction of *E. coli* performed three to seven times higher than the spin column reference method. Prominently, a seven- and five-fold increase was achieved for the SwiftX protocol with PK or a combination of PK and BB, respectively. Likewise, the DNA of *C. parvum* was recovered in a six- to ten-fold higher amount with all variations of the SwiftX protocol compared to the spin column reference method. Nevertheless, the best results were achieved using pre-treatment with PK, PK + BB or PK + AT.

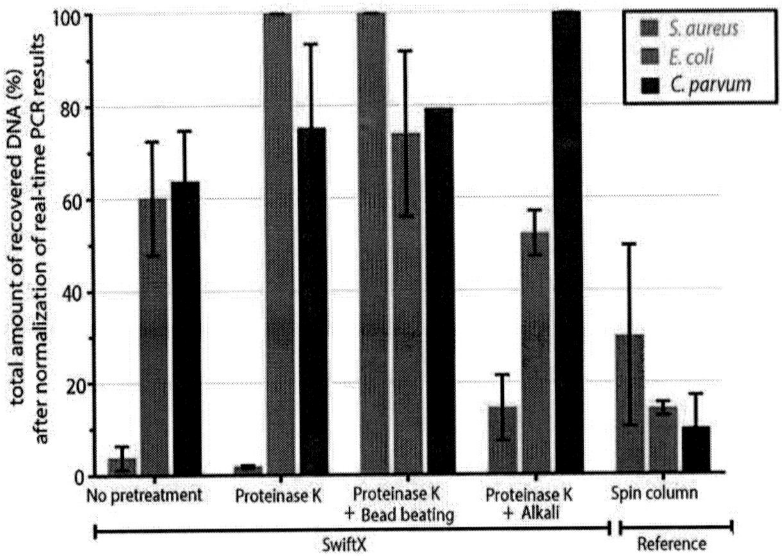

Figure 3. Results of the combination of various pre-treatment protocols. Between 10^6 and 10^8 of bacterial cells of either *S. aureus* or *E. coli*, as well as oocysts of *C. parvum*, were prepared to test a maximum dual pre-treatment based on the best performer in Figure 2. Highest percentage of recovered DNA was achieved using SwiftX combined with proteinase K and bead beating for *S. aureus*. For *E. coli*, proteinase K or a combination of proteinase K and bead beating proved to be most efficient, while proteinase K or a combination of proteinase K and either bead beating or alkaline treatment worked the best for *C. parvum*.

Influence of Different Bead-Beating Methods and Glass Bead Sizes on the DNA Extraction Performance

DNA was extracted from a bacterial cell suspension of *S. aureus* and *E. coli* using the SwiftX protocol combined with a BB step with glass beads in sizes 0.1 mm, 0.5 mm or 1.0 mm. Additionally, performances of a simple hulamixer or Vortexer for the BB step were compared to each other to avoid the use of an expensive complex BB device. The use of 0.1 mm glass beads together with the Vortexer outperformed all tested extraction methods for *S. aureus* (Figure 4). In contrast, the different BB variations for the DNA extraction of *E. coli* did not show a significant difference. In the case of *C. parvum*, glass beads in sizes 0.1 mm and 0.5 mm, as well as 0.1 mm zirconium beads, were used for DNA extraction with the SwiftX protocol. Results were comparable to the use of SwiftX with PK; no advantages were recorded for *C. parvum* DNA recovery.

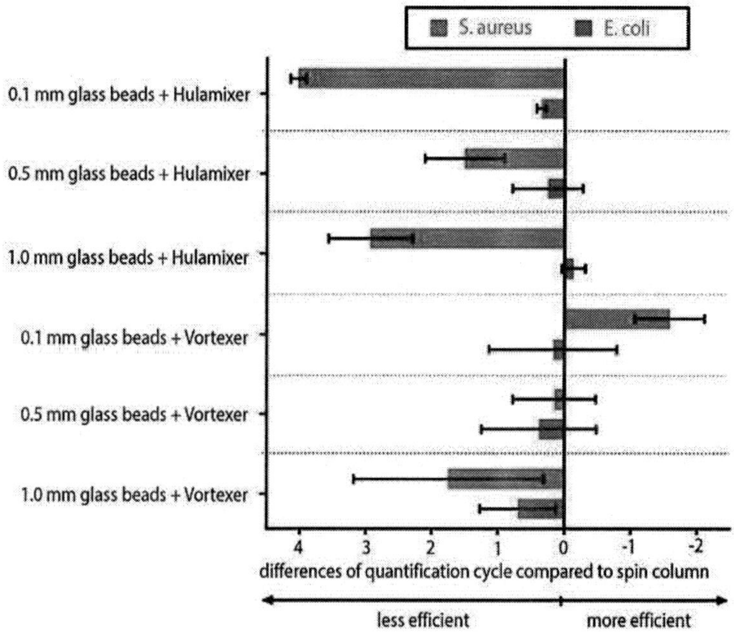

Figure 4. Effect of glass bead size and bead beating force on the extraction performance. To identify the optimal protocol for DNA recovery, SwiftX was combined with bead beating using glass beads with different sizes (0.1 mm, 0.5 mm or 1.0 mm). The real-time PCR results of SwiftX protocols and the spin column reference technique were compared. The use of 0.1 mm glass beads combined with the Vortexer showed the best results for *S. aureus*, while equal performance was achieved for *E. coli*.

Correspondence of Quantification Cycle Determined by Real-Time PCR and Nucleic Acid Concentration Measured by Nanodrop and Qubit

No substantial correlation could be identified between the nucleic acid concentration measured by Nanodrop or Qubit and the C_q values by real-time PCR for *S. aureus*, *E. coli* and *C. parvum*.

Time and Pipetting Steps of Various Extraction Protocols

To identify the best protocol for rapid extraction time, working steps, reagents volume and number for electrical devices for each protocol were compared. While SwiftX required three to five working steps in a total of 30 or 35 min, the spin column reference method needed more time (up to 270 min) and seven to nine pipetting steps. A BB step needs larger volumes of reagents (400–480 μL) and a tissue homogenizer or Vortexer. A heat block was crucial for all protocols and a high-speed centrifuge was a must for the spin column reference method, while it was not required for the SwiftX technology (Table 3).

Table 3. Number of working steps, time (min.), added volume of reagents (in μL) and the number of additional electric devices for different extraction protocols for *S. aureus*, *E. coli* and *C. parvum*

Extraction Method	**Working Steps**	**Time (min.)**	**Added Reagents (μL)**	**Use of Electric Devices**
SwiftX + no pre-treatment	3	30	200	-
SwiftX + proteinase K	3	30	200	-
SwiftX + proteinase K + bead beating	4	35	480	Tissue homogenizer (or Vortexer)
SwiftX + proteinase K + alkali 95 °C	5	35	300	-
Spin column				
S. aureus	7	40	400	Centrifuge + tissue homogenizer
E. coli	6	150	200	Centrifuge
C. parvum	9	270	200	Centrifuge

Determination of LOD for the Extraction Method of Choice

The combination of the SwiftX protocol with the use of PK + BB was chosen as the method of choice for *S. aureus* and *E. coli*. For *C. parvum*, the SwiftX protocol including PK treatment was selected. The LOD of the DNA extraction method for each pathogen was determined in a ten-fold serial dilution of spiked wastewater to simulate the real case scenario. An amount between 10^3 and 10^6 bacterial cells or oocysts per microliter was used to spike the wastewater and was extracted with the respective protocol using the spin column reference method as control.

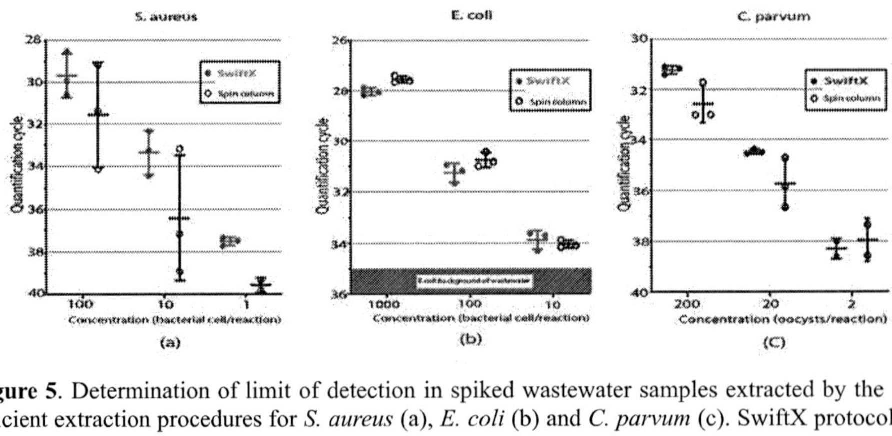

Figure 5. Determination of limit of detection in spiked wastewater samples extracted by the most efficient extraction procedures for *S. aureus* (a), *E. coli* (b) and *C. parvum* (c). SwiftX protocol was combined with proteinase K and a bead-beating step for *S. aureus* and *E. coli*, whereas for *C. parvum*, the proteinase K and SwiftX protocol was applied. Ten-fold serial dilutions of spiked wastewater were screened. After extraction, the quantification cycle of each dilution was measured using real-time PCR. All results were compared to a spin column reference method. Down to one bacterial cell of *S. aureus* per reaction was detected (a), while the threshold was ten with *E. coli* (b). For *C. parvum*, the limit of detection was two oocysts per reaction (c). Because of the *E. coli* pre-existence in wastewater, the shaded zone in (b) represents the background values.

Down to one bacterial cell of *S. aureus* per reaction was detected by combining the methods of choice with real-time PCR. The detected amount of DNA for each dilution was on average 0.7 log levels higher than the spin column reference method (Figure 5a). The number of detected cells per microliter in each dilution of *E. coli* sample after extraction with SwiftX and PK + BB were comparable to those achieved with the spin column reference method. In lower dilutions, ten DNA molecules per reaction were consistently detected due to the background level of *E. coli* in the wastewater (Figure 5b). Down to two oocysts of *C. parvum* per reaction were detected by both the SwiftX and spin column reference techniques (Figure 5c). With a 95% probability, 0.74 copies per reaction with SwiftX and 2.33 copies per reaction with the spin column reference method were calculated for *S. aureus*. In the case of *E. coli*, 9.94 and 115.1 copies per reaction were identified for SwiftX and the spin column reference method, respectively. For the extraction of *C. parvum* DNA, both methods, the SwiftX protocol and the spin column reference method, achieved 13.55 copies per reaction. The probability of detection curves are shown in Figure 6.

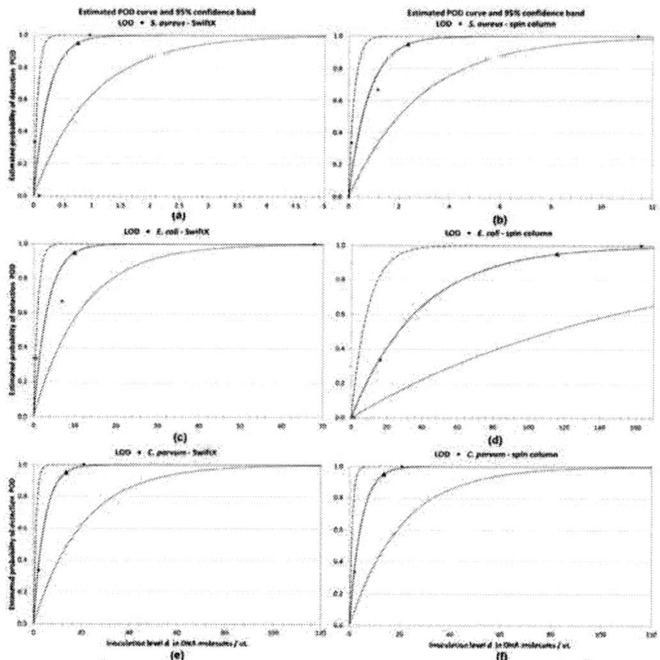

Figure 6. Probability of detection of method of choice for the extraction of *S. aureus* (a,b), *E. coli* (c,d) and *C. parvum* (e,f). Between 10^3 and 10^6 bacterial cells or oocysts per microliter were spiked into wastewater in a ten-fold serial dilution. In the case of *S. aureus* and *E. coli*, DNA was extracted using SwiftX in combination with proteinase K and bead beating. For *C. parvum*, the SwiftX protocol was combined in a preincubation with proteinase K. The efficiency of the extraction protocols was compared to a spin column reference method. The probability of the detection function was calculated by the Wilrich and Wilrich model using quantification cycles measured by real-time PCR. The 95% probability is depicted as a triangle. For *S. aureus*, 0.74 copies per reaction with SwiftX (a) and 2.33 with the spin column reference method (b) were calculated. For *E. coli*, 9.94 and 115.1 copies per reaction were measured for SwiftX (c) and the spin column reference method (d), respectively. In the case of *C. parvum*, 13.55 copies per reaction were determined for both the SwiftX (e) and the spin column reference method (f).

DISCUSSION

In this study, a portable rapid DNA extraction method based on reverse purification separation was established for the extraction of pathogen DNA from wastewater. The method included a pre-treatment with PK and BB for bacteria and a pre-treatment with PK for protozoa, respectively.

In all experiments, molecular testing (real-time PCR) was selected over culture-based detection methods which required 12 h of incubation and specially trained laboratory staff. Real-time PCR is much faster while enabling a high sensitivity and specificity of the analysis [20,27]. As clearly shown in our study and by other groups, DNA extraction is a very crucial step to obtain a sufficient amount and quality of DNA for real-time PCR, which is instrumental in avoiding false negative results [21,22]. In this regard, it is not only the quality of the assay that affects the sensitivity of the detection method, but also the extraction procedure.

Although all tested combinations of sample pre-treatment led to detectable amounts of DNA, the quality and yield varied among the different treatments. This was expected, as the outer layer structures of the tested pathogens are very different. Gram-positive bacteria such as *S. aureus* have a thick homogeneous cell wall (20–40 nm) containing a wide peptidoglycan layer [28,29]. The cell wall of Gram-negative bacteria such as *E. coli* is much thinner (15 nm) and composed of an inner membrane, a thin peptidoglycan monolayer and an outer membrane [28,29,30]. The oocyst wall of *C. parvum* is very rigid. It is 40 nm thick and contains an inner filamentous and an outer glycoprotein layer [31]. When PK was used separately or in combination, the amount of extracted DNA increased, especially for *E. coli* and *C. parvum*, as the PK eliminates interfering proteins in the solution and protects free DNA by inactivating DNases [32]. Moreover, the protease degrades the filamentous layer of the oocyst wall resulting in an increase in extraction efficiency for *C. parvum* [31]. For *S. aureus*, PK was likely not adequate to disrupt the thick cell wall of the Gram-positive bacterium. An additional BB step proved to be essential for the extraction of DNA from *S. aureus*. These results are in accordance with data obtained from previous studies [33,34,35]. Modification of the BB method improved the extraction efficiency for *E. coli*. This emphasizes that bead size, BB duration and BB device can influence the DNA yield and need to be adjusted to the specific pathogen. Likewise, Proctor et al. have previously made the same observation [36]. With the use of the reverse purification principle, the cleared lysate still contains certain organic and inorganic compounds, which can influence measurements by real-time PCR [37], which is why an applicability testing of reverse purification-based methods is advised before implementation in the subsequent workflow. A previous study by Hansen et al. reported a significant inhibitory effect when using the SwiftX DNA kit for direct DNA extraction from fecal samples [38]. Thus, our observation that there was no difference in the performance of DNA extraction from PBS and wastewater, respectively, was somewhat surprising. This may be explained by the significantly lower concentration of fecal matter in wastewater compared to actual fecal samples. In our case, the lysate after DNA extraction was clear and colorless. However, direct extraction of DNA from solid fecal samples may not be successful as substances such as bilirubin, which gives the brownish fecal coloration and can interfere with the real-time PCR, might only be insufficiently removed [39].

The developed method comprises several advantages. First, DNA can be extracted very rapidly with a maximum working time of 35 min. Second, the procedure involves no more than four steps and is therefore easy to learn and to implement. Third, it requires only two basic electrical devices: a heating block and a small Vortexer. Both can be operated as part of a mobile suitcase lab under field conditions [40]. Fourth, the reagents are heat stable and do not require refrigeration or freezer storage, which again improves field applicability. In contrast, the spin column reference method requires an expensive tissue homogenizer, a high-speed centrifuge and more handling time.

Down to one bacterial cell per reaction was detected for *S. aureus*, ten bacterial cells for *E. coli* and two oocysts for *C. parvum*, which was similar to the spin column reference method. Establishing a highly sensitive extraction and detection procedure is crucial, especially in the case of water testing, where pathogen concentrations might be low [41,42]. Rainfall and runoff, as well as regional and seasonal differences, can cause huge variations in the pathogen's quantity and may result in a drastic dilution effect of the wastewater [43]. Despite the efficacy of the method established in this study, a concentration step (e.g., ultrafiltration) might be needed in a future application to avoid false negative results. Additionally, this would provide the capability to study larger volumes of wastewater. In the experiments performed to determine the best pre-treatment options, the SwiftX protocols resulted in an up to 10-fold increase of recovered DNA compared to the spin column reference method. The differences can be explained by the loss of DNA due to the number of working steps and the need for a high-speed centrifuge in the reference method. In the case of the reverse purification method, fewer working and sample transfer steps are required, which results in less stress and loss of DNA molecules.

Despite the many advantages of the reverse purification methods, their compatibility with the sample type of interest must be examined to avoid any potential inhibitors impairing the downstream applications. The method was successfully implemented for nucleic acid extraction from skin [44], feces [38], urine [45], cervicovaginal lavage [46] and blood [40], but in combination with isothermal amplification methods, which are known to resist several common inhibitors of real-time PCR chemistries [47]. Sample purity and the concentration of nucleic acids are usually measured by Nanodrop or Qubit. In our experiment, no correlation was found between the results of these measurements and the detectability in the molecular assays.

Even though nucleic acid concentrations could be measured by Nanodrop, the dynamic ranges and the ratios of wavelengths indicate that they are due to background noise. Quantification of DNA concentration by Nanodrop is based on UV absorption measurement at a DNA-specific wavelength, while the Qubit instrument conducts a fluorescence-based measurement of a DNA-bound dye. Li and Wu et al. found that the UV absorption method and the fluorescence method can be affected by the presence of organic and chemical contaminants [48].

Since in the reverse purification both remnants of cells and lysis buffer components remain as background, the measurements of DNA concentrations by Nanodrop and Qubit have likely been influenced. Consequently, the use of DNA concentration measurement in combination with the established extraction method is not recommended. Overall, our findings suggest that the rapid extraction methods formulated in this study are field-applicable and need further controlled trials to confirm. Moreover, the effectiveness of the extraction of nucleic acids also needs to be determined in the detection of antimicrobial resistance genes and viruses, as these are important contributors to the health risks imposed by wastewater.

REFERENCES

1. Li, J.; Zhu, Y.; Wu, X.; Hoffmann, M.R. Rapid Detection Methods for Bacterial Pathogens in Ambient Waters at the Point of Sample Collection: A Brief Review. Clin. Infect. Dis. 2020, 71, S84–S90.
2. Hendriksen, R.S.; Munk, P.; Njage, P.; van Bunnik, B.; McNally, L.; Lukjancenko, O.; Röder, T.; Nieuwenhuijse, D.; Pedersen, S.K.; Kjeldgaard, J.; et al. Global monitoring of antimicrobial resistance based on metagenomics analyses of urban sewage. Nat. Commun. 2019, 10, 1124.
3. Hovi, T.; Shulman, L.M.; van der Avoort, H.; Deshpande, J.; Roivainen, M.; EM, D.E.G. Role of environmental poliovirus surveillance in global polio eradication and beyond. Epidemiol. Infect. 2012, 140, 1–13.
4. Medema, G.; Heijnen, L.; Elsinga, G.; Italiaander, R.; Brouwer, A. Presence of SARS-Coronavirus-2 RNA in Sewage and Correlation with Reported COVID-19 Prevalence in the Early Stage of the Epidemic in The Netherlands. Environ. Sci. Technol. Lett. 2020, 7, 511–516.
5. Dufour, A. Animal Waste, Water Quality and Human Health; World Health Organization: Geneva, Switzerland, 2012; p. 488.
6. Berendes, D.M.; Yang, P.J.; Lai, A.; Hu, D.; Brown, J. Estimation of global recoverable human and animal faecal biomass. Nat. Sustain. 2018, 1, 679–685.
7. Surveillance for waterborne disease outbreaks associated with drinking water and other nonrecreational water—United States, 2009–2010. MMWR Morb. Mortal. Wkly Rep. 2013, 62, 714–720.
8. Rhoden, K.; Alonso, J.; Carmona, M.; Pham, M.; Barnes, A.N. Twenty years of waterborne and related disease reports in Florida, USA. One Health 2021, 13, 100294.
9. Jenkins, M.; Ahmed, S.; Barnes, A.N. A systematic review of waterborne and water-related disease in animal populations of Florida from 1999–2019. PLoS ONE 2021, 16, e0255025.
10. Tong, S.Y.; Davis, J.S.; Eichenberger, E.; Holland, T.L.; Fowler, V.G., Jr. Staphylococcus aureus infections: Epidemiology, pathophysiology, clinical manifestations, and management. Clin. Microbiol. Rev. 2015, 28, 603–661.
11. Haag, A.F.; Fitzgerald, J.R.; Penadés, J.R. Staphylococcus aureus in Animals. Microbiol. Spectr. 2019, 7.
12. Bélanger, L.; Garenaux, A.; Harel, J.; Boulianne, M.; Nadeau, E.; Dozois, C.M. Escherichia coli from animal reservoirs as a potential source of human extraintestinal pathogenic E. coli. FEMS Immunol. Med. Microbiol. 2011, 62, 1–10.
13. Xiao, L.; Feng, Y. Zoonotic cryptosporidiosis. FEMS Immunol. Med. Microbiol. 2008, 52, 309–323.
14. Robertson, L.J.; Björkman, C.; Axén, C.; Fayer, R. Cryptosporidiosis in Farmed Animals. Cryptosporidium Parasite Dis. 2013, 149–235.
15. Food and Agriculure Organization of the United Nations; Word Organization for Animal Health; World Health Organization. Technical Brief on Water, Sanitaion, Hygiene and Wastewater Management to Prevent Infections and Reduce the Spread of Antimicrobial Resistance; Food and Agriculture Organization of the United Nations: Rome, Italy; World Organisation for Animal Health: Paris, France; World Health Organization: Geneva, Switzerland, 2020.
16. European Union. Directive (EU) 98/83/EC of the European Parliament and of the Council of 3 November 1998 on the Quality of Water Intended for Human Consumption. Available online: https://eur-lex.europa.eu/legal-content/EN/TXT/?uri=celex%3A31998L0083 (accessed on 3 January 2023).
17. Ontario Ministry of the Environment and Climate Change, Laboratory Services Branch. Protocol for the Sampling and Analysis of Industrial/Municipal Wastewater of the 01 January

2016. Available online: https://files.ontario.ca/protocol_for_the_sampling_and_analysis_of_industrial_municipal_wastewater.pdf (accessed on 3 January 2023).

18. Federal Government, U.S. Code of Federal Regulations of 1 July 2021. Title 40; Part 136—Guidelines establishing test procedures for the analysis of pollutants. Available online: https://www.ecfr.gov/current/title-40/chapter-I/subchapter-D/part-136 (accessed on 3 January 2023).

19. Valledor, S.; Valledor, I.; Gil-Rodríguez, M.C.; Seral, C.; Castillo, J. Comparison of several Real-Time PCR Kits versus a Culture-dependent Algorithm to Identify Enteropathogens in Stool Samples. Sci. Rep. 2020, 10, 4301.

20. Call, D.R.; Brockman, F.J.; Chandler, D.P. Detecting and genotyping Escherichia coli O157:H7 using multiplexed PCR and nucleic acid microarrays. Int. J. Food Microbiol. 2001, 67, 71–80.

21. Mumy, K.L.; Findlay, R.H. Convenient determination of DNA extraction efficiency using an external DNA recovery standard and quantitative-competitive PCR. J. Microbiol. Methods 2004, 57, 259–268.

22. Knudsen, B.E.; Bergmark, L.; Munk, P.; Lukjancenko, O.; Priemé, A.; Aarestrup, F.M.; Pamp, S.J. Impact of Sample Type and DNA Isolation Procedure on Genomic Inference of Microbiome Composition. mSystems 2016, 1, e00095-16.

23. Luciani, L.; Inchauste, L.; Ferraris, O.; Charrel, R.; Nougairède, A.; Piorkowski, G.; Peyrefitte, C.; Bertagnoli, S.; de Lamballerie, X.; Priet, S. A novel and sensitive real-time PCR system for universal detection of poxviruses. Sci. Rep. 2021, 11, 1798.

24. Tillman, G.E.; Simmons, M.; Wasilenko, J.L.; Narang, N.; Cray, W.C., Jr.; Bodeis-Jones, S.; Martin, G.; Gaines, S.; Seal, B.S. Development of a real-time PCR for Escherichia coli based on gadE, an acid response regulatory gene. Lett. Appl. Microbiol. 2015, 60, 196–202.

25. Dresely, I.; Daugschies, A.; Lendner, M. Establishment of a germ carrier assay to assess disinfectant efficacy against oocysts of coccidian parasites. Parasitol. Res. 2015, 114, 273–281.

26. Wilrich, C.; Wilrich, P.T. Estimation of the POD function and the LOD of a qualitative microbiological measurement method. J. AOAC Int. 2009, 92, 1763–1772.

27. Klein, M.; Brown, L.; van den Akker, B.; Peters, G.M.; Stuetz, R.M.; Roser, D.J. Monitoring bacterial indicators and pathogens in cattle feedlot waste by real-time PCR. Water Res. 2010, 44, 1381–1388.

28. Giesbrecht, P.; Kersten, T.; Maidhof, H.; Wecke, J. Staphylococcal cell wall: Morphogenesis and fatal variations in the presence of penicillin. Microbiol. Mol. Biol. Rev. 1998, 62, 1371–1414.

29. Salton, M.R.J.K.K. Chapter 2: Structure. In Medical Microbiology; Baron, S., Ed.; University of Texas Medical Branch: Galveston, TX, USA, 1996; Volume 4.

30. Matuła, K.; Richter, Ł.; Janczuk-Richter, M.; Nogala, W.; Grzeszkowiak, M.; Peplińska, B.; Jurga, S.; Wyroba, E.; Suski, S.; Bilski, H.; et al. Phenotypic plasticity of Escherichia coli upon exposure to physical stress induced by ZnO nanorods. Sci. Rep. 2019, 9, 8575.

31. Harris, J.R.; Petry, F. Cryptosporidium parvum: Structural components of the oocyst wall. J. Parasitol. 1999, 85, 839–849.

32. Gautham, A. DNA and RNA Isolation Techniques for Non-Experts, 1st ed.; Springer International Publishing; Imprintin Springer: Cham, Switzerland, 2022; p. 48.

33. Halstead, F.D.; Lee, A.V.; Couto-Parada, X.; Polley, S.D.; Ling, C.; Jenkins, C.; Chalmers, R.M.; Elwin, K.; Gray, J.J.; Iturriza-Gómara, M.; et al. Universal extraction method for gastrointestinal pathogens. J. Med. Microbiol. 2013, 62, 1535–1539.

34. Guo, F.; Zhang, T. Biases during DNA extraction of activated sludge samples revealed by high throughput sequencing. Appl. Microbiol. Biotechnol. 2013, 97, 4607–4616.

35. Mary, C.; Chapey, E.; Dutoit, E.; Guyot, K.; Hasseine, L.; Jeddi, F.; Menotti, J.; Paraud, C.;

Pomares, C.; Rabodonirina, M.; et al. Multicentric evaluation of a new real-time PCR assay for quantification of Cryptosporidium spp. and identification of Cryptosporidium parvum and Cryptosporidium hominis. J. Clin. Microbiol. 2013, 51, 2556–2563.

36. Proctor, C.; Soldat, S.M.; Easparro, B.; Nash, R.; Atwood, J. Evaluating the impact of bead media diameter and material composition on bacterial cell lysis and genomic DNA extraction. Fed. Amaerican Soc. Exp. Biol. 2019, 33, 648.6.

37. Wilson, I.G. Inhibition and facilitation of nucleic acid amplification. Appl. Environ. Microbiol. 1997, 63, 3741–3751.

38. Hansen, S.; Roller, M.; Alslim, L.M.A.; Böhlken-Fascher, S.; Fechner, K.; Czerny, C.P.; Abd El Wahed, A. Development of Rapid Extraction Method of Mycobacterium avium Subspecies paratuberculosis DNA from Bovine Stool Samples. Diagnostics 2019, 9, 36.

39. Al-Soud, W.A.; Rådström, P. Purification and characterization of PCR-inhibitory components in blood cells. J. Clin. Microbiol. 2001, 39, 485–493.

40. Mondal, D.; Ghosh, P.; Khan, M.A.; Hossain, F.; Böhlken-Fascher, S.; Matlashewski, G.; Kroeger, A.; Olliaro, P.; Abd El Wahed, A. Mobile suitcase laboratory for rapid detection of Leishmania donovani using recombinase polymerase amplification assay. Parasit. Vectors 2016, 9, 281.

41. Hamilton, K.A.; Waso, M.; Reyneke, B.; Saeidi, N.; Levine, A.; Lalancette, C.; Besner, M.C.; Khan, W.; Ahmed, W. Cryptosporidium and Giardia in Wastewater and Surface Water Environments. J. Environ. Qual. 2018, 47, 1006–1023.

42. Sidhu, J.P.; Toze, S.G. Human pathogens and their indicators in biosolids: A literature review. Environ. Int. 2009, 35, 187–201.

43. Lipp, E.K.; Kurz, R.; Vincent, R.; Rodriguez-Palacios, C.; Farrah, S.R.; Rose, J.B. The Effects of Seasonal Variability and Weather on Microbial Fecal Pollution and Enteric Pathogens in a Subtropical Estuary. Estuaries 2001, 24, 266–276.

44. Gunaratna, G.; Manamperi, A.; Böhlken-Fascher, S.; Wickremasinge, R.; Gunawardena, K.; Yapa, B.; Pathirana, N.; Pathirana, H.; de Silva, N.; Sooriyaarachchi, M.; et al. Evaluation of rapid extraction and isothermal amplification techniques for the detection of Leishmania donovani DNA from skin lesions of suspected cases at the point of need in Sri Lanka. Parasites Vectors 2018, 11, 665.

45. Frimpong, M.; Kyei-Tuffuor, L.; Fondjo, L.A.; Ahor, H.S.; Adjei-Kusi, P.; Maiga-Ascofare, O.; Phillips, R.O. Evaluation of a real-time recombinase polymerase amplification assay for rapid detection of Schistosoma haematobium infection in resource-limited setting. Acta Trop. 2021, 216, 105847.

46. Archer, J.; Patwary, F.K.; Sturt, A.S.; Webb, E.L.; Phiri, C.R.; Mweene, T.; Hayes, R.J.; Ayles, H.; Brienen, E.A.T.; van Lieshout, L.; et al. Validation of the isothermal Schistosoma haematobium Recombinase Polymerase Amplification (RPA) assay, coupled with simplified sample preparation, for diagnosing female genital schistosomiasis using cervicovaginal lavage and vaginal self-swab samples. PLoS Negl. Trop. Dis. 2022, 16, e0010276.

47. El Wahed, A.A.; Patel, P.; Maier, M.; Pietsch, C.; Rüster, D.; Böhlken-Fascher, S.; Kissenkötter, J.; Behrmann, O.; Frimpong, M.; Diagne, M.M.; et al. Suitcase Lab for Rapid Detection of SARS-CoV-2 Based on Recombinase Polymerase Amplification Assay. Anal. Chem. 2021, 93, 2627–2634.

48. Li, X.; Wu, Y.; Zhang, L.; Cao, Y.; Li, Y.; Li, J.; Zhu, L.; Wu, G. Comparison of three common DNA concentration measurement methods. Anal. Biochem. 2014, 451, 18–24.

6

Nonlinear Effects Induced by Interactions among Functional Groups of Bacteria and Fungi Regulate the Priming Effect in Malagasy Soils

Benoît Jaillard[1], Kanto Razanamalala[2], Cyrille Violle[3] and Laetitia Bernard[1]

[1]Eco & Sols, University Montpellier, IRD, INRAE, CIRAD, Institut Agro, 2 place Viala, 34060 Montpellier, France
[2]Laboratoire des Radio-Isotopes, Antananarivo 101, Madagascar
[3]CEFE, University Montpellier, CNRS, EPHE, IRD, 1919 Route de Mende, 34293 Montpellier, France

ABSTRACT

The priming effect (PE) occurs when fresh organic matter (FOM) supplied to soil alters the rate of decomposition of older soil organic matter (SOM). The PE can be generated by different mechanisms driven by interactions between microorganisms with different live strategies and decomposition abilities. Among those, stoichiometric decomposition results from FOM decomposition, which induces the decomposition of SOM by the release of exoenzymes by FOM-decomposers. Nutrient mining results from the co-metabolism of energy-rich FOM with nutrient-rich SOM by SOM-decomposers. While existing statistical approaches enable measurement of the effect of community composition (linear effect) on the PE, the effect of interactions among co-occurring populations (non-linear effect) is more difficult to grasp. We compare a non-linear, clustering approach with a strictly linear approach to separately and comprehensively capture all linear and non-linear effects induced by soil microbial populations on the PE and to identify the species involved. We used an already published data set, acquired from two climatic transects of Madagascar Highlands, in which the high-throughput sequencing of soil samples was applied parallel to the analysis of the potential capacity of microbial communities to generate PE following a ^{13}*C-labeled wheat straw input. The linear and clustering approaches highlight two different aspects of the effects of microbial biodiversity on SOM decomposition. The comparison of the results enabled identification of bacterial and fungal families, and combinations of families, inducing either a linear, a non-linear, or no effect on PE after incubation. Bacterial families mainly favoured a PE proportional to their relative abundances in soil (linear effect). Inversely, fungal families induced strong non-linear effects resulting from interactions among them and with bacteria. Our findings suggest that bacteria support stoichiometric decomposition in the first days of incubation, while fungi support mainly the nutrient mining of soil's organic matter several weeks after the beginning of incubation. Used together, the clustering and linear approaches therefore enable the estimation of the relative importance of linear effects related to microbial relative abundances, and non-linear effects related to interactions among microbial populations on soil properties. Both approaches also enable the identification of key microbial families that mainly regulate soil properties.*

***Keywords**: Assembly motif, Bacteria, Biodiversity, Combinatorial analysis, Ecosystem functioning, Fungi, Organic matter, Priming effect, Soil*

INTRODUCTION

The positive priming effect (PE), i.e., the acceleration of the soil's organic matter (SOM) decomposition by the input of a fresh, easily decomposable, organic matter (FOM), is a key ecosystem process [1]. PE has long been explained by two major processes: (i) stoichiometric decomposition, which results from FOM decomposition, which induces the decomposition of SOM by the release of exoenzymes by FOM-decomposers; (ii) nutrient mining results from the co-metabolism of energy-rich FOM with nutrient-rich SOM by SOM-decomposers [2,3]. Energy-rich FOM can also come from organic matter desorbed by carboxylic acids released by FOM-decomposers [4]. The microbial actors and the biotic and abiotic determinants of the priming effect are therefore multiple [5]. All the proposed processes involve interactions among microbial communities, including competitive interactions among microbial populations for access to FOM and complementarity between the enzymatic activities of different microbial functional groups [6]. In order to improve the understanding of the priming effect, therefore, the identification of the microbial populations that favored each of the different processes is needed, either because of their own activities or because of their interactions with other soil microbial populations. DNA–SIP has been described as a direct method to identify microbial populations feeding on ^{13}C-labeled organic matter [7]. However, as the PE generated by nutrient mining results from the co-metabolism between different sources of organic matter (labeled and unlabeled), such a method cannot discriminate the true FOM-decomposers implied in stoichiometric decomposition from the SOM-decomposers benefiting from labeled FOM catabolites and implied in "nutrient mining" [6]. Therefore, an appropriate statistical approach could help to better disentangle the involved processes.

Microbial biodiversity generates diverse effects on soil functions. The effects are most often decomposed into interaction effect, sensu stricto, and composition effect [8]. The composition effect reflects the specific activities of certain key species in the realization of a soil function and in the absence of interaction with other co-occurring species. It is therefore assumed to be cumulative and responds linearly to the presence of these species and their relative abundance within the community. The interaction effect gathers all positive and negative diversity effects other than the composition effect: it is therefore, by definition, non-linear. Several authors [8,9] separate the interaction effect from the composition effect on the basis of the linearity of the response of the composition effect to the relative abundance of key species [10]. The observed function of a community is compared with the sum of properties, characterizing all populations composing the community as they were grown in monoculture, weighted by their relative abundance. Using molecular methods, it is possible to discriminate between different populations of an assemblage and evaluate their relative abundance. However, the properties of each population grown in monoculture cannot be known because of the impossibility to isolate and cultivate many soil-native microorganisms. In this context, it is not possible to separate the two biodiversity effects on the basis of the linearity of the response of the composition effect to community biodiversity and species' relative abundance using classical approaches.

Most statistical methods are based on the linearity of the response of a variable to be explained by a set of explanatory variables: variance analysis, linear regression, and principal component analysis. In the absence of interactions among species, a linear analysis of the property of a community explained by its biodiversity, especially species' relative abundances, would therefore approximate the effect of community composition only. Conversely, a non-linear analysis of the community property would approximate the overall biodiversity effect of a community, i.e., the product of the composition effect and the interaction effect. Jaillard et al. [11,12] recently proposed an approach to explain ecosystem property by the co-occurrence of species in an ecosystem. This approach searches for species combinations that best account for observed variations in the ecosystem property. The approach enables the cluster of species into functional groups whose co-occurrence determines the ecosystem property. This clustering approach is non-linear. It can therefore be used to analyze the overall biodiversity effect of a microbial community. Compared with a linear approach, this non-linear approach allows for the inference of the effect of interactions among species on community properties.

Here, we aim to identify microbial taxa that predominantly contribute to the generation of PE in Malagasy Ferralsols, either by their own activities or through their interactions with other microbial taxa. Our approach is based on the comparison between linear and non-linear analyses of the same dataset. Three soil properties associated with SOM decomposition activity were analyzed: basal soil respiration, mineralization of ^{13}C labeled wheat straw supplied to soil, and the PE generated by the straw supplied [13]. PE was calculated by removing the total carbon mineralized in the part resulting from wheat-straw and that which was registered in the non-amended subsample (i.e., basal respiration). These three soil properties were measured after seven and 42 days of incubation, because those times likely corresponded to different processes of PE generation. The composition of bacterial and fungal communities was assessed in pristine soils before incubation, by high throughput molecular analysis of 16S and 18S ribosomal genes, respectively. The gene sequences were assigned at the family level.

MATERIALS AND METHODS

Dataset

The dataset used here was already partly published by [13]. Ferralsols from the Highlands of Madagascar were collected (May 2014, 57 sites) under herbaceous savannah dominated by the Poaceae *Aristida* sp., along gradients of temperature and rainfall. At each site, five soil cores were sampled from 0–10 cm depth and mixed to form a composite soil sample. The 57 composite soil samples were sieved to 2 mm, stored at 4 °C, then sent to the Genosol platform in Dijon, France. A 50 g aliquot of each composite soil sample was subsampled, then freeze-dried prior to genetic analysis.

Bacterial and fungal community compositions were assessed on 57 soil samples. Banks of 16S and 18S ribosomal sequences were prepared prior to pyrosequencing analyses as fully described in [14]. Pyrosequencing was carried out on a GS FLX Titanium (Roche 454 Sequencing System). Biocomputing analysis of the sequences was performed using the GnS-PIPE [15] as described in detail in Tardy et al. [16]. In order to compare the datasets efficiently and avoid biased community comparisons, the sample reads were reduced by random selection closed to the lowest datasets (3000 reads for 16S- and 18S-rRNA gene sequences, respectively, for each soil sample). The retained high-quality reads were used for taxonomy-based analysis using similarity approaches and dedicated reference databases from SILVA [17]. Assignments published in Razanamalala et al. [13] were made at the highest taxonomic level, i.e., the phylum level. However, in the present study, we preferred to perform assignments at a more functionally relevant level, i.e., the family level. Actually, we tested the class, order, and family phylogenetic levels, and family appeared as the best compromise to improve functional inference without drastically reducing the dataset due to the lack of known species and even genera in the SILVA database. In order to compare this work with that of Razanamalala et al. [13], the links between families and phyla. The relative abundance matrices had a dimension of $n = 57$ soils for $p = 60$ bacterial or fungal families, respectively. This number of families was chosen in order to be at the limit of the recommendations of the linear approaches in terms of the number of variables, which must be lower compared with the number of samples. Relative abundances per soil aliquot ranged from 1 to 1486, and from 5 to 1048, out of 3000 sequences, with a median of 4.0 and 11.5, for bacteria and fungi, respectively. The observation frequency of each family ranges from 32 to 100%, and 35 to 100% of soils, for bacteria and fungi, respectively.

In parallel, the soils were incubated in the absence or presence of ^{13}C-enriched wheat straw (for details, see [13]). CO_2 release was measured after seven and 42 days of incubation. Those two times were chosen because they likely corresponded to different processes of PE generation [13]. Three measurements were made: the CO_2 released by soil in the absence of straw, the CO_2 released by soil with straw supplied, and the ^{13}C-labeled CO_2 release due to the mineralization of the straw supplied, which was previously enriched with ^{13}C. The measurements enabled the determination of three soil properties concerning SOM decomposition activity carried out by microbial communities: (i) basal soil respiration, equal to the release of CO_2 by soil in absence of straw, (ii) straw mineralization, equal to the release of ^{13}C-labeled CO_2 due to the mineralization of the straw supplied only, and (iii) the priming effect (PE) generated by the straw supply, equal to the CO_2 release by soil with straw supplied, minus the CO_2 resulting from soil basal respiration and straw mineralization.

Linear Analyses

Modeling SOM Decomposition by the Relative Abundance of Microbial Families

A multi-linear analysis without interactions assumes that each microbial family contributes to SOM decomposition in proportion to its relative abundance. The relative abundance of each family is then assumed to be independent of the relative abundance of other families. A multi-linear analysis therefore models SOM decomposition as a linear combination of the relative abundances of families that co-occur in soil. The model consisted of weighing the relative abundance of each family to optimize the fit to SOM decomposition.

Evaluation of the Model Quality

The explanatory power of the model was measured by its coefficient of determination, R^2, that is the ratio of the variance explained by multi-linear analysis on the total observed variance. The model quality, i.e., the compromise between the model precision and the number of explanatory variables, hereafter, the number of families (plus one for the regression intercept) was measured by its Akaike Information Criterion AICc, corrected for small sample sets [18].

Model Reduction by Variable Selection

A multi-linear analysis is improved by reducing the number of explanatory variables. We used a backward stepwise variable selection, based on the progressive removal of microbial families considered as irrelevant explanatory variables because of non-significant contributions to SOM decomposition. Each family was successively removed from the set of explanatory variables, and the effect of each of these removals on model quality was evaluated. The family whose removal maximized the model quality was considered irrelevant and was definitively removed from the set of explanatory variables. We repeated the procedure while the removal of a family increased the model quality. We stopped when removing any remaining families decreased model quality. This means that all remaining families were then identified as relevant explanatory variables, because their contribution to SOM decomposition was significant and because their inclusion in the set of explanatory variables improved model quality. Throughout the variable selection procedure, the quality of the model was measured by its AICc.

A linear model consists of a system of n equations with p unknowns, hereafter, n observed soils for p microbial families: it requires a non-zero number of degrees of freedom, i.e., a number n of observations greater than the number p of families, plus one ($n > p + 1$). The bacteria and fungus relative abundance matrices comprised $n = 57$ soils for $p = 60$ families: this mathematical constraint imposed to keep only $p = 55$ families for $n = 57$ soils. When analyzing only the bacterial families, or only the fungal families, we therefore removed the five least abundant families from the bacteria and fungi relative abundance matrices, respectively.

Clustering Analysis

Modeling SOM Decomposition by the Co-Occurring of Relative Abundance Classes of Microbial Families

A clustering analysis is based on the occurrence of families in microbial communities, i.e., qualitative data. The presence of each microbial family in soil, however, was measured by their relative abundance, i.e., quantitative data. The relative abundance of each family was therefore converted into classes of relative abundance, then each quantitative matrix of relative abundance was converted into a qualitative one-shot encoding table. Clustering methods are all the more effective when each family to be clustered is equitably observed. The least frequent bacterial and fungal families were observed in 32% and 35% of sampled soils, respectively. The distribution of relative abundance of each family was therefore segmented into classes of relative abundance, centered on an observation frequency of 30%. The ubiquitous families, i.e., the families observed in 100% of soils, were segmented into three classes of relative abundance, noted 1/3, 2/3, and 3/3 from the least to the most abundant classes. The least frequent families were not segmented and were noted 1/1 as a reminder. Families in between were segmented into two classes and noted as 1/2 and 2/2. The segmentation thresholds were determined in such a way that the numbers of observations in each class were equal to, within one unit. The resulting one-hot encoding tables contained 153 and 175 classes of family relative abundance, with an average observation frequency of 31.7% and 32.4% (median 32.2% and 33.3%) for bacteria and fungi, respectively. The clustering analysis then aimed to group classes of family relative abundance whose co-occurrence best accounted for variations of SOM decomposition. The method then looked to maximize the inter-group variance of SOM decomposition associated with different combinations of functional groups, i.e., the different assembly motifs [11]. As in the linear modelling, the explanatory power of the model was measured by the coefficient of determination, R^2, that is the ratio of the variance explained by the clustering analysis on the total observed variance.

Model Reduction by Variable Selection

As a linear model, a clustering model is improved by reducing the number of explanatory variables. We used a backward stepwise selection similar to the one applied to linear analysis. The first difference was that each family was segmented into several classes of relative abundance: removing a family here therefore meant removing all the classes of relative abundance from the family. A second difference is that a clustering model enables the clustering of families into functional groups and observations into assembly motifs, i.e., combinations of functional groups: we imposed that for a family to be considered as an irrelevant variable, its removal must change neither the functional groups nor the assembly motifs. A third difference is that all the least significant classes of family relative abundance are clustered in the same functional group by default, with the residual group labeled by the letter of highest rank: only the removal of families belonging to this group are therefore tested.

Hierarchy of Functional Groups

A clustering analysis ultimately provided a hierarchical tree of the functional groups of classes of family relative abundance that best accounted for SOM decomposition. The functional groups are sorted from left to right, from those that best to least explain SOM decomposition. Within each functional group, the classes of family relative abundance were also sorted from left to right, based on their ability to explain SOM decomposition. The residual group that clusters the least significant classes of family relative abundance is therefore on the right, labeled by the letter of highest rank, and the least significant classes of family relative abundance belonging to this group is on the right of this functional group.

Evaluation of the Model Quality

As for a multi-linear model, the explanatory capacity of a clustering model was measured by its coefficient of determination, R^2, that is the ratio of variance explained by the clustering analysis on the total observed variance. The quality of the model was measured by its AICc, i.e., the trade-off between model precision and the number of explanatory variables, hereafter, the number of families were considered relevant. As explained above, the variable selection procedure was based on constant numbers of functional groups and observed assembly motifs. However, the number of families on which the clustering analysis was based decreased. The number of variables taken into account in the AICc calculation were the family numbers, instead of the numbers of observed assemblage motifs that stayed constant [11].

Linear Effects Associated with Each Functional Group

The clustering analysis looks to maximize the inter-group variance of SOM decomposition associated with the different assembly motifs, which are the combinations of functional groups. It is also possible to assess the linear effects explained by clustering analysis using a variance analysis of SOM decomposition explained by each functional group of classes of family relative abundance and their statistical interactions.

Statistical Computations

All computations were performed using R-software [19]. Linear and multi-linear regressions were performed using the lm function, and variance analyses using the aov function of the R-package stats. Clustering analyses were performed using the fclust function of the R-package functClust. Backward stepwise selections were performed using the lm_step and fclust_step functions. Comparison of medians was performed using a non-parametric Kruskal–Wallis test (function kruskal.test of the R-package stats). All statistical tests were performed at the probability threshold of $p < 0.001$. All scripts are available on the INRAE dataverse at https://doi.org/10.15454/LRY3M2 (accessed on 20 March 2023).

RESULTS

Linear Analyses of the Relationship between SOM Decomposition Activity and Environmental Conditions of Sampling Sites

Basal soil respirations after seven and 42 days of incubation were positively correlated ($R^2 = 0.773$; $p < 10^{-10}$). Straw mineralization after 42 days did not depend on that observed after seven days of incubation ($R^2 = 0.007$; $p = 0.238$), and the priming effects after seven and 42 days of incubation were negatively correlated ($R^2 = 0.203$; $p = 0.256 \times 10^{-3}$). This means that soils with a high PE after seven days had a low PE after 42 days of incubation.

In general, SOM decomposition functions did not vary with precipitation at sampling sites. In contrast, basal soil respirations after seven and 42 days were negatively correlated ($R^2 = 0.496$; $p = 0.601 \times 10^{-9}$ and $R^2 = 0.391$; $p = 0.118 \times 10^{-7}$, respectively) with temperatures, and PE after seven and 42 days were negatively and positively correlated, respectively ($R^2 = 0.043$; $p = 2.064 \times 10^{-5}$; and $R^2 = 0.180$; $p = 0.588 \times 10^{-3}$), with temperatures at the sample sites.

Multi-Linear and Clustering Analyses of the Relationship between Initial Composition of Bacterial and Fungal Communities and SOM Decomposition Activity

Both multi-linear and clustering approaches to the relative abundance of bacterial families accurately explained SOM decomposition functions, i.e., basal soil respiration, straw mineralization, and the priming effect, after seven and 42 days of incubation (Table 1). The six multi-linear models selected, in median, 26 key families out of 55, with model degrees of freedom of 28 and R^2 of 0.959. The Fisher ratios were around 25.0, all associated with a probability lower than 10^{-10}.

The median AICc of the six models was −316.6. The clustering analyses selected, in median, only 14 key families out of 60, with model degrees of freedom of 46 and R^2 of 0.965. The Fisher ratio equaled 49.3 and the AICc −356.2. Regarding fungal communities (Table 1), the variable selection procedure applied in the multi-linear and clustering models was almost as efficient as for bacteria communities, with 18 and 16 selected key families, respectively. While the median R^2 of the multi-linear models were around 0.632, those of clustering models reached 0.933, indicating the same accuracy for fungal communities as bacterial communities.

Table 1. Statistics of multi-linear and clustering analyses of the relationships between relative abundance of bacterial and fungal families and basal soil respiration, straw mineralization, and the priming effect. Analyses of relative abundance of bacteria, fungi, and bacteria and fungi get together

	Mineralization	Duration of Incubation	Statistical Model	Initial Number of Families	Number of Key Families	Degrees of Freedom	R^2	F-Ratio	AICc
bacteria	soil	7 days	lm	55	32	22	0.993	112.1	−319.1
			fclust	60	17	43	0.966	39.3	−328.2
		42 days	lm	55	28	26	0.981	50.8	−304.9
			fclust	60	12	48	0.966	84.6	−354.8
	straw	7 days	lm	55	38	16	0.985	30.4	−91.3
			fclust	60	13	47	0.963	59.2	−246.9
		42 days	lm	55	19	35	0.883	14.6	−314.0
			fclust	60	15	45	0.927	24.9	−357.5
	priming effect	7 days	lm	55	22	32	0.879	11.2	−351.6
			fclust	60	20	40	0.985	99.0	−480.5
		42 days	lm	55	24	30	0.936	19.6	−347.8
			fclust	60	13	47	0.939	32.5	−401.0
fungi	soil	7 days	lm	55	11	43	0.598	6.1	−209.3
			fclust	60	26	34	0.977	30.7	−302.4
		42 days	lm	55	23	31	0.666	4.3	−193.4
			fclust	60	14	46	0.929	18.2	−307.1
	straw	7 days	lm	55	13	41	0.585	4.7	−109.6
			fclust	60	24	36	0.982	40.4	−236.9
		42 days	lm	55	7	47	0.557	8.8	−280.6
			fclust	60	10	50	0.540	4.2	−269.9
	priming effect	7 days	lm	55	24	30	0.724	3.5	−293.1
			fclust	60	17	43	0.937	23.3	−412.7
		42 days	lm	55	23	31	0.848	8.0	−304.2
			fclust	60	8	52	0.838	20.5	−361.0
bacteria and fungi	soil	7 days	fclust	120	13	107	0.949	181.4	−320.0
		42 days	fclust	120	14	106	0.971	59.3	−358.2
	straw	7 days	fclust	120	14	106	0.938	37.1	−214.7
		42 days	fclust	120	20	100	0.979	29.2	−407.4
	Priming effect	7 days	fclust	120	19	101	0.959	49.3	−428.1
		42 days	fclust	120	13	107	0.933	145.1	−395.7

Coefficient of determination (R^2), Fisher ratio (F-ratio), and Akaike Information Criterion corrected for small samples (AICc) of the models.

The variable selection procedure retained, in median, only 14 key families out of 120, for the six models (Table 1). The number of degrees of freedom was thus 106, the coefficient of determination R^2 0.954, and the F-ratio 54.3. All F-ratio were associated with a probability lower than 10^{-10}. The resulting AICc was −377.0 in median, i.e., the best mean AICc among all models. Applied to soil bacteria and fungus communities combined together, the clustering analyses provided parsimonious and accurate models.

Identifying Bacterial and Fungal Families That Regulate SOM Decomposition Activity

Both multi-linear and clustering approaches enable the identification of bacterial or fungal families as the key actors in basal soil respiration, straw mineralization, and the priming effect after seven and 42 days of incubation, by separately analyzing each of the two communities. The results are summarized in Table 2.

Table 2. Bacterial and fungal families identified separately by multi-linear (lm) and clustering analyses (fclust) as key actors in basal soil respiration (soil), straw mineralization (straw), and the priming effect

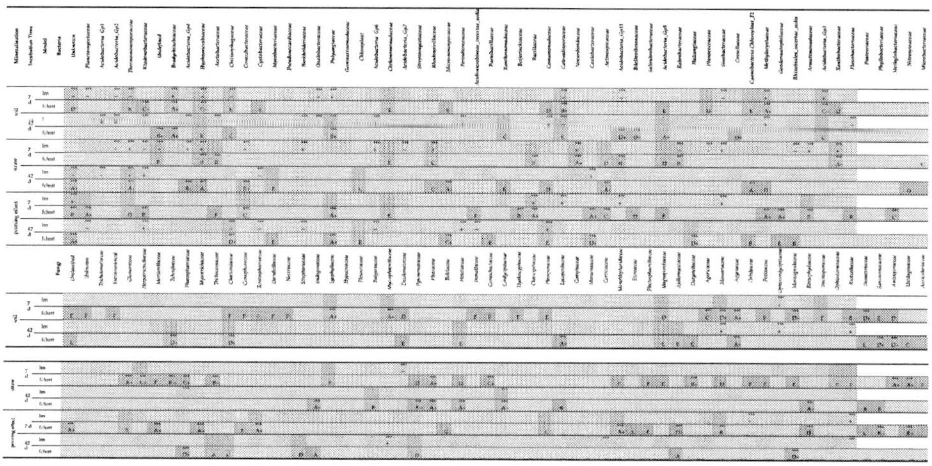

A midpoint (·) indicates that the family was identified as key by the variable selection procedure and (***) indicates that the significance was at $p < 0.001$. Cells are colored depending on if the family is identified as key by (pink) both the multi-linear and clustering models, (yellow) the multi-linear model alone, (green) the clustering model alone, (blue) as negligible by both the multi-linear and clustering models, or (white) as not analyzed by the multi-linear model. The sign indicates the direction, positive (+) or negative (−), of the family's contribution to SOM decomposition activity. For clustering analysis, the letter (A to F) indicates the most significant functional group to which a class of relative abundance of the family was assigned. Families were ranked from left to right in descending order of relative abundance.

For each SOM decomposition function and time of incubation, families identified as key actors in initial soil communities by either the multi-linear or the clustering approach accounted for 47% and 42% of the total number of bacterial and fungal families, respectively. Only 13% and 7% of bacterial and fungal families were commonly identified as key for using both approaches, while 37% and 51% were commonly rejected as non-significant (Table 2). This indicates that multi-linear and clustering analyses modeled different aspects of the relationship between microbial families of initial soil communities and SOM decomposition, and this difference was stronger for fungi than for bacteria.

The clustering analyses of bacterial and fungal families gathered together in the same dataset confirmed the results (summarized in Table 3). The variable selection procedure retained less than 14% of total families for a given SOM decomposition function and a given incubation duration, and also rejected 44% of total families showing no relationship for any SOM decomposition function at any incubation duration. This indicates that a small number of microbial families of initial soil communities explained a large part of SOM decomposition after seven and 42 days of incubation.

Table 3. Bacterial and fungal families identified altogether by clustering analyses (fclust) as key actors in basal soil respiration (soil), straw mineralization (straw), and the priming effect

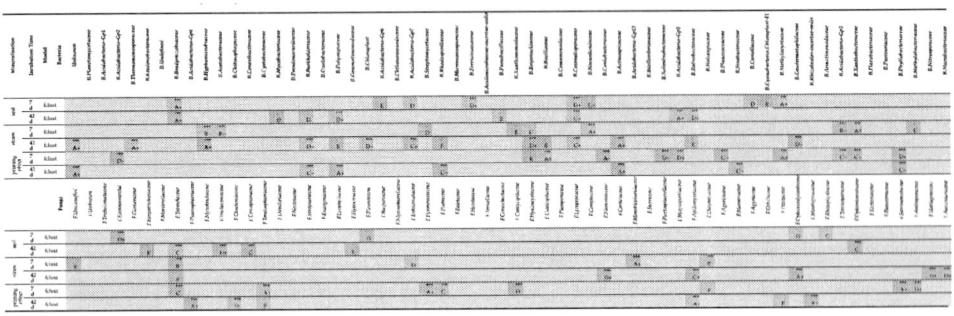

Although each family was observed in about 30% of soils, the extent of the relative abundances of bacterial and fungal families were very broad, ranging from 1 to 1486, and from 5 to 1048 out of 3000 sequences, respectively (Table 2 and Table 3). However, a comparison of medians confirmed that key families were not related to their relative abundance, whatever the SOM decomposition function, the time of duration, or the modelling approach.

Identity of Potentially Key Bacterial and Fungal Controlling the Priming Effect

The main results of the clustering analyses of bacterial and fungal families gathered together in the same dataset are reported in Figure 1, Figure 2 and Figure 3. Figure 1 shows the clustering of relative abundance classes of the microbial families of initial soil communities identified as key for basal soil respiration (Figure 1a,b) and straw mineralization (Figure 1c,d) after seven and 42 days of incubation. Figure 2 and Figure 3 report the clustering analyses of key bacterial and fungal families for the priming effect after seven and 42 days of incubation, respectively.

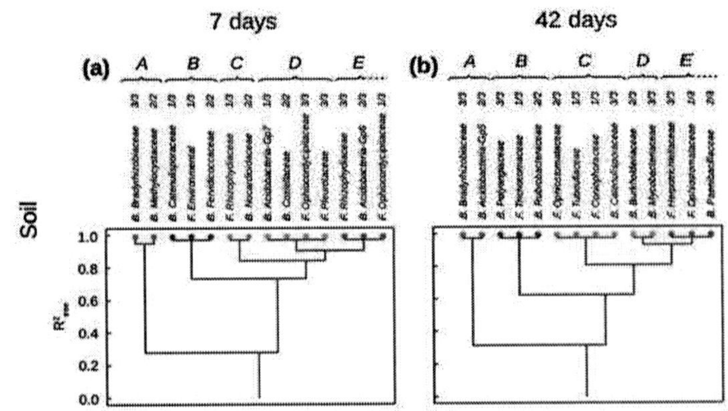

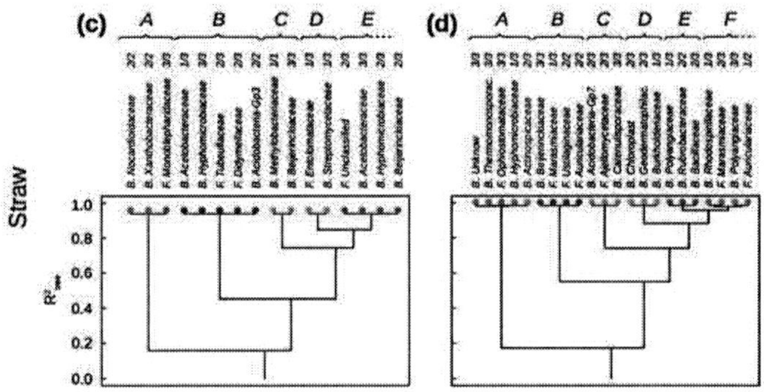

Figure 1. Clustering analysis of basal soil respiration (a,b) and straw mineralization (c,d) after seven (a,c) and 42 days of incubation, explained by the relative abundance classes of bacterial and fungal families in soil. The functional groups and the classes of family relative abundance inside each functional group are sorted from left to right by their decreasing effects on the soil property. Each functional group has a color attributed: red for A, dark blue for B, yellow for C, light blue for D, pink for E, and green for F.

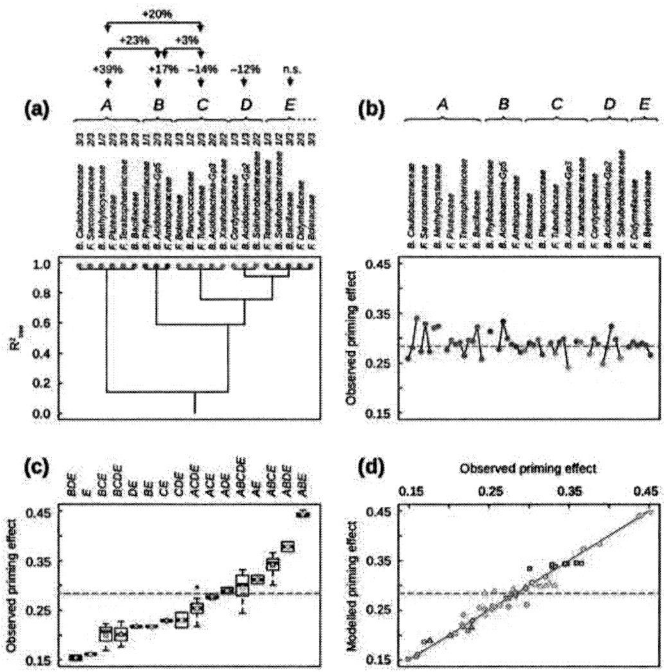

Figure 2. Clustering analysis of the priming effect after seven days of incubation, explained by the relative abundance classes of bacterial and fungal families in soil. (a) Clustering tree of classes of family relative abundance. The functional groups and the classes of family relative abundance inside each functional group are sorted from left to right by their decreasing effects on the priming effect. Each functional group has a color attributed: red for A, dark blue for B, yellow for C, light blue for D, pink for E. The above values indicate the significant effects (at $p < 0.001$) of the different functional groups and their interactions. (b) Mean observed priming effect of soils containing a given class of family relative abundance. The linked points correspond to the different classes of increasing relative

abundance (from left to right) for each family. The used symbols are the same as those used in (a). (c) Boxplots of the observed priming effect sorted by assembly motifs, i.e., combinations of functional groups. The used symbols are the same as those used in (b). (d) Modeled versus observed priming effect. Different symbols correspond to different assembly motifs, i.e., combinations of functional groups. The red line is the bisector. (b–d) The dotted line is the mean observed priming effect.

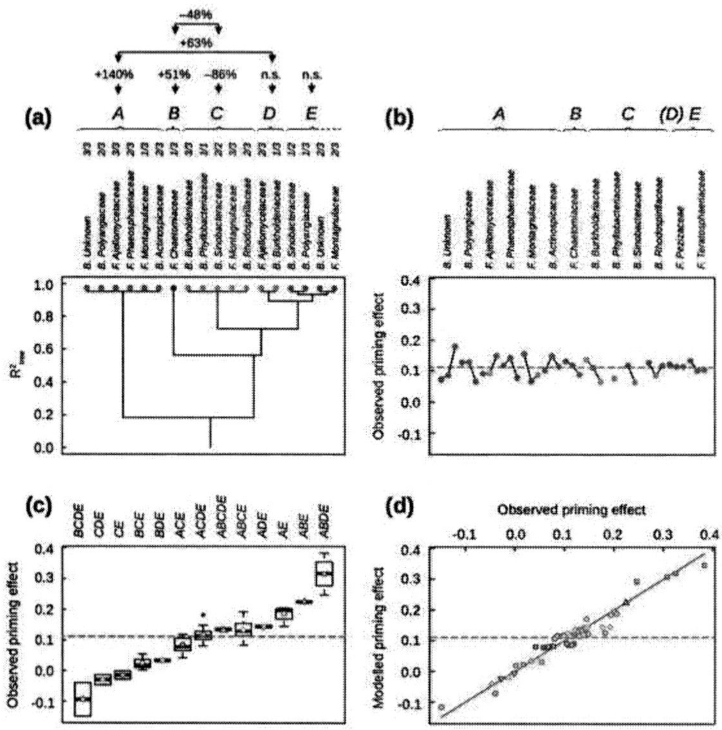

Figure 3. Clustering analysis of the priming effect after 42 days of incubation, explained by the relative abundance classes of bacterial and fungal families in soil. (a) Clustering tree of classes of family relative abundance. The functional groups and the classes of family relative abundance inside each functional group are sorted from left to right by their decreasing effects on the priming effect. The above values indicate the significant effects (at $p < 0.001$) of the different functional groups and their interactions. (b) Mean observed priming effect of soils containing a given class of family relative abundance. The linked points correspond to the different classes of increasing relative abundance (from left to right) for each family. The used symbols are the same as those used in (a). (c) Boxplots of the observed priming effect sorted by assembly motifs, i.e., combinations of functional groups. The used symbols are the same as those used in (b). (d) Modeled versus observed priming effect. Different symbols correspond to different assembly motifs, i.e., combinations of functional groups. The red line is the bisector. (b–d) The dotted line is the mean observed priming effect.

Ten bacterial and nine fungal families of initial soil communities were identified as key for the priming effect after seven days of incubation. The 19 microbial families were clustered into five functional groups (Figure 2). Functional groups were labeled from A to E by their decreasing contribution to PE (Figure 2a). Within each group, the relative abundance classes of microbial families are sorted from left to right, by their decreasing contribution to PE (Figure 2a). The specific contribution of the relative abundance classes of family ranged from −15% to +20% of the median PE (Figure 2b). Some families showed a linear contribution, such as the bacteria *Caulobacteraceae*, while others displayed a non-linear contribution, such as the fungus *Sarcosomataceae* and the bacteria *Bacillaceae* (Figure 2b). The first main functional group, noted A, included three bacterial families, *Caulobacteraceae* in its highest relative abundance (class 3/3), *Methylocystaceae* in its lowest relative abundance (class 1/2), and *Bacillaceae* in its medium relative abundance (class 2/3), and three fungal families, *Sarcosomataceae* (class 2/3), *Pluteaceae* (class 2/3), and *Teratosphaeriaceae* (class 3/3) (Figure 2a). The functional group B contained two bacterial families, *Phyllobacteriaceae* (class 1/1) and *Acidobacteria*-Gp5 (class 2/3), and the fungal family *Ambisporaceae* (class 2/3) (Figure 2a). A variance analysis indicates that the functional groups A and B are associated with a PE that is 39% and 17% higher on average, respectively, than the median priming effect ($P(A) < 10^{-10}$; $P(B) = 0.63 \times 10^{-9}$). Moreover, their statistical interaction is associated with an even higher PE of 23% ($P(A{:}B) = 0.51 \times 10^{-6}$). As a corollary, all assembly motifs containing the functional group A were associated with high PE, and the assembly motifs containing both the functional groups A and B were associated with the highest PE (Figure 2c). At the opposite, the functional groups C and D are associated with a PE of an average 14% and 12%, respectively ($P(C) = 0.37 \times 10^{-6}$; $P(D) = 0.53 \times 10^{-6}$), lower than the median priming effect. However, the functional group C interacts positively with the A and B groups and is associated with a PE of 20% and 3%, respectively ($P(A{:}C) = 0.44 \times 10^{-7}$; $P(B{:}C) = 0.62 \times 10^{-3}$), higher than the median. The functional group C clustered three bacterial families, *Planococcaceae* (class 1/2), *Acidobacteria*-Gp3 (class 2/2), and *Xanthobacteraceae* (class 2/2), and two fungal families, *Boletaceae* (class 1/3) and *Tubeufiaceae* (class 2/3). The functional group D included two bacterial families, *Acidobacteria*-Gp2 (class 1/3) and *Solirubrobacteraceae* (class 2/3), and the fungal family *Cordycipitaceae* (class 1/3): it did not interact with other functional groups. The last functional group E gathered all other bacterial and fungal families identified as key: it is not associated with any significant variation in the priming effect. Finally, the clustering of 19 families of initial soil communities identified as key accurately explained the priming effect after seven days of incubation ($R^2 = 0.959$; AICc = −428.1; $p < 10^{-10}$) (Figure 2d). The clustering was related neither to precipitation ($p = 0.503$) nor to temperature ($p = 0.027$) at sampling sites.

The priming effect intensity was lower after 42 days than seven days of incubation. Seven bacterial and six fungal families of initial soil communities were identified as key for the PE. The 13 microbial families were clustered into five functional groups (Figure 3). The specific effect of relative abundance classes of family ranged from −43% to +60% of the median PE (Figure 3b). The main first functional group A included the group of unknown bacteria (class 3/3), two bacterial families, *Polyangiaceae* (class 2/3) and *Actinospicaceae* (class 2/3), and three fungal families, *Ajellomycetaceae* (class 3/3), *Phaeosphaeriaceae* (class 2/3), and *Montagnulaceae* (class 1/3): the group A is associated with a PE 140% higher than the median ($P(A) < 10^{-10}$) (Figure 3a). This means that the co-occurrence of at least two families belonging to the group A doubled the PE variation associated with only a single family (Figure 3b); all assembly motifs containing the functional group A were therefore associated with high PE (Figure 3c). The functional group B is also associated with a PE 51% higher than the median ($P(B) = 0.85 \times 10^{-9}$); yet it contained only one fungal family, *Chaetomiaceae,* in its lowest relative abundance (Figure 3a). The functional group

C clustered the bacterial families *Burkholderiaceae* (class 3/3), *Phyllobacteriaceae* (class 1/1), *Sinobacteraceae* (class 2/2), and *Rhodospirillaceae* (class 2/3), and the fungal family *Montagnulaceae* (class 3/3) (Figure 3a). This group is associated with a PE 86% lower than the median ($P(C) < 10^{-10}$). It strongly interacted with the functional group B, associated with a PE 48% even lower than the median ($P(B{:}C) = 0.42 \times 10^{-3}$). As a consequence, the assembly motifs containing the functional group C, and even more when associated with B, showed the lowest PE (Figure 3c). In addition, functional group D is associated with no specific variation of PE, but it strongly interacted with A, which is associated with a PE 63% higher than the median ($P(A{:}D) = 0.34 \times 10^{-3}$): it included the fungal family *Ajellomycetaceae* (class 2/3) and the bacterial family *Burkholderiaceae* (class 1/3) (Figure 3a). Finally, the clustering of only 13 families identified as key in initial soil communities accurately and parsimoniously modeled the PE after 42 days of incubation ($R^2 = 0.933$; AICc = −395.7; $p < 10^{-10}$) (Figure 3d). The clustering was related neither to precipitation ($p = 0.148$) nor to temperature ($p = 0.003$) at sample sites.

Except for the bacterial family *Phyllobacteriaceae* and the fungal family *Cordycipitaceae*, all families identified as key in initial soil communities for the priming effect were different after seven and 42 days of incubation (Figure 2b and Figure 3b).

DISCUSSION

A Few Microbial Families Were Associated with Significant Variations in SOM Decomposition Functions

A striking result is that whatever the soil function, a small number of microbial families of initial soil communities explain most of the SOM decomposition functions after seven and 42 days of incubation. When analyzing bacterial and fungal families gathered together, the clustering analysis identified less than sixteen families as key out of 120, i.e., less than 14% of observed families. These findings confirm that, for a given ecosystem property, biodiversity is most often a saturating function; only a fraction of the identified species contribute significantly to the emergence of the property studied [20,21,22]. They highlight the importance of procedures of variable selection for analyzing the relationships between biodiversity and ecosystem functioning; these procedures reduce the communities to only the species that are key, at one time or another, for the property studied [23,24]. Note that our analyses are based on microbial composition of initial soil communities before incubation; the microbial communities obviously changed without our knowledge during incubation, mainly by changing their relative abundances. The initial composition of soil microbial communities is therefore key in anticipating SOM decomposition functions after seven and 42 days of incubation, especially the priming effect.

Another striking result is that when bacterial and fungal families were analyzed together, all functional groups contained both bacteria and fungi. This means that some bacteria and fungi are functionally redundant. This functional redundancy suggests that, despite their morphological and physiological differences, bacteria and fungi may be associated with similar processes. However, it is possible that this functional redundancy is only a façade. Like any statistical analysis, a clustering analysis is not causal; it only relates a variable to be explained with explanatory variables. The clustering of families or classes of families in relative abundance in the same functional group therefore does not prejudge the role played by each of the clustered families. It only indicates that different combinations of microbial families are associated with different variations in SOM decomposition activity which, moreover, take place seven and 42 days after analysis of the initial composition of soil microbial communities. The functional groups generated by clustering analysis can therefore be composed of microbial families that directly and actively affect SOM decomposition activity after seven or 42 days of incubation, and families that contribute to variations in biotic or abiotic conditions are associated with variations in SOM decomposition.

For instance, the bacterial *Methylocystaceae* family is identified as key in the initial soil community for basal soil respiration, straw mineralization, and the priming effect after seven days of incubation. As the *Methylocystaceae* family is a strictly methanotrophic family that releases CO_2 by oxidizing CH_4 [25], they could not have contributed to any heterotrophic respiration. Therefore, our results highlight that soil conditions favorable to the *Methylocystaceae* family promote the priming effect after seven days of incubation. As another example, the bacterial *Polyangiaceae* family is identified as key in the initial soil community for basal soil respiration and the priming effect after 42 days of incubation; it then belongs to the functional group A, which is associated with a high priming effect. *Polyangiaceae* are bacteria that prey on other bacteria [26]; this family possibly plays a positive role in regulating specific populations having a negative effect on PE.

Our results also show that key families are neither the most frequent nor the most abundant families. For instance, when the functional groups A and B co-occurred in the initial soil community, the highest PE was observed after seven days of incubation. All bacterial families identified, *Caulobacteraceae*, *Methylocystaceae,* and *Bacillaceae,* in functional group A, and *Phyllobacteriaceae* and *Acidobacteria*-Gp5 in functional group B, are not highly abundant. Likewise, the fungal families *Sarcosomataceae* and *Pluteaceae* in functional group A, and *Ambisporaceae* in functional group B, are not very abundant. Only the ubiquist fungus *Teratosphaeriaceae* was moderately abundant and co-occurred in its highest relative abundance class in its initial soil community. All the microbial families were, however, associated with high PE. When the functional groups A and B co-occurred in the initial soil community, the highest PE was observed after 42 days of incubation. The unknown bacteria were very abundant and co-occurred in their most abundant relative class, although they correspond to a phylogenetically and functionally heterogeneous group. The fungus families *Phaeosphaeriaceae* and *Ajellomycetaceae*, however, were much less abundant in soils and co-occurred in the medium relative abundance class. It is possible that the most abundant families play an active role in SOM mineralization functions after seven or 42 days of incubation, while the less abundant families were rather associated with biotic or abiotic conditions favoring SOM decomposition.

We should, however, remember that (i) first, next generation sequencing technology is not a quantitative molecular method [14]; (ii) second, the occurrence of each microbial family was determined by only a few sequences, although it was observed in about 30% of soils. This lack of relationship between observed effects and frequency or abundance of microbial families should nevertheless be a question to us. In ecology, it is common to eliminate the least frequent or least abundant families because these rare species are a priori assumed to be inefficient [27,28]. This practice tends to underestimate the contribution of rare families to community functioning, even though some of them may play a key role [29,30,31]. In bacterial communities, the clustering analysis confirmed that most of the families were eliminated in the multi-linear analysis because of their low frequency or abundance not being key. In fungal communities, clustering analysis identified more than half of the families as key that were eliminated in the multi-linear analysis due to their low frequency or abundance. Our results thus highlight that taxonomic rarity is not a relevant criterion. Clustering analysis enables us to more deeply explore the relationship between biodiversity and ecosystem functioning than multi-linear analysis. It should be favored in looking for species that play a key role in the relationships between biodiversity and ecosystem functioning.

Multi-Linear and Clustering Analyses Enable the Identification of Microorganisms That Stimulate SOM Decomposition Activities after Seven and 42 Days of Incubation

Our results show that SOM decomposition activities are accurately explained by variations in the relative abundance of bacterial families in pristine soil. It is more accurately and parsimoniously explained by the co-occurrence of bacterial families at different levels of relative abundance. However, the improvement is marginal. Multi-linear and combinatorial approaches are therefore equally relevant. These results support the observations of Razanamalala et al. [13] made at the phylum level on the same samples, who found that bacteria were strongly linearly correlated with PE. The effect induced by bacteria on SOM decomposition activity would therefore be close to a composition effect.

Contrastingly, the relationship between fungi occurrence and any SOM decomposition activity at any time duration are hardly explained by multi-linear analyses, in contrast to the clustering analysis, which remains accurate. The relationships between fungi occurrence and SOM decomposition activities are thus non-linear; their occurrence moderately explains the PE after seven days of incubation, but much more explains the PE after 42 days. At this time, the occurrence of some functional groups composed of both bacteria and fungi in initial soil communities is related to a double PE, while the occurrence of other functional groups is related to significantly reduced PE. The main bacterial and fungal families selected for their potential involvement in PE recorded after 42 days of incubation are not the same as at the beginning of incubation, and non-linear processes of high intensity have taken over linear processes.

Linear and Clustering Analyses Enlighten the Priming Effect

Several authors have suggested that mechanisms underlying the priming effect can occur simultaneously: one may dominate for a period of time and then be replaced by another depending on changes in environmental conditions, including the availability of mineral nitrogen in soil solution [2,32,33]. Based on the literature, Razanamalala et al. [13] proposed that the PE measured after seven days was mainly generated by stoichiometric decomposition, and that the PE measured after 42 days was mainly the result of nutrient mining. Strikingly, we showed that microbial families favoring PE measured after seven and 42 days of incubation were not the same.

After seven days of incubation, the functional group A associated with the highest priming effect seems functionally convergent as it is mainly composed of bacterial families endowed with specific enzymatic capacities for the decomposition of lignin (*Caulobacteraceae,* [34]) and cellulose (*Bacillaceae*, [35]). This group also contains saprotrophic fungi well known for their lignocellulolytic capacities [36]. These results support the stoichiometric decomposition hypothesis after seven days of incubation, yet none of these families appeared to have a preponderant role, either in basal soil respiration or in straw mineralization. Although they might play a key role in PE, they are not among the most abundant nor the most frequent families. These families could therefore benefit from the exoenzymatic activity of other populations directly involved in straw mineralization as suggested in the stoichiometric hypothesis. Our results also show that PE depended on positive and negative interactions between families of group A and other functional groups. For instance, group B, which increased the effect of group A, is composed of two bacterial families' characteristics of rich media, the *Phyllobacteriaceae* [37], or at least enriched in nutrients, the *Acidobacteria*-GP5 [38], and whose common feature is their ability to denitrify. Group C has a rather negative effect on PE as well as on group A, and is functionally more diversified than groups A and B.

When the labile part of FOM and the available nitrogen is exhausted, SOM-decomposers can use the energy of FOM catabolites to mine nitrogen in SOM [5]. Fontaine et al. [36] suggested that fungi are the main decomposers of cellulose and are thus the main actors of the nutrient mining PE. This important role in nutrient mining is also linked to the ability of fungi to explore a large volume of soil, having their mycelium on FOM and SOM simultaneously. It is indeed reasonable to assume that interactions between bacteria are limited due to their relative immobility. In contrast, fungi develop an extensive mycelial network that allows them to interact over long distances with other populations of bacteria and fungi. After 42 days of incubation, unlike after seven days of incubation, the functional group A that increased PE by 140% is functionally quite heterogeneous. It is composed of two families of saprotrophic Ascomycetes (*Phaeosphaeriaceae* and *Ajellomycetaceae*, [39,40]), a family of acidophilic Actinomycetes (*Actinospicaceae*, [41]) known for their ability to produce secondary metabolites [42], and unknown bacteria, which are functionally heterogenous but generally considered oligotrophic because they do not grow in the too-rich conditions of laboratory environments. Against all expectations, it is the bacteria (unknown and *Actinospicaceae*) that seem to engage in co-metabolism between FOM and SOM, not the fungi. However, as the group of unknown bacteria brings together various families under the same name, it can actually be divided into families specialized in either the breakdown of FOM or SOM, without co-metabolism. Enrichment of the databases should gradually reduce the size of this group in future studies. It has recently been suggested that PE could also be generated by the release of molecules with a high affinity for soil minerals, making it possible to desorb the initially associated labile organic matter rich in N and P [5]. Representatives of *Burkholderiaceae* are able to weather minerals by the release of gluconic acid [43]. However, in our study, *Burkholderiaceae* have a strong inhibitory role on PE after 42 days of incubation, linked to a density effect (their lowest and highest abundance classes are found in functional groups C and D). At the same time, they have an inhibiting role in straw mineralization. *Burkholderiaceae* have other capacities, such as exopolysaccharide production, antifungal release, and organic and inorganic *p* solubilization via siderophores production [44,45]. All those capacities can interfere directly or indirectly in the PE generation process. Therefore, the role of this family in the late priming effect has to be more deeply investigated in the future.

CONCLUSIONS

The clustering approach makes it possible to highlight taxa with non-linear effects on a flow resulting from complex processes, such as the priming effect, but also the effect on this flow of interactions between certain taxa. This approach has the advantage of not being constrained by the ratio between the number of variables and the number of samples, unlike linear statistical approaches. Normally applied to occurrence matrices, it has been adapted here to an abundance matrix by dividing each taxon into one, two or three abundance classes according to their respective densities. The results obtained are surprising and open up new challenges for their interpretation. This approach has proven its interest and deserves to be applied to more recent datasets resulting from sequencing techniques and more advanced bioinformatics analysis, which could only improve the quality and precision of the results. It is obvious that the biofunctioning of the soil is subservient to interactions between various functional entities and that this type of method considerably increases the field of possibilities in terms of understanding its various workings.

REFERENCES

1. Kuzyakov, Y.; Friedel, J.; Stahr, K. Review of mechanisms and quantification of priming effects. Soil Biol. Biochem. 2000, 32, 1485–1498.
2. Fontaine, S.; Mariotti, A.; Abbadie, L. The priming effect of organic matter: A question of microbial competition? Soil Biol. Biochem. 2003, 35, 837–843.
3. Chen, R.; Senbayram, M.; Blagodatsky, S.; Myachina, O.; Dittert, K.; Lin, X.; Blagodatskaya, E.; Kuzyakov, Y. Soil C and N availability determine the priming effect: Microbial N mining and stoichiometric decomposition theories. Glob. Chang. Biol. 2014, 20, 2356–2367.
4. Keiluweit, M.; Bougoure, J.J.; Nico, P.S.; Pett-Ridge, J.; Weber, P.K.; Kleber, M. Mineral protection of soil carbon counteracted by root exudates. Nat. Clim. Chang. 2015, 5, 588–595.
5. Bernard, L.; Basile-Doelsch, I.; Derrien, D.; Fanin, N.; Fontaine, S.; Guenet, B.; Karimi, B.; Marsden, C.; Maron, P.-A. Advancing the mechanistic understanding of the priming effect on soil organic matter mineralisation. Funct. Ecol. 2022, 36, 1355–1377.
6. Bernard, L.; Maron, P.-A.; Mougel, C.; Nowak, V.; Lévêque, J.; Marol, C.; Balesdent, J.; Gibiat, F.; Ranjard, L. Contamination of Soil by Copper Affects the Dynamics, Diversity, and Activity of Soil Bacterial Communities Involved in Wheat Decomposition and Carbon Storage. Appl. Environ. Microbiol. 2009, 75, 7565–7569.
7. Friedrich, M.W. Stable-isotope probing of DNA: Insights into the function of uncultivated microorganisms from isotopically labeled metagenomes. Curr. Opin. Biotechnol. 2006, 17, 59–66.
8. Wilson, J.B. Shoot competition and root competition. J. Appl. Ecol. 1988, 25, 279–296.
9. Loreau, M.; Hector, A. Partitioning selection and complementarity in biodiversity experiments. Nature 2001, 412, 72–76.
10. Loreau, M.; Hector, A. Not even wrong: Comment by Loreau and Hector. Ecology 2019, 100, e02794.
11. Jaillard, B.; Deleporte, P.; Loreau, M.; Violle, C. A combinatorial analysis using observational data identifies species that govern ecosystem functioning. PLoS ONE 2018, 13, e0201135.
12. Jaillard, B.; Deleporte, P.; Isbell, F.; Loreau, M.; Violle, C. Consistent functional clusters explain the effects of biodiversity on ecosystem productivity in a long-term experiment. Ecology 2021, 102, e03441.
13. Razanamalala, K.; Razafimbelo, T.; Maron, P.-A.; Ranjard, L.; Chemidlin, N.; Lelièvre, M.; Dequiedt, S.; Ramaroson, V.H.; Marsden, C.; Becquer, T.; et al. Soil microbial diversity drives the priming effect along climate gradients: A case study in Madagascar. ISME J. 2018, 12, 451–462.
14. Maron, P.-A.; Mougel, C.; Ranjard, L. Soil microbial diversity: Methodological strategy, spatial over-view and functional interest. Comptes Rendus Biol. 2011, 334, 403–411.
15. Terrat, S.; Christen, R.; Dequiedt, S.; Lelièvre, M.; Nowak, V.; Regnier, T.; Bachar, D.; Plassart, P.; Wincker, P.; Jolivet, C.; et al. Molecular biomass and MetaTaxogenomic assessment

of soil microbial communities as influenced by soil DNA extraction procedure. Microb. Biotechnol. 2012, 5, 135–141.

16. Tardy, V.; Spor, A.; Mathieu, O.; Lévèque, J.; Terrat, S.; Plassart, P.; Regnier, T.; Bardgett, R.D.; van Der Putten, W.H.; Roggero, P.P.; et al. Shifts in microbial diversity through land use intensity as drivers of carbon mineralization in soil. Soil Biol. Biochem. 2015, 90, 204–213.
17. Quast, C.; Pruesse, E.; Yilmaz, P.; Gerken, J.; Schweer, T.; Yarza, P.; Peplies, J.; Glöckner, F.O. The SILVA ribosomal RNA gene database project: Improved data processing and web-based tools. Nucleic Acids Res. 2013, 41, 590–596.
18. Burnham, K.P.; Anderson, D.R. Multimodel Inference—Understanding AIC and BIC in Model Selection. Sociol. Methods Res. 2004, 33, 261–304.
19. R Development Core Team. R: A Language and Environment for Statistical Computing; R Foundation for Statistical Computing: Vienna, Austria, 2009; ISBN 3-900051-07-0. Available online: https://www.R-project.org (accessed on 20 March 2023).
20. Isbell, F.; Gonzalez, A.; Loreau, M.; Cowles, J.; Díaz, S.; Hector, A.; Mace, G.M.; Wardle, D.A.; O'Connor, M.I.; Duffy, J.E.; et al. Linking the influence and dependence of people on biodiversity across scales. Nature 2017, 546, 65–72.
21. Yu, X.; Polz, M.F.; Alm, E.J. Interactions in self-assembled microbial communities saturate with diversity. ISME J. 2019, 13, 1602–1617.
22. Clements, C.S.; Hay, M.E. Biodiversity has a positive but saturating effect on imperiled coral reefs. Sci. Adv. 2021, 7, eabi8592.
23. Maire, E.; Villéger, S.; Graham, N.A.; Hoey, A.S.; Cinner, J.; Ferse, S.C.; Aliaume, C.; Booth, D.J.; Feary, D.A.; Kulbicki, M.; et al. Community-wide scan identifies fish species associated with coral reef services across the Indo-Pacific. Proc. R. Soc. B Biol. Sci. 2018, 285, 20181167.
24. Delalandre, L.; Gaüzère, P.; Thuiller, W.; Cadotte, M.; Mouquet, N.; Mouillot, D.; Munoz, F.; Denelle, P.; Loiseau, N.; Morin, X.; et al. Functionally distinct tree species support long-term productivity in extreme environments. Proc. R. Soc. B 2022, 289, 20211694.
25. Chowdhury, T.R.; Dick, R.P. Ecology of aerobic methanotrophs in controlling methane fluxes from wetlands. Appl. Soil Ecol. 2013, 65, 8–22.
26. Petters, S.; Groß, V.; Söllinger, A.; Pichler, M.; Reinhard, A.; Bengtsson, M.M.; Urich, T. The soil microbial food web re-visited: Predatory myxobacteria as keystone taxa? ISME J. 2021, 15, 2665–2675.
27. Gaston, K.J.; Lawton, J.H. The population ecology of rare species. J. Fish Biol. 1990, 37, 97–104.
28. Marchant, R. How important are rare species in aquatic community ecology and bioassessment? A comment on the conclusions of Cao et al. Limnol. Oceanogr. 1999, 44, 1840–1841. Available online: http://pascal-francis.inist.fr/vibad/index.php?action=getRecordDetail&idt=1209822 (accessed on 20 March 2023).
29. Cao, Y.; Larsen, D.P. Rare species in multivariate analysis for bioassessment: Some considerations. J. N. Am. Benthol. Soc. 2001, 20, 144–153.
30. Cao, Y.; Williams, D.D.; Williams, N.E. How important are rare species in aquatic community ecology and bioassessment? Limnol. Oceanogr. 1998, 43, 1403–1409.
31. Violle, C.; Thuiller, W.; Mouquet, N.; Munoz, F.; Kraft, N.J.; Cadotte, M.W.; Livingstone, S.W.; Mouillot, D. Functional Rarity: The Ecology of Outliers. Trends Ecol. Evol. 2017, 32, 356–367.
32. Derrien, D.; Plain, C.; Courty, P.E.; Gelhaye, L.; Moerdijk-Poortvliet, T.C.; Thomas, F.; Versini, A.; Zeller, B.; Koutika, L.S.; Boschker, H.T.; et al. Does the addition of labile substrate destabilise old soil organic matter? Soil Biol. Biochem. 2014, 76, 149–160. Available online:

https://www.sciencedirect.com/science/article/pii/S0038071714001606 (accessed on 20 March 2023).

33. Blagodatskaya, E.; Khomyakov, N.; Myachina, O.; Bogomolova, I.; Blagodatsky, S.; Kuzyakov, Y. Microbial interactions affect sources of priming induced by cellulose. Soil Biol. Biochem. 2014, 74, 39–49.
34. Wilhelm, R.C.; Singh, R.; Eltis, L.D.; Mohn, W.W. Bacterial contributions to delignification and lignocellulose degradation in forest soils with metagenomic and quantitative stable isotope probing. ISME J. 2019, 13, 413–429.
35. Mandic-Mulec, I.; Stefanic, P.; van Elsas, J. Ecology of Bacillaceae. Microbiol. Spectr. 2015, 3, TBS–0017–2013.
36. Fontaine, S.; Hénault, C.; Aamor, A.; Bdioui, N.; Bloor, J.M.G.; Maire, V.; Mary, B.; Revaillot, S.; Maron, P.A. Fungi mediate long term sequestration of carbon and nitrogen in soil through their priming effect. Soil Biol. Biochem. 2011, 43, 86–96.
37. Xing, X.; Xu, H.; Zhang, W.; Hou, H.; Qin, H.; Liu, Y.; Zhang, L.; Fang, Y.; Wei, W.; Sheng, R. The characteristics of the community structure of typical nitrous oxide-reducing denitrifiers in agricultural soils derived from different parent materials. Appl. Soil Ecol. 2019, 142, 8–17.
38. Diamond, S.; Andeer, P.F.; Li, Z.; Crits-Christoph, A.; Burstein, D.; Anantharaman, K.; Lane, K.R.; Thomas, B.C.; Pan, C.; Northen, T.R.; et al. Mediterranean grassland soil C–N compound turnover is dependent on rainfall and depth, and is mediated by genomically divergent microorganisms. Nat. Microbiol. 2019, 4, 1356–1367.
39. Karunarathna, A.; Papizadeh, M.; Senanayake, I.C.; Jeewon, R.; Phookamsak, R.; Goonasekara, I.D. Novel fungal species of Phaeosphaeriaceae with an asexual/sexual morph connection. Mycosphere 2017, 8, 1818–1834.
40. Marin-Felix, Y.; Stchigel, A.M.; Cano-Lira, J.F.; Sanchis, M.; Mayayo, E.; Guarro, J. Emmonsiellopsis, a new genus related to the thermally dimorphic fungi of the family Ajellomycetaceae. Mycoses 2015, 58, 451–460.
41. Cavaletti, L.; Monciardini, P.; Schumann, P.; Rohde, M.; Bamonte, R.; Busti, E.; Sosio, M.; Donadio, S. Actinospica robiniae gen. nov., sp. nov. and Actinospica acidiphila sp. nov.: Proposal for Actinospicaceae fam. nov. and Catenulisporinae subord. nov. in the order Actinomycetales. Int. J. Syst. Evol. Microbiol. 2006, 56, 1747–1753.
42. Guo, X.; Liu, N.; Li, X.; Ding, Y.; Shang, F.; Gao, Y.; Ruan, J.; Huang, Y. Red Soils Harbor Diverse Culturable Actinomycetes That Are Promising Sources of Novel Secondary Metabolites. Appl. Environ. Microbiol. 2015, 81, 3086–3103.
43. Uroz, S.; Christophe, C.; Turpault, M.-P.; Frey-Klett, P. Mineral weathering by bacteria: Ecology, actors and mechanisms. Trends Microbiol. 2009, 17, 378–387.
44. Emmett, B.D.; Lévesque-Tremblay, V.; Harrison, M.J. Conserved and reproducible bacterial communities associate with extraradical hyphae of arbuscular mycorrhizal fungi. ISME J. 2021, 15, 2276–2288.
45. Wang, S.; Walker, R.; Schicklberger, M.; Nico, P.S.; Fox, P.M.; Karaoz, U.; Chakraborty, R.; Brodie, E.L. Microbial Phosphorus mobilization strategies across a natural nutrient limitation gradient and evidence for linkage with Iron solubilization traits. Front. Microbiol. 2021, 12, 572212.

7

Helminths and their Role in Environmental Engineering

Blanca Jiménez, Catalina Maya, José A. Barrios and Inés Navarro

Institute of Engineering, UNAM, Mexico, D.F., Mexico

ABSTRACT

Helminth eggs represent an important challenge to environmental engineers as they are among the most difficult biological parasites to inactivate in wastewater and sludge. Even though no official data on helminthiasis exist, it is estimated that more than 2.6 billion people are affected. These parasites are of concern in developing countries, particularly in those areas where the reuse of wastewater and sludge for agriculture is common. With regard to this, the unrestricted use of wastewater for irrigation presents a serious health risk due to the dissemination of pathogens, particularly helminth eggs. Helminth eggs survive in water, soil, and crops for several months and over much longer periods than other microorganisms. Therefore, and in order to minimize risk, several guidelines and regulations exist which limit their content in wastewater and sludge. Risk assessment estimates that such regulations may be less strict in developing countries where higher concentrations of helminth eggs occur in wastewater and sludge. These eggs need to be removed from wastewater and inactivated in sludge using certain treatment processes, some of which are not feasible in developing countries. Adequate methods are needed to precisely identify and quantify helminth eggs in environmental samples. Therefore, a multidisciplinary approach is needed to address helminthiasis in environmental engineering issues.

Keywords: *Biosolids, Guidelines and Regulations, Helminth Eggs, Helminthiasis, Inactivation Processes, Microbial Risk Assessment, Wastewater*

INTRODUCTION

For centuries, wastewater has been used for agricultural irrigation throughout the world, and this is still a common practice in several countries. There are many examples that show wastewater reuse is key to increasing food production and improving local economies. This is simply due to the high water demand for irrigation. In developing countries, this amounts to 81% of the total water extracted and to around 45% in developed countries [1]. As an example, in Mexico, where 75% of the territory is semiarid, wastewater reuse for agriculture is often practiced. Mexican farmers have long appreciated wastewater use because it contains, in addition to water, organic matter, nitrogen, and phosphorus, which act as fertilizers, increasing crop yield. Jiménez [2] summarized the reasons why wastewater is reused for irrigation: (a) it significantly saves fresh water; (b) it provides nutrients to soil; (c) it reduces or eliminates the need for chemical fertilizers; (d) it contributes to the expansion of agricultural land in arid and semi-arid areas; (e) it increases farmers' income; and (f) it is a relatively cheap disposal method for wastewater, reducing surface water pollution. It is estimated that there are 20 million hectares in at least 50 developing countries where wastewater is used to irrigate [3], representing around 10% of the total irrigated land. Even though the reuse of wastewater for agricultural irrigation has several benefits, it poses a public health risk due its pathogenic content. Among these pathogens, helminth eggs are of particular concern.

Helminths are parasitic worms transmitted to humans via their eggs (infective life stage, Figure 1). They are considered to be the biological structures most resistant to inactivation in the environmental engineering field [4]. Most helminths are transmitted by direct contact with contaminated soil, crops, or wastewater (e.g., *Ascaris lumbricoides*, *Trichuris trichiura*, and hookworms), but some require the presence of intermediate hosts (e.g., freshwater snails in the case of schistosomiasis) [5].

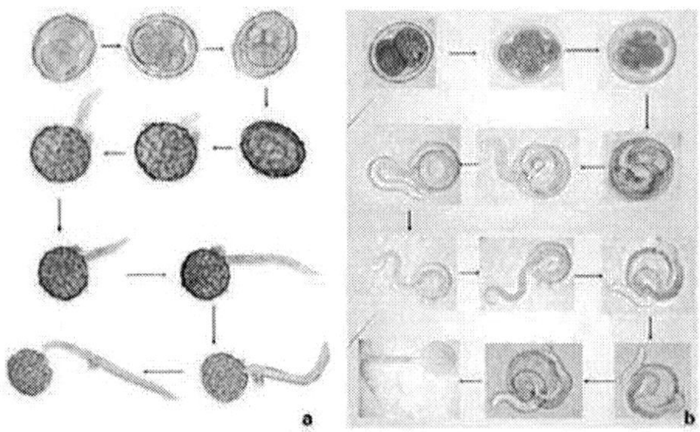

Figure 1. Fertilized eggs with larval growth and development of the worm for (a) Ascaris lumbricoides and (b) Toxocara canis (Photographic archives, Treatment and Reuse Group, Instituto de Ingeniería, UNAM).

Concerns about their presence are related to their very low infectious dose, their high rate of survival in the environment for extended periods of time (up to several years, compared to weeks for other pathogens), and their high resistance to conventional disinfection processes [6]. Helminth eggs are a particular threat to health where sanitation conditions are poor, polluted water is used for irrigation, or where excreta or non-treated sludge is disposed of in an uncontrolled manner. They cause a set of diseases call "helminthiasis" that are given specific names based on the genera involved (for instance, ascariasis for genus *Ascaris*). Symptoms include deterioration of the intestines, toxic effects, blood loss, diarrhea, undernourishment, and anemia. Some helminths gnaw away at the intestinal wall causing hemorrhages while simultaneously secreting an anti-coagulant. The damage caused by inflammation, and the wounds they open generate tumors and excrescences. In addition, helminths can block conduits (for example, biliary) or cause intestinal obstruction and perforation of the digestive tract causing peritonitis [6, 7].

Helminthiases may lead to serious collateral effects limiting the physical and mental development of children, notably when repeated infection occurs between 5 and 15 years of age. It is estimated that 182 million children of preschool age are infected, that is, around

33% of those living in developing countries [8–10]. These children display lower height and weight due to undernourishment compared to well-nourished children living in healthy environments. At the same time, malnutrition results in a low school performance and a decrease in intelligence quotient (IQ) [11, 12]. Other effects, such as epileptic seizures, violent headaches, vertigo, local paralysis, vomiting, and optical and physical perturbations have been reported [7].

In spite of that, the control of helminth eggs was neglected until the late 1980s when the World Health Organization (WHO) developed guidelines for water and sludge reuse in agriculture. In 2006 the World Health Organization [6] confirmed the need to control the associated health hazards through an updated version of the guidelines for safe use of wastewater, excreta, and sludge in agriculture and aquaculture. These guidelines recommend limiting the helminth egg content in wastewater, excreta, and sludge; however, to achieve this, it is necessary to remove and inactivate the eggs. The following sections discuss the data collected for helminth eggs in environmental matrices, public health risks, regulations in different countries, treatment methods for wastewater and sludge, and analytical methods to determine their concentrations in environmental matrices.

HELMINTH EGG CONTENT IN WASTEWATER AND SLUDGE

Helminths are multi-cellular organisms (worms) with a wide variety of shapes and sizes. Some of them are free-living (like earthworms), while others are parasites. Helminths can be classified in different ways, but the classification most frequently used considers their body shape. Roundworms are called Nematodes while flatworms are called Plathelminthes; if the latter have segments then are referred to as Cestodes while non-segmented ones are termed Trematodes [5]. As mentioned previously, helminths reproduce via the production of eggs, which are microscopic structures whose shape, size (20–180 m), and density (1.06–1.23) vary.

A fertilized *Ascaris lumbricoides* female roundworm can lay around 200,000 eggs per day and up to 27,000,000 eggs over a lifespan of 10–24 months, while the *Taenia saginata*, a beef tapeworm, can produce as many as 800,000 eggs per segment per day (a typically sized worm may have around 1000 segments) [13–15]. Helminth eggs contained in wastewater, sludge, or excreta may be viable (alive) but not infective. To be infective, the eggs need to develop into larvae, which require a temperature of around 25°C combined with a moisture content of at least 5% [16]. These conditions are found in soils or crops where eggs develop into larvae within a few days, remaining viable for several months or years [6]. In addition, infective doses are very low, within the range of 1–10 eggs. Most helminthiases are, therefore, transmitted via the eggs through a human-water-soil-crop-human pathway.

The content of helminth eggs in developing countries' wastewater and sludge differs considerably from that of developed ones (Table 1). Helminth egg concentrations may be 7–80 times greater in developing countries. For instance, the helminth egg content in developing countries ranges from 70 to 3000 helminth eggs per liter (HE/L) in wastewater and 70–735 helminth eggs per gram of total dry solids (HE/g TS) in sludge. In comparison, for developed countries, the content in wastewater is only 1–9 HE/L and that for sludge is 2–13 HE/g TS [17]. Not all eggs are viable, but, in general, mean viability generally reaches 88%, with an even higher percentage for *Ascaris* spp. (90%) as a result of their high environmental resistance [4, 18, 19].

Table 1. Helminth ova content in wastewater and sludge for selected countries

Country/region	Helminth eggs in wastewater (HE/L)	Helminth eggs in sludge (HE/gTS)	References
Developing countries	70–3000	67–735	[13, 18, 20]
Tropical countries		300–3000	[18]
Brazil	166–202	1–76	[21]
Cayman islands	100–1230		[14]
China	840	2300	[22]
France	9	5–7	[20]
Egypt (liquid primary)	6–42	Mean: 67, Max: 735	[23–24]
Egypt (dewatered primary)		Mean: 8, Max: 124	[24]
Ghana		76	[20, 24]
Germany		<1	
Great Britain		<6	
Japan	80	1–51	[25]
Jordan	300		[14]
Mexico	6–98 (up to 330 in poor areas)	73–177 (viable eggs)	[17]
Morocco	840		[26]
South Africa	772	2–40	[27, 28]
Syria	800		[29]
Tunisia	30		[15]
Ukraine	60		[13]
United States of America	1–8	2–13	[20]

PREVALENCE OF HELMINTHIASIS

Stoll N. [30] calculated that there were 2200 million nematode infections worldwide and predicted that by 1991, there would be 5000 million infected people. Similarly, he estimated that the Chinese population produced a total of 18,000 tons of *Ascaris* eggs per year. Currently, it is estimated that more than 2.6 billion people are infected with helminths (Table 2), and although helminthiases are globally distributed, the prevalence of disease is mostly limited to developing countries [5, 7, 31]. They are endemic in regions of Africa, Central America, South America, and the Far East, with incidence rates as high as 90% for specific regions and sectors of the population [6, 7]. The dominant species depends on local conditions. However, most of the information related to procedures to control helminth eggs in sludge was gathered in developed countries where the low concentrations found render it difficult to utilize the data collected [20].

Around 96% of the helminthiases reported are induced by infection by Nematoda and Trematoda classes, with 4% due to Cestoda [5, 32]. The most common genus is *Ascaris lumbricoides* [33] with more than 819 million people infected. The eggs are highly infective (commonly, one egg suffices), very persistent in the environment, and very resistant to conventional disinfection/inactivation processes [10–12, 34]. For example, embryonated eggs of *Ascaris* spp. can survive for 20 days at temperatures of -20.9 to -27°C and survive in frozen Siberian soils for 10 years [35]. This resistance comes from the fact that eggs are surrounded by a series of layers functioning as a barrier that protects the larva against harsh environmental conditions. Indeed, the different helminth egg species possess 3–4 layers with different physical and chemical characteristics: (a) The 1–2 outer layers are formed of mucopolysaccharides and proteins; (b) the middle layers have chitin which provides structure and mechanical resistance; and (c) the inner layer, composed of lipids and proteins, protect the egg from desiccation, strong acid and bases, oxidants, reductive agents, detergents and proteolytic compounds [36–39].

The interaction of the layers' components with external agents may cause a change in their chemical composition, as well as in the specific function of each layer, which in turn modifies their permeability, their mechanical and chemical resistance and, finally, the egg viability. These mechanisms may be similar to those that take place during the hatching process, during which the larva secretes certain enzymes that induce the loss of permeability of the ascaroside layer and attack the outer eggshell layers. However, in this case, the layer remains intact until the hatching of the larva with no detectable chemical change [40–41].

The impact on the quality of life of infected populations may be illustrated using an estimation made in 2013 for years lived with disabiliy (YLDs) [42]. This amounted worldwide to 1,004,000 years for anemia caused by hookworm disease, and 671,000 years for schistosomiasis. Based on the analysis of YLDs estimates, ascariasis was among the eight most prevalent causes of disease, affecting more than 10% of world's population in 2013, such that if the mean prevalence of chronic sequelae is selected, for periods longer than 3 months, the impact of ascariasis was estimated in 819 million cases.

Table 2. Common helminth species and helminthiasis by region

Helminth species	Common name	Prevalence (million inhabitants)	Regional presence
Nematoda			
Ascaris lumbricoides	Roundworm	819	Many regions of South-East Asia, Africa, and Central and South America
Ancylostoma duodenale	Hookworm	439	Tropical and subtropical countries (Sub-Saharan Africa), Central and South America, the Caribbean, Asia and in the Pacific islands
Necator americanus			
Strongyloides stercoralis		370	
Trichuris trichiura	Whipworm	465	Moist, warm, tropical regions of Asia, Africa, Central and South America, and the Caribbean islands

Trichostrongylus orientalis	Roundworm	Several	Mainly rural communities in Asia
Cestoda			
Hymenolepis diminuta	Rat tapeworm	50	Most occurrences in areas which lack adequate sanitation but may be found around the world in South America, Southeast Asia, Western Africa and East Africa; and in areas of the tropics and subtropics and some areas of Southern and Eastern Europe, the United States of America and Mexico.
Hymenolepis nana	Dwarf tapeworm		
Taenia saginata	Beef tapeworm	50	
Taenia solium	Pork tapeworm		
Trematoda			
Schistosoma mansoni	Blood fluke	207	Tropical and subtropical regions. This species occurs widely throughout Africa and South America, especially in Brazil, Venezuela, Surinam, Guyana and several Caribbean islands, including Puerto Rico, St. Lucia, Martinique, and Guadalupe
Clonorchis sinensis *Echinostoma* spp. *Fasciola gigantica* *Fasciola hepatica* *Fasciolopsis buski* *Heterophyes* spp. *Metagonimus* spp. *Opisthorchis felineus* *Opisthorchis viverrini* *Paragonimus* spp.	Food-borne Trematodes	56	Largely in Southern and Eastern Asia but also in Central and Eastern Europe.
Fasciolopsis buski	Intestinal fluke		
Other groups		100	Worldwide
Total		Over 2.6 billion infections worldwide	

Source: Ref. [5].

GUIDELINES AND REGULATIONS

As mentioned previously, the use of domestic wastewater for irrigation, even without treatment, is an established practice in many countries. However, it leads to the proliferation of helminthiasis in the exposed population [6, 43]. Following a series of epidemiological studies, since 1989, the World Health Organization has recommended a limit for the content of nematode eggs in wastewater reused for agricultural irrigation [44]. Similarly, sludge produced during wastewater treatment may be reused in agriculture or soil remediation after adequate treatment to reduce its microbial content. Once treated, wastewater and sludge need to meet national regulations or international criteria in order to be safely reused. For instance, in 2006, the World Health Organization suggested that a limit of less than 1 viable helminth egg per liter (HE/L) in wastewater makes it acceptable for agricultural reuse, while less than 1 viable helminth egg per gram of total dry solids (1 HE/g TS) is required in sludge [6]. However, these limits are difficult to meet in countries or regions with endemic diseases, requiring effective inactivation processes to control the high concentrations of helminth eggs.

Following the WHO guidelines [6], many countries have set standards for helminth eggs in treated water, including Brazil, Colombia, Costa Rica, Chile, Israel, Jordan, Mexico, Saudi Arabia, and Tunisia. These standards also set recommendations for the types of crops to be irrigated, irrigation methods, and other intervention measures to manage risks. In addition, sludge and biosolids (treated sludge) regulations have been developed by several countries, led principally by the United States (Tables 3 and 4).

Table 3. Regulations for helminth egg content in treated wastewater use in agriculture

Country	**Regulation-standard-guidelines**	**Type**	**Helminth eggs limit, eggs/L**
Australia	Australian regulations, 1995	U	–
		N/A	Absent
Argentina	Resolución 778/96	U	–
		R	<1 Nematode
Chile	Norma 1333 (1978)	U	-
		R	<1 Nematode
Mexico	NOM-001-SEMAR-NAT-1996	U	<1
		R	<5
United States of America	Department of Health Services (DHS), California, 1918.	N/A	Absent
WHO	WHO, 2006	U	≤1 (arithmetic mean)[t1,t2]
		R	
		Localized (drip) irrigation)	Low-growing crops: ≤1 (arithmetic mean)[t2] High-growing crops: no recommendati[on]t3

[a]When children under 15 years of age are exposed, additional health protection measures should be used (e.g., treatment to ≤0.1 egg per liter, protective equipment such as gloves or shoes /boots or chemical treatment);

[b]An arithmetic mean should be determined throughout the irrigation season. The mean value of ≤1 egg per liter should be obtained for at least 90% of samples in order to allow for the occasional high-value sample (i.e., with >10 eggs per liter). In some wastewater

treatment processes (e.g., waste stabilization ponds), the hydraulic retention time can be used as a surrogate to assure compliance with a limit of ≤1 egg per liter;

[c]Including fruit trees and olives, not crops harvested directly from the soil.

U: Unrestricted irrigation: For agricultural irrigation of all kinds of crops, including those that are eaten uncooked (lettuce, onion); R: Restricted irrigation: For agricultural irrigation of all kinds of crops, except that are eaten uncooked (highly mechanized, labor intensive).

Source: Refs. [6, 45–47].

Table 4. Regulations for helminth egg content in sludge

Country	Regulation standard guidelines	Class/ type	Helminth egg limit, eggs/g TS
Brazil	CONAMA 375/2006	A	0.25 [t4]
		B	10 [t4]
Chile	No. 123 (30/08/2006)	A	0.25[t4]
		B	-
France	Directive 86/278	-	0.3
Mexico	NOM-004-SEMARNAT-2002	A	1 [t4]
		B	10
		C	35
New Zealand	Guidelines for the safe application of biosolids to land in New Zealand	A	0.25
Norway	Regulations for the treatment, use and disposal of sewage sludge	–	Absent
South Africa	Guidelines for the utilisation and disposal of wastewater sludge (Vol. 2)	A	0.25
		B	1
The United States of America	CFR 40 Part 503 /1993	A	0.25[t4]
The WHO	WHO, 2006		1

[V]Viable eggs.

In general, the standard values have been set to protect human health, allowing sludge application at sites where human contact may occur [48]. Under those conditions, a value of <1 HE/g is to be achieved (Class A). Only Brazil and Mexico allow higher concentrations of helminth eggs. However, in the case of Brazil, the regulation states that Class B sludge may be land applied only after risk assessment determines that this is a secure practice. In contrast, the limits for Class B and C sludge in the Mexican regulations refer to total eggs, assuming not all of them are viable, and is intended for land application without human contact (e.g., agriculture, soil restoration, forestry). However, to enforce these limits, it is necessary to correctly measure the helminth egg content in wastewater and sludge (treated or untreated).

QUANTITATIVE MICROBIAL RISK ASSESSMENT (QMRA)

WHO guidelines and US EPA limits for helminth eggs were based on limited epidemiological evidences, and on the performance of different sludge treatment methods, rather than the results of a risk assessment. Neither of the organizations based their considerations on results of a dose response-curve "because methodologies had not been developed sufficiently enough to make such calculations" [6, 49]. As a result, no human risk assessment was conducted, due to the lack of a dose-response model appropriate to describe helminth eggs infection. At the time, of the three different methods used to evaluate microbial risks: microbiology laboratory analysis, epidemiological studies, and quantitative microbial risk assessment (QMRA), only the first two have been applied to helminth data [50–52]. In contrast, a number of human dose-response relationships have been developed for bacteria, viruses, and protozoa [53–59]; consequently, a dose-response function for helminth infections was required for applying a QMRA.

QMRA is a modeling approach used to predict the human health risks from exposure to pathogens and has been shown to be effective in assessing the transmission of water and food-borne infections. It estimates the risk of infection or illness based on the concentration of infectious pathogens in wastewater, on surfaces or in drinking water, or from other environmental sources (e.g., crops, biosolids, air), the estimated ingestion rate, and the established dose-response models for a given population.

Since 2009 a dose-response curve is only available for *Ascaris* [60], although other helminths genus are highly relevant in wastewater and sludge reuse, especially in developing countries [61]. This curve was derived from *A. lumbricoides* prevalence data obtained from stools of a large sample of children in the Mezquital Valley in Mexico, rather than conducting human *Ascaris* dose-challenge studies. Navarro et al. [60] found that their *Ascaris* infection data best fitted the β-Poisson dose-response equation [Eq. (1)].

$$P(d)=1-[1+(d/N_{50})(2^{1/\alpha}-1)]^{-\alpha} \qquad (1)$$

where P(d) is the risk of infection in an individual who has ingested *d Ascaris* eggs on one occasion; N_{50} is the mean *Ascaris* infective dose; and α is an *Ascaris* 'infectivity constant'. They found the values of N_{50} and α to be 859 and 0.104, respectively.

Use of the QMRA tool allowed an initial target estimation of *Ascaris* concentration in sludge and wastewater. These values were greater than WHO and US EPA limits [62], but with an estimated probability of infection smaller than the prevalence rate observed on site. Such scenarios may allow a gradual improvement in population health conditions, as well as working towards an *Ascaris* eggs content in sludge and/or wastewater which gradually should approach regulation limits. The authors concluded from these risk analyses that regulations targeting biosolids reuse in developing countries should address the challenge of firstly deciding an acceptable infection risk and, secondly, putting in place an integrated framework for risk management, involving additional health protection measures. They suggested factors to be considered, which include, amongst others: (a) an affordable treatment process, (b) crop restriction policy, (c) different sludge application rates, and (d) efficient produce washing methods.

Further research should focus on QMRAs with the β-Poisson dose-response model for *Ascaris lumbricoides*, which have demonstrated through case studies its application to analyze the tolerable risk and to evaluate additional control measures, considered as potential interventions for health risk reduction. They illustrates the importance of two recommendations from WHO guidelines [3]: The first is that in some circumstances, "it is recommended that, initially, a national standard is established for a locally appropriate level of tolerable additional burden of disease based on the local incidence of diarrheal disease," and the second that post-treatment health-protection control measures can achieve significant pathogen reductions, so that wastewater treatment does not have to achieve the total pathogen reduction required to protect consumer health.

In the first case, it was shown that a maximum tolerable additional disability-adjusted life year (DALY) loss per person per year (pppy) of 10^{-4} is an appropriate value, especially in low-income countries [63]. It is more applicable than the WHO guidelines [3] default value of $\leq 10^{-6}$ DALY loss for the tolerable additional burden of disease due to wastewater pathogens. A tolerable *Ascaris* infection risk of 1.2×10^{-2} [64] corresponds to a tolerable DALY loss of 10^{-4} pppy. Therefore, the QMRA results, applying the β-Poisson dose-response model, indicate that a ova reduction to 10 eggs/L results in a risk of $\sim 3 \times 10^{-3}$, which could be used as a guideline value. This is in agreement with previous recommendations of ≤15 eggs/L [65, 66] who also suggested that pathogen reduction may be achieved by simple wastewater treatment.

QMRA applications using the β-Poisson dose-response model have illustrated the health protection levels that may be achieved with some control measures. Experimental work by [67] showed that a waiting period of 120 days at 25°C or 90 days at 37°C following land application of biosolids to lettuce fields would result in acceptable yearly risks of less than 10^{-4} for *Ascaris* for the planting of the crop and acceptable yearly risks of less than 10^{-4} for *Ascaris* from the consumption of lettuce. They were able to evaluate the effect of different incubation temperatures of biosolids on the inactivation of *Ascaris* eggs and estimated an appropriate time between the application of biosolids to land and the harvesting of lettuce to achieve an acceptable risk for consumers at the end of the exposure pathway.

An important topic with regard to the safe use of wastewater in agriculture is the estimation of the number of days of irrigation cessation required to achieve tolerable annual infection risk. The on-site die-off of pathogens through irrigation cessation is considered a potential intervention for health risk reduction. Seidu et al. [68] undertook the challenge of comparing the best fit die-off model for *Ascaris* derived in their study with existing die-off models in a QMRA. The β-Poisson dose-response model was used in order to assess the effect of different die-off models on the days required to achieve the tolerable annual infection risk associated with the consumption of wastewater-irrigated lettuce. The study showed that none of the survival curves of *Ascaris suum* fitted the log-linear model, indicating that the classical first-order kinetic approach is inadequate in many cases. The implication of using die-off models for health risk assessment was an underestimation of the number of days of irrigation cessation necessary to reduce *Ascaris* infection risk for the log-linear die-off rate compared to the biphasic die-off rate of their study. Therefore, cessation of irrigation as a health risk reduction measure appeared to be impractical, given the prevailing conditions, in their study area. This also indicated that assessing the health risk reduction efficacy of intervention using QMRA models is dependent on accurate characterization of the die-off of pathogenic organisms.

Studies of Barker *et al* [69] and Kundu *et al* [70] assessed the risk of gastrointestinal infections caused by *Ascaris lumbricoides*, among other pathogens, associated with the consumption of raw vegetables. They used a QMRA in two developing regions (Kumasi, Ghana, and the Arias-Arenales River, Argentina). Both studies are examples of risk estimations that consider the *Ascaris* infection risk as a result of the quality of the water resource used for irrigation, the results after harvesting, and due to crops being eaten raw. They also included the *Ascaris* infection risk from accidental ingestion of contaminated water and produce washing behaviors of the population. They developed different approaches for following the steps of a QMRA, showing that a wide range of assumptions may be made for specific exposure scenarios to identify the reduction measures needed to protect human health. Their results and discussion also made it evident that the variability observed is a consequence of the inherent characteristics of each case study and that the uncertainties analyzed in the different scenarios illustrated the variables that played a major role in the risk estimates. Barker et al. [69] concluded that "particularly in the context of developing countries, it is important to balance the risks with the benefits of access to fresh vegetables. It is important that the consideration of the benefits is not lost in the discussion of the risks, which remain real and significant".

Finally, it was shown that these case studies illustrate that QMRA is a useful tool for developing standards for human exposure to pathogens. Clearly, additional interventions and changes in behavior need to be investigated and implemented to reduce the risks to acceptable levels; however, in the meantime, a more efficient and rapid analytical technique of helminth egg detection in environmental samples is needed, as well as high-quality control of local data to improve the exposure scenarios.

WASTEWATER TREATMENT PROCESSES

In order to remove helminth eggs from wastewater, processes that remove particles, such as sedimentation, filtration, or coagulation-flocculation, are employed [71–73]. In practice, and in contrast to other microorganisms, helminth ova cannot be inactivated with chlorine, UV light, or ozone (in the latter case at least not with economical doses since a concentration of >36 mg/L ozone is required with 1 h of contact time). As discussed previously, their morphology, in terms of their external structure, protects them from inactivation.

The main removal mechanisms employed during wastewater treatment are associated with the size and density of helminth eggs. Since they are denser than water, they may be correlated with solid particles in wastewater [measured as total suspended solids (TSS)] and this, therefore, aids their separation. This correlation is used to indirectly measure their content and evaluate the performance of treatment processes in terms of their removal [74]. Due to their size and adhesiveness, helminth eggs can also be removed from wastewater through filtration [33, 71, 75, 76]. In terms of wastewater treatment, the following processes may achieve good removal of helminth eggs [33, 73].

- *Stabilization ponds (SP).* Stabilization ponds are large shallow basins enclosed by earth embankments, in which raw wastewater is treated by entirely natural processes. Several factors contribute to removing helminths, namely sedimentation, temperature, sunlight, pH, microorganism predation, adsorption, and absorption, although sedimentation is the most effective. There are three types of SP: anaerobic, facultative, and maturation ponds. Anaerobic (1-day retention time) and facultative ponds (5–15 days) are best for helminth ova removal.
- *Reservoirs.* Similarly to stabilization ponds, reservoirs and dams can remove helminth ova from wastewater if retention times longer than 20 days are used.
- *Coagulation-flocculation.* This process promotes aggregation of solid particles with the use of metallic salts (mainly alum or iron salts) and produces water suitable for agricultural reuse. When this process uses low coagulant doses

(50–65 mg/L) combined with synthetic polymers as flocculants (0.8–1.2 mg/L), it is called chemical enhanced primary treatment (CEPT) or advanced primary treatment (APT). CEPT or APT promote particle aggregation, including helminth eggs, into flocs that increase their settling velocity and allow separation via sedimentation.

- *Filtration.* This consists of passing primary or secondary effluent through a porous material that retains the solids and produces a good quality effluent. Rapid filtration (rate >2 m/h) is one of the most useful treatments to remove helminth eggs from effluents, either physicochemical or biological, with values consistently below 1 HE/L.
- *Constructed wetlands.* These are designed to operate by gravity, and they are generally shallow to allow a better removal of pollutants. The plants typically used are as follows: (a) large plants with floating or aerial leaves; (b) plants with well-developed and submerged roots, such as rushes, water hyacinth, reeds, and water lilies; and (c) very small floating plants with few roots or no roots at all, such as those of the *Lamenacea* family, *Lemna* or duckweed, *Spirodela*, *Wolffia*, *Wolffiela*, and *Salvinia* [77, 78]. Most of the removal of helminth eggs occurs within the first 25 m in a horizontal flow gravel bed wetland (100 m long), reaching 100% after the entire process [79, 80].

SLUDGE STABILIZATION

Once separated from wastewater, most helminth eggs are concentrated in sludge, which needs to be adequately treated before its land application or disposal. Since helminth eggs are the most resistant form of the parasites [4, 18–19], sludge treatment processes must consider their initial concentrations to achieve their inactivation and comply with regulations. In this respect, helminth eggs have the ability to survive for long periods of time in raw sludge and soil (up to 6 years from their initial application [81]). As a result, different sludge treatment processes may be used to inactivate helminth eggs, often including thermal treatment.

As an example, some of the best results for helminth egg inactivation in sludge have been obtained using thermal treatment at 108°C, irradiation at 1000 Gy or greater, pasteurization at 70°C, and thermophilic (55°C) anaerobic digestion [82–85]. In addition, the US EPA [48] allows the use of different alternatives to produce a sludge that meets class A limits (<0.25 HE/g TS) which include processes such as composting, irradiation, pasteurization, and heat treatment. However, all these advanced treatments require investments that are not always feasible in developing countries, where basic sanitation strategies are of greater importance.

With respect to more conventional treatment processes, mesophilic aerobic or anaerobic digestion do not reduce viable eggs of *Ascaris, Trichuris, Toxocara,* or *Capillaria* [84]. When mesophilic anaerobic digestion has been evaluated, at least 50% of *Ascaris suum* eggs were found to survive for up to 5 weeks [86]. In contrast, studies of alkaline pre- and post-stabilization with 40% (w/w) lime [71, 87] have reported inactivation efficiencies between 92 and 95%.

Several studies have evaluated the combination of different adverse conditions to inactivate helminth eggs, with some of them including the use of a range of chemicals. For example, Ghiglietti *et al* [88] found that a combination of sludge alkalinization with ammonium hydroxide (NH_4OH) at 30°C causes the inactivation of *A. lumbricoides, A. suum,* and *Trichuris muris*, and that a temperature of 40°C, with or without ammonia, was unfavorable for the development of the eggs; however, at 22°C, there was no effect, even with the addition of ammonia.

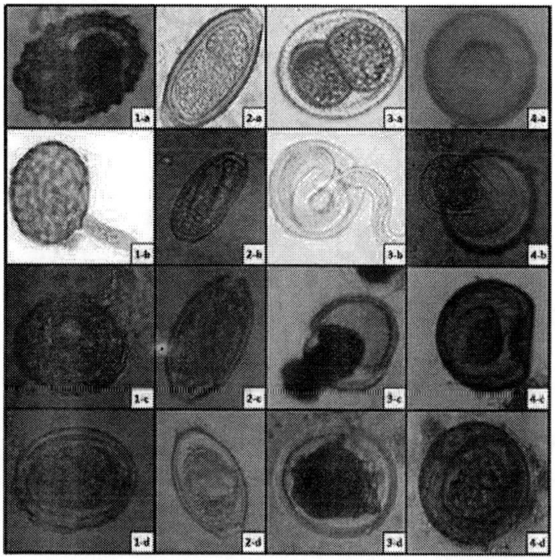

Figure 2. Viable eggs: 1-a Ascaris; 2-a Trichuris; 3-a, Toxocara; and 4-a Hymenolepis diminuta. Larval eggs: 1-b Ascaris; 2-b Trichuris; 3-b Toxocara; 4-b Hymenolepis. Morphological damage observed when eggs were subjected to different chemical reagents: 1-c and 1-d Ascaris; 2-c and 2-d Trichuris; 3-c and 3-d Toxocara; and 4-c and 4-d Hymenolepis. (Photographic archives, Treatment and Reuse Group, Instituto de Ingeniería, UNAM).

Another study [87] also obtained a 69% reduction of viable helminth eggs after 2h contact time with 10% (w/w) ammonia. When 50% ammonia was added, inactivation reached 94%. In addition, optimal conditions for egg inactivation have been found to include a combination of temperature, pH, and dryness of the sludge (45°C, pH of 5.3 and 90% dryness within 6days or 45°C, pH of 12.7 and 90% dryness within 19days) [4]. These results also confirm that the acidification process with peracetic acid was more effective than lime treatment. In this respect, Barrios *et al* [89] also evaluated the use of peracetic acid for microbial inactivation in sludge; results showed that the application of 550 ppm for 30min reduced viable helminth eggs by 94% from an initial concentration of 93 viable HE/g TS. Aguilar et al. [90] evaluated the use of silver for inactivating high concentrations of helminth eggs in sludge (168–215 viable HE/g TS); the use of silver alone was not sufficient for complete inactivation. However, when silver was applied with copper and a synergistic agent (5:50:13.3mg Ag–Cu–SA/g TS), total inactivation was achieved after 60min.

Following some of those studies, the effect of different chemicals on the morphology of helminth eggs has been evaluated. After the addition of peracetic acid, lime, increased temperature, and desiccation, serious malformations of the embryos and larva, and even the destruction of the embryo, have been documented (Figure 2).

ANALYTICAL TECHNIQUES

In order to quantify helminth eggs in wastewater, sludge, and excreta, an analytical procedure based on their visual identification and enumeration is used. However, current methodologies are not always effective for identification since experienced technicians are required, and therefore, results are often neither accurate nor reliable. Moreover, there is no universally accepted method to quantify them in sludge and biosolids [91]. The available analytical procedures commonly have two steps: (a) the separation of as many eggs as possible from other particles in the sample and (b) their visual identification under the microscope, where the concentrated sediment (pellet) contains many other types of particles. Only a properly trained technician is able to discriminate such particles from the eggs, and this technician has to visually identify the different species of helminth eggs. This is critical and constitutes the main source of error and uncertainty in the methodology. In particular, it is problematic when processing samples with a high content of helminth eggs because the discrimination process is tedious and time-consuming. In short, the challenge for the analysis is to separate, correctly identify, and enumerate helminth eggs in samples that, even after processing, contain many impurities, which render this difficult. Several alternative methods have been proposed to quantify helminths, considering the complexity of dealing with environmental samples. However, the efficacy of their application is yet to be proven.

As part of newly proposed analytical techniques, molecular methods have reported variable results. Some of these have been tested with synthetic samples and as a result, they still need to demonstrate their feasibility where actual environmental samples are analyzed. A recent study [92] compared different methods to detect hookworm ova over a range of concentrations and concluded that direct DNA extraction exhibited some limitations due to polymerase chain reaction (PCR) inhibitors present in environmental samples. In contrast, another study reported a sensitivity of one to four hookworm ova in wastewater samples [93]. Using quantitative PCR methods, *Ascaris* eggs may be detected [94, 95]; however, this technique still has some limitations, such as the low recovery rates obtained in samples with low numbers of eggs or the production of false positives.

A recent approach has proposed the use of image processing algorithms to identify and quantify helminth eggs from photographs taken using a microscope. This method is based on selected characteristics of helminth eggs that allow their correct identification without the need for a highly trained technician; it is capable of identifying up to eight species of helminths with a specificity (capacity to discriminate between species of helminth eggs and other objects) and sensitivity (capacity to correctly identify and classify the different species of helminth eggs) of 0.99 and 0.90, respectively [5].

FINAL REMARKS

Much knowledge has been gained since the early 80s but there are still major challenges in the field of environmental engineering. A large number of species of helminth eggs are excreted by humans and are discharged into wastewater, representing a significant source of pollution to the environment. In particular, when untreated or partially treated wastewater is discharged or used for agriculture, the risk of transmitting these types of diseases increases. The concentrations of helminth eggs in environmental matrices (wastewater and sludge) are directly related to public health. Therefore, until the millennium goals of 100% sanitation worldwide are met, about 2.6 billion cases of helminthiasis will prevail. Meanwhile the integrated management of wastewater and sludge remains as an engineering challenge.

Wastewater and sludge regulations focus on public health protection, assuming agricultural reuse and land application is practiced. Very low concentrations are permitted in treated effluents and biosolids (<1 HE/L or gram of dry solids, respectively). In some cases, these levels are not easy to achieve, considering the high concentrations occurring in developing countries. Helminth eggs are associated with solid particles in wastewater, either because they behave in the same way or they are part of aggregated solids. As a result, processes related to solids removal (e.g., sedimentation, filtration, or coagulation-flocculation) will also remove most of the helminth eggs contained in wastewater. Once separated, they will concentrate in sludge where they need to be inactivated before the sludge is reused or disposed of. For this purpose, processes that increase temperature and/or pH, reduce sludge humidity, as well as the use of certain chemicals (e.g., lime, organic acids, or ammonia) achieve high inactivation (>90%). Within conventional sludge treatment methods, the use of quicklime has proven effective where high concentrations occur. However, in developing countries where high concentrations of helminth eggs are found, there is still a need for economic yet efficient inactivation methods.

In order to demonstrate that these processes meet the strict limits established by regulations and guidelines, adequate methods for identification and quantification are required. Current analytical techniques to quantify helminth eggs in environmental samples are usually time-consuming and require a high level of expertise to differentiate between species. Promising alternative methods are being developed, including the use of molecular tools as well as image processing technologies that could improve sensitivity and reduce processing time. Further validation will prove their applicability under different laboratory and/or field conditions.

Quantitative microbial risk assessment has been used to predict the human health risks from exposure to *Ascaris* eggs. Some QMRA applications suggest that helminth egg limits estimated may be initial targets and may be included in national regulations (wastewater and sludge for agricultural reuse), even though they may be less strict than those proposed by WHO and US EPA, but still they will gradually reduce infection risks from these parasites. Moreover, several QMRA results have demonstrated that additional interventions and behavior changes may be implemented to reduce the risks to acceptable levels. Nonetheless, more high-quality data is needed to improve the evaluation of different exposure scenarios and to reduce uncertainties in risk estimates.

From the point of view of environmental engineering, helminth eggs are relevant since they need to be removed from wastewater and inactivated once in sludge to break their life cycle. However, to further improve public health, other strategic measures, such as preventive chemical treatment, and specific agricultural practices, must be implemented, and thus, a multidisciplinary approach is needed to address this global problem.

REFERENCES

1. Navarro I, Chávez A, Maya C, Becerril E, Barrios JA, Lucario S, Jimenez B. Wastewater reuse for irrigation. In: Muhammad Salik Javaid, editor. Practices, Safe Reuse and Perspectives, Irrigation and Drainage—Sustainable Strategies and Systems. Rijeka, Croatia: InTech; 2015.
2. Jiménez B. Irrigation in developing countries using wastewater. International Review for Environmental Strategies 2006;6(2):229–250. ISBN/ISSN: 1345-7594.
3. World Health Organization, editor. Guidelines for the Safe Use of Wastewater, Excreta and Greywater. Vol. 2. Wastewater Use in Agriculture World Health Organization. Geneva, Switzerland; 2006. 196p. ISBN: 92-4-154683-2.

4. Maya C, Torner-Morales FJ, Lucario ES, Hernández E, Jiménez B. Viability of six of larval and non-larval helminth eggs for different conditions of temperature, pH and dryness. Water Research 2012;46:4770–4782. doi:10. 1016/j. watres. 2012. 06. 014. ISSN: 0043-1354.
5. Jiménez B, Maya C, Velásquez G, Torner F, Arambula F, Barrios JA, Velasco M. Identification and quantification of pathogenic helminth eggs using a digital image system. Experimental Parasitology 2016;166:164–172. doi:10. 1016/j. exppara. 2016. 04. 016.
6. World Health Organization, editor. Guidelines for the Safe Use of Wastewater, Excreta And Greywater. Vol. 1. Policy and Regulatory Aspects. Geneva, Switzerland; World Health Organization; 2006. 100 p. ISBN:92-4-154682-4.
7. Bogitsh BJ, Carter CE, Oeltmann TN. Blood and tissue nematodes. In: Elsevier (ed.) Human Parasitology. UK: Academic Press; 2013. pp. 329–345. ISBN: 978-0-12-415915-0.
8. Mascarini-Serra L. Prevention of soil-transmitted helminth infection. Journal of Global Infectious Diseases 2011;3(2):175–182. doi:10. 4103/0974-777X. 81696.
9. Vercruysse J, Levecke B, Prichard R. Human soil-transmitted helminths: implications of mass drug administration. Current Opinion on Infectious Diseases 2012;25:703–708. ISSN: 0951-7375.
10. Strunz EC. Water, sanitation, hygiene, and soil-transmitted helminth infection: a systematic review and meta-analysis. PLOS Medicine 2014;11:e1001620. doi:10. 1371/journal. pmed. 1001620.
11. World Health Organization, editor. Helminth Control in School-Age Children: A Guide for Managers of Control Programs. Geneva, Switzerland; World Health Organization; 2011. 75 p. ISBN: 978924154826–7.
12. World Health Organization, editor. Eliminating Soil-Transmitted Helminthiasis as a Public Health Problem in Children: Progress Report 2001–2010 and Strategic Plan 2011–2020. Geneva, Switzerland; World Health Organization; 2012. 79 p. ISBN: 97592 4150312-9.
13. Feachem, RG. ; Bradley, DJ. ; Garelick, H; Mara, D. Sanitation and disease : health aspects of excreta and wastewater management. World Bank studies in water supply and sanitation; no. 3. NY: John Wiley & Sons.
14. Ellis K, Rodrigues P, Gomez C. Parasite ova and cysts in waste stabilization ponds. Water Research 1993;27(9):1455–1460. doi:10. 1016/0043-1354(93)90025-D.
15. Alouini Z, Jemli M. Destruction of helminth eggs by photosensitized porphyrin. Journal Environmental Monitoring 2001;3:548–551. doi:10. 1039/B103471P.
16. Silva de NR, Chan MS, Bundy AP. Morbidity and mortality due to ascariasis: re-estimation and sensitivity analysis of global numbers at risk. Tropical Medicine and International Health 1997;2(6):519–528. ISSN: 13602276.
17. Jiménez B, Maya C, Sánchez E, Romero A, Lira L, Barrios JA. Comparison of the quantity and quality of the microbiological content of sludge in countries with low and high content of pathogens. Water Science and Technology 2002;46(10):17–24. ISSN: 0273-1223.
18. Strauss M, Drescher S, Zurbrügg CH, Montangero A. Co-composting of faecal sludge and municipal organic waste. A Literature and State-of-Knowledge Review. Dübendorf, Switzerland: Swiss Federal Institute of Environmental Science and Technology (EAWAG) and IMWI; 2003.
19. Jimenez B, Austin A, Cloete E, Phasha C. Using Ecosan sludge for crop production. Water Science and Technology 2006;5(54):169–177. ISSN: 0273-1223.
20. Jiménez B, Wang L. Sludge treatment and management. Chap. 10. In: Ujang Z, Henze M (eds.) Municipal Wastewater Management in Developing Countries: Principles and Engineering. London, UK: IWA Publishing; 2006. pp. 237–292. ISBN: 1-84339-030-2.

21. Thomas-Soccol V, Paulino RC, Castro EA. Metodologia para análise parasilógica em lodo de esgoto (Methodology for parasitological analysis of sewage sludge). In: Andreoli, Bonnet (eds.). Manual de métodos para análises microbiológicas e parasitológica em reciclagem agrícola de lodo de esgoto (Handbook of microbial and parasitological methods for agricultural recycling of sewage sludge). Curitiva, Brazil; 2000. 28–41 (Portuguese).
22. McGarry MG, Stainforth J. Compost, Fertilizer and Biogas Production from Human and Farm Wastes in the Peoples' Republic of China. Ontario, Canada: International Development Research Centre (IDRC) Ottawa; 1978. 94 pp. ISSN: 0889361401.
23. Stott R, Jenkins T, Shabana M, May E. A survey of the microbial quality of wastewater in Ismailia, Egypt and the Implications for wastewater reuse. Water Science and Technology 1997;35(11–12):211–217. doi:10. 1016/S0273-1223(97)00261-8.
24. Hall J. Sludge management in developing countries. In: Lowe P, Hudson JA (eds.) Proceedings of the Joint CIWEM, 5th European Biosolids and Organic Residuals Conference Seminar 1, Paper 3. November 2000, Wakefield, UK. Aqua Enviro Consultancy Services; 2000.
25. Sudo R, Aiba S. Advances in water pollution research. In: Jaag O, Baars JK, Pearson EA. (eds.) Proceedings: 2nd International Conference, August 1964, Tokyo, Japan. Oxford: Pergamon Press; 1964. pp. 282–284. doi: 10. 1002/iroh. 19670520415
26. Schwartzbrod J, Stien JL, Bouhoum K, Baleux B. Impact of wastewater treatment on helminth eggs. Water Sciences and Technology 1989;21(3):295–297.
27. Chale-Matsau JRB. Persistence of human pathogens in a crop grown from sewage sludge treated soil. PhD thesis. Faculty of Engineering, University of Pretoria, Pretoria; 2005.
28. Pillay S, Foxon K, Rodda N, Smith M, Buckley C. The use of effluent from an anaerobic baffled reactor (ABR) for irrigation in a peri-urban community. In: Ecosan GTZ (ed.) 3rd International Ecological Sanitation Conference. Durban, South Africa: DFID, EcoSanRes, CSIR; 2005. pp. 445–449.
29. Bradby RM, Hadidy S. Parasitic infestation and the use of untreated sewage for irrigation of vegetables with particular reference to Aleppo, Syria. Public Health Engineer 1981;9: 154–157.
30. Stoll N. This wormy world. Journal of Parasitology 1947;33(1):1–43.
31. Jiménez B, Maya C, Galván M. Helminth ova control in wastewater and sludge for advanced and conventional sanitation. Water Science and Technology 2007;56(5):43–51. doi:10. 2166/wst. 2007. 555.
32. Gaspard P, Wiart J, Schwartzbrod J. Parasitological contamination of urban sludge used for agricultural purposes. Waste Management and Research 1997;14:429–436. doi:10. 1006/wmre. 1996. 0097.
33. Jiménez B, Maya C, Salgado G. The elimination of helminth ova, faecal coliforms, Salmonella and protozoan cysts by various physicochemical processes in wastewater and sludge. Water Science and Technology 2001;43(12):179–182. ISSN: 0273-1223.
34. Pullan RL, Smith JL, Jasrasaria R, Brooker SJ. Global numbers of infection and disease burden of soil transmitted helminth infections in 2010. Parasites and Vectors. 2014;7(1):37. ISSN: 1756-3305. http://researcholine. lshtm. ac. uk/1496142/
35. Brown HW, Belding LD. Parasitología Clínica. Interamericana, Buenos Aires: S. A. ; 1965 (Spanish).
36. Wharton DA. Nematode egg-shells. Parasitology 1980;81:447–463. doi:10. 1017/S003118200005616X.
37. Fairweather I, Threadgold LT. Hymenolepis nana: the fine structure of the embryonic envelopes. Parasitology 1981;82:429–443. doi:10. 1017/S0031182000066968.

38. Lýsek H, Malínský J, Janisch R. Ultrastructure of eggs of Ascaris lumbricoides Linneaeus, 1758 I. Egg-shells. Folia Parasitologica 1985;32:381–384. ISSN: 1803-6465.

39. Quilès F, Balandier JY, Capizzi-Banas S. In situ characterization of a microorganism surface by Raman microspectroscopy: the shell of Ascaris eggs. Analytical and Bioanalytical Chemistry 2006;386:249–255. doi:10. 1007/s00216-006-0638-4.

40. Barret J. Studies on the induction of permeability in Ascaris lumbricoides eggs. Parasitology 1976;73(1):109–121. PMID: 987567.

41. Clarke AJ, Perry RN. The induction of permeability in egg shells of Ascaris suum prior to hatching. International Journal for Parasitology 1988;18(7):987–990. doi:10. 1016/0020-7519(88)90182-8.

42. Vos T, et al. Global, regional, and national incidence, prevalence, and years lived with disability for 301 acute and chronic diseases and injuries in 188 countries, 1990–2013: a systematic analysis for the Global Burden of Disease Study 2013. The Lancet 2015;386(9995):743–800. doi:10. 1016/S0140-6736(15)60692-4.

43. Kassai T, Cordero del Campillo M, Euzeby J, Gaafar S, Hiepe T, Himonas CA. Standardized nomenclature of animal parasitic diseases (SNOAPAD). Veterinarian Parasitology 1988;29:299–326. doi:10. 1016/0304-4017(88)90148-3.

44. World Health Organization, editor. Health Guidelines for the Use of Wastewater in Agriculture and Aquaculture, Technical Report Series No. 778. Geneva, Switzerland; World Health Organization;1989. ISBN: 924120778-7.

45. Asano T, editor. Wastewater Reclamation and Reuse: Water Quality Management Library. Vol. 10. Lancaster, Pennsylvania, USA: Techonomic Publishing Inc. ; 1998. doi:10. 5772/59361.

46. Cotruvo J. Water Reclamation and Groundwater Recharge in the USA Ongoing and Planned Water Reuse Related Project in EU and Mediterranean countries. WHO Expert Consultation on Health Risks in Aquifer Recharge by Reclaimed Water. Budapest; 2001.

47. Dillon P, Toze S, Pavelic P. Australian water quality guidelines and research on subsurface storage of reclaimed water Ongoing and Planned Water Reuse Related Project in EU and Mediterranean Countries. WHO Expert Consultation on Health Risks in Aquifer Recharge by Reclaimed Water. Budapest; 2001.

48. US Environmental Protection Agency. Part 503—Standards for the Use and Disposal of Sewage Sludge. Rules and Regulations. Federal Register 1993;58(32):9248–9415.

49. US Environmental Protection Agency. A Guide to the Biosolids Risk Assessment for the EPA Part 503 Rule. Washington, DC, USA: Environmental Protection Agency; 1995.

50. Tellez A, Morales W, Rivera T, Meyer E, Leiva B, Linder E. Prevalence of intestinal parasites in the human population of León, Nicaragua. Acta Tropica 1997;66:119–125. doi:10. 1016/S0001-706X(97)00037-5.

51. Howard SC, Donnelly CA, Kabatereine NB, Ratard RC, Brooker S. Spatial and intensity-dependent variations in associations between multiple species Helminth infections. Acta Tropica 2002;83:141–149. doi:10. 1016/S0001-706X(02)00093-1.

52. Berhe N, Madhin G, Erko B, Smith T, Gedamu S, Bereded D, Moore R, Habte E, Redda A, Gebre-Michael T, Gundersen SG. Variations in helminth faecal egg counts in Kato-Katz thick smears and their implications in assessing infection status with Schistosoma mansoni. Acta Tropica 2004;92:205–212. doi:10. 1016/jactatropica. 2003. 06. 011.

53. Regli S, Rose JB, Haas CN, Gerba CP. Modeling risk from Giardia and viruses in drinking water. American Water Works Association Journal 1991;83(11):76–84.

54. Rose JB, Haas CN, Regli S. Risk assessment and control of waterborne Giardiasis. American Journal of Public Health 1991;81(6):709–713. doi:10. 2105/AJPH. 81. 6. 709.

55. Haas CN, Rose JB, Gerba CP. Quantitative Microbial Risk Assessment. New York: Wiley; 1999.

56. Crockett CS, Haas CN, Fazil A, Rose JB, Gerba CP. Prevalence of shigellosis in the U. S. : consistency with dose-response information. International Journal of Food Microbiology 1996;30(1–2):87–100.

57. Fazil AM. A Quantitative Risk Assessment Model for Salmonella. M. S. Thesis, Drexel University, Philadelphia, PA, USA; 1996.

58. Medema GJ, Teunis PF, Havelaar AH, Haas CN. Assessment of the dose-response relationship of Campylobacter jejuni. International Journal of Food Microbiology 1996;30(1–2):101–111. doi:10. 1016/0168-1605(96)00994-4.

59. Teunis PF, Nagelkerke NJ, Haas CN. Dose response models for infectious gastroenteritis. Risk Analysis 1999;19(6):1251–1260.

60. Navarro I, Jimenez B, Cifuentes E, Lucario S. Application of helminth ova infection dose curve to estimate the risks associated with biosolid application on soil. Journal of Water and Health 2009;7(1):31–44. doi:10. 2166/wh. 2009. 113.

61. Haas CN. Microbial dose response modeling: past, present & future. Environmental Science and Technology 2014;49(3):1245–1259. doi:10. 1021/es504422q.

62. Navarro I, Jiménez B. Evaluation of the WHO helminth eggs criteria using a QMRA approach for the safe reuse of wastewater and sludge in developing countries. Water Science and Technology 2011;63(7):1499–1505. doi:10. 2166/wst. 2011. 394. ISSN: 0273-1223. ISSN: 0273-1223.

63. Mara D, Hamilton AJ, Sleigh A, Karavarsamis N. Tools for risk analysis: updating the 2006 WHO guidelines. In: Dreschsel P, Scott CA, Raschild-Sally L, Redwood M, Bahri A (eds.) Wastewater Irrigation and Health: Assessing and Mitigating Risks in Low-Income Countries. London: Earthscan; 2010. pp. 89–100.

64. Mara D, Sleigh A. Estimation of norovirus and Ascaris infection risks to urban farmers in developing countries using wastewater for crop irrigation. Journal of Water and Health 2010;8(3):572–576.

65. Ayres RM, Stott R, Mara DD, Lee DL. Wastewater reuse in agriculture and the risk of intestinal nematode infection. Parasitologica Today 1992;8(1):32–35. doi:10. 1016/0169-4758(92)90309-P.

66. Ensink JHJ, van der Hoek W. Implementation of the WHO guidelines for the safe use of wastewater in Pakistan: balancing risks and benefits. Journal of Water Health 2009;7(3):464–468.

67. Williams DL, Pepper IL, Gerba CP. Survival of Ascaris ova in desert soils: a risk assessment. Journal of Residuals Science and Technology 2012;9(4):151–157. doi:10. 2166/wh. 2009. 061.

68. Seidu R, Sjølander I, Abubakari A, Amoah D, Larbi JA, Stenström TA. Modeling the die-off of E. coli and Ascaris in wastewater irrigated vegetables: implications for microbial health risk reduction associated with irrigation cessation. Water Science and Technology 2013;68(5):1013–1021. doi:10. 2166/wst. 2013. 335.

69. Barker SF, Amoah P, Drechsel P. A probabilistic model of gastroenteritis risks associated with consumption of street food salads in Kumasi, Ghana: Evaluation of methods to estimate pathogen dose from water, produce or food quality. Science of the Total Environment 2014;487(1):130–142. doi:10. 1016/j. scitotenv. 2014. 03. 108.

70. Kundu A, Poma HR, Jenkins MW, Rajal VB, Wuertz S. QMRA of intestinal nematode infection via multimedia exposure pathways. In: Proceedings 7th International Congress on

Environmental Modelling and Software: Bold Visions for Environmental Modeling, IEMSs 2014; vol. 3. pp. 1482–1491.

71. Jiménez B, Barrios JA, Maya C. Class B biosolids production from wastewater sludge with high pathogenic content generated in an advanced primary treatment. Water Science and Technology 2000;42(9):103–110. ISSN: 0273-1223.

72. Mara D. Domestic Wastewater Treatment in Developing Countries. London: Earth Scan; 2003.

73. Jiménez B. Helminth ova removal from wastewater for agriculture and aquaculture reuse. Water Science and Technology 2007;55(1–2):485–493. ISSN: 0273-1223.

74. Chavez A, Jimenez B, Maya C. Particle size distribution as a useful tool for microbial detection, Water Science and Technology 2004;50(2):179–186. ISSN: 0273-1223.

75. Landa H, Capella A, Jiménez B. Particle size distribution in an effluent from an advanced primary treatment and its removal during filtration. Water Science and Technology 1997;36(4):159–165. doi:10. 1016/S0273-1223(97)00435-6.

76. Jimenez B, Chavez A. Low cost technology for reliable use of Mexico city's wastewater for agricultural irrigation. Environmental Technology 2002;9(1–2):95–108. doi:10. 1016/j. resconrec. 2009. 08. 002.

77. Brix H. Chapter 2: wastewater treatment in constructed wetlands: system design, removal process and treatment performance. In: Moshiri G (eds.) Constructed Wetlands for Water Quality Improvement. USA: CRC Press; 1993. pp. 9–22.

78. Olguin EJ, Hernandez E. Use of aquatic plants for recovery of nutrients and heavy metals from wastewater. Inter-America program for environmental technology cooperation in the key industry sector. Roundtable on Municipal Water 15–17 Mars 1998, Vancouver Canada. http:/ www. idrc. ca/industry/canada_el4html.

79. Rivera F, Warren A, Curds CR, Robles E, Gutierrez A, Gallegos E, Calderon A. The application on the root zone method for the treatment and reuse of high-strength abattoir waste in Mexico. Water Science and Technology 1997;35(5):271–278.

80. Stott R, Jenkins T, Baghat M, Shalaby I. Capacity of constructed wetlands to remove parasite eggs from wastewater in Egypt. Water Science and Technology 1999;40(3):117–123. PII: SO273-1223(99)00454-0.

81. Krasnonos LI. Many-years viability of Ascaris eggs (Ascaris lumbricoides) in soil of Samarkand. Medicine and Parasitology 1978;47:103–106. (Abstract in: Trop. Dis. Bull. 1978;75(10):991–992).

82. Popat SC, Yates MV, Deshusses MA. Kinetics of inactivation of indicator pathogens during thermophilic anaerobic digestion. Water Research 2010;44:5965–5972. doi:10. 1016/j. watres. 2010. 07. 045.

83. Kato S, Fogarty E, Bowman DD. Effect of aerobic and anaerobic digestion on the viability of Cryptosporidium parvum oocysts and Ascaris suum eggs. International Journal Environmental Health Research 2003;13:169–179. doi:10. 1080/096031203100 0098071.

84. Gantzer C, Gaspard P, Galvez L, Huyard A, Dumouthier N, Schwartzbrod J. Monitoring of bacterial and parasitological contamination during various treatment of sludge. Water Research 2001;35 3763–3770. doi:10. 1016/S0043-1354(01)00105-1. 12230157

85. Capizzi-Banas S, Schwartzbrod J. Irradiation of Ascaris ova in sludge using an electron beam accelerator. Water Research 2001;135:2256–2260. doi:10. 1016/S0043-1354(00) 00503-0.

86. Johnson PW, Dixon R, Ross AD. An in-vitro test for assessing the viability of Ascaris suum eggs exposed to various sewage treatment processes. International Journal Parasitology 1998;28:627–633.

87. Méndez JM, Jiménez BE, Barrios JA. Improved alkaline stabilization of municipal wastewater sludge. Water Science and Technology 2002;46(10):139–146. ISSN: 0273–1223.

88. Ghiglietti R, Gench C, Mateo L, Calcaterra E, Colombi A. Survival of Ascaris suum in amonia treated wasterwater sludge. Bioresource Technology 1998;59:195–198.

89. Barrios J, Jiménez B, Maya C. Treatment of sludge with peracetic acid to reduce the microbial content. Journal of Residuals Science and Technology 2004;1(1):69–74. ISSN: 1544-8053.

90. Aguilar P, Jiménez B, Maya C, Orta T, Luna V. Disinfection of sludge with high pathogenic content using silver and other compounds. Water Science and Technology 2006;54(5):179–187. doi:10. 2166/wst. 2006. 561. ISSN: 0273-1223.

91. Bowman DD, Little MD, Reimers RS. Precision and accuracy of an assay for detecting Ascaris eggs in various biosolid matrices. Water Research 2003;37:2063–2072. doi:10. 1016/S0043-1354(02)00597-3.

92. Gyawali P, Ahmed W, Jagals P, Sidhu JPS, Toze S. Comparison of concentration methods for rapid detection of hookworm ova in wastewater matrices using quantitative PCR. Experimental Parasitology 2015;159:160–167. doi:10. 1016/j. exppara. 2015. 09. 002.

93. Gyawali P, Sidhu JPS, Ahmed W, Jagals P, Toze S. Rapid concentration and sensitive detection of hookworm ova from wastewater matrices using a real-time PCR method. Experimental Parasitology 2015;159:5–12. doi:10. 1016/j. exppara. 2015. 08. 009.

94. Raynal M, Villegas EN, Nelson KL. Enumeration of viable and non-viable larvated Ascaris eggs with quantitative PCR. Journal of Water and Health 2012;10:594–604. doi:10. 2166/wh. 2012. 101.

95. Pecson BM, Barrios JA, Johnson DR, Nelson KL. A real-time PCR method for quantifying viable Ascaris eggs using the first internally transcribed spacer region of ribosomal DNA. Applied and Environmental Microbiology 2006;72:7864–7872. doi:10. 1128/AEM. 01983-06.

8 Fungi and Oomycetes–Allies in Eliminating Environmental Pathogens

Iasmina Luca

Faculty of Veterinary Medicine, Banat's University of Agricultural Sciences and Veterinary Medicine "King Michael I of Romania", Timişoara, Romania

ABSTRACT

Fungi and oomycetes are the subjects of numerous current research studies. These are natural agents that can control parasitic populations, and arthropod populations with a role in the transmission of various diseases but can also eliminate various pollutants that are found in the external environment. Therefore, their conservation and exploitation are a global necessity, due to the benefits they confer on the quality of life of animals, but also of humans. Science must be aimed at finding a balance between the different constituents of the ecosystem and establishing coexistence relationships that are beneficial to all. Thus, research should be directed at investigating the potential actions of fungi and oomycetes against the various agents with which they coexist naturally in the external environment. This chapter provides information regarding the mechanism of action of these natural constituents and updates information on the species of fungi and oomycetes that have been studied so far. Thus, readers can have a base in this field and can further exploit what they have discovered to continue to improve the welfare of animals, addressing an ecological and healthy vision.

Keywords: *Ecological Action, Fungi, Oomycetes, Cleaning*

INTRODUCTION

Plants and animals coexist in a certain balance within the ecosystem, together with fungi, oomycetes, bacteria, viruses, and parasites.

Currently, about 75.000 species of fungi have been described, many of which are still unclassified [1]. Also, in the category of fungi, oomycetes have been included in the past. Detailed studies have highlighted their morphological and functional differences, the oomycetes being now included in the phylum *Oomycota* [2]. Both fungi and oomycetes are found in various symbiotic relationships and can be saprophytes or parasites [3]. These relationships can be exploited in creating ideal habitats for animals.

Many bacteria, viruses, and single-celled parasites can be carried by arthropods (insects, mites) or other vectors (amoebas) and can be sources of infection, causing many diseases in animals. Fungi and oomycetes can use different mechanisms by which they can eliminate these vectors. They can also be involved in the detoxification of the environment from numerous pollutants and can be considered important agents in the biocontrol of some animal parasites. In removing amoebae, fungi use hyphae that function as "sticky extensions" that capture "prey" or can parasitize internally, causing amoebae death by sporulation [4]. Sprayed in the form of a solution on the body of insects, more precisely on the body of mosquitoes, the fungi attach themselves through the conidia to their cuticle. Then begins the germination and dispersal of spores in the hemocoel. At this level, the evolutionary cycle of fungi continues with the multiplication of hyphae, which gradually kill the host by colonizing the trachea and producing toxins, after which the fungi leave their body [5, 6]. In eliminating the larval forms of some insects, the fungi also through the conidia block the siphon region and thus determine the death by asphyxiation of the hosts [6]. The same mechanisms have been reported in the elimination of evolutionary stages of ticks. An important role in the fixation and adhesion of conidia at the cuticular level is played by hydrophobins and adhesins, as proteins, but also lipase and esterase, as enzymes [7, 8, 9].

Certain pollutants, such as pesticides, can be battered by various fungi through numerous chemical processes (deoxygenation, hydroxylation, esterification, or dehydrogenation) [10]. Certain heavy metals in the environment can be inactivated by organic acids and siderophores (metabolites) of fungi [11]. Enzymes also play an important role in bioremediation, among them can be mentioned: cellulase, lipase, protease, peroxidase, amylase, chitinase, catalase, laccase, xylanase, etc. [12].

In the management of parasitic populations, especially nematode populations found in animals, fungi use complex mechanisms to eliminate these pathogens. The first stage is the recognition between the fungus and the nematode. Fungi adhere to the body of nematodes through lecithin that binds to carbohydrate receptors located in the cuticle of the parasite [13, 14]. Adhesion is facilitated by fungal spores and protein fibrils that form nematode-trapping traps. The fibrils are arranged in a network or perpendicular to the external surface of the nematodes, after which they easily penetrate their body. The penetration step involves the release of hydrolytic enzymes and the application of progressive pressure on the parasite's cuticle [15]. After complete penetration of the cuticle, the formation and multiplication of hyphae begin. Gradually the fungi digest the nematodes internally. Nutrients are captured in the hyphae in lipid droplets or are fixed and carried by lecithin [16]. The same steps are observed in the case of oomycetes. They adhere to the surface of parasite eggs or larvae, through hyphae, after which they penetrate the egg wall or larval cuticle, releasing various enzymes (various exoglycosidases, kinases, endo-β-1,3-glucanases, and cellulases). Gradually, they digest and destroy the internal contents through hyphae and zoospores that form continuously [17].

Another method of removing nematodes is using adhesive nets, hyphae, or knobs forming constricting rings together. Through the movements and body heat, the nematodes trigger the complete tightening of the rings around them and the exteriorization of a penetrating tube where the internal multiplication of the hyphae begins [18]. Certain fungi can spread to the surface of the body of nematodes or larvae, including the wall of nematode eggs. Gradually the sporulation takes place internally, having an ovicidal, larvicidal, or adulticidal effect [19, 20]. An ovicidal effect can be exerted by fungi also through hyphae, more precisely through oppressors, secondary metabolites, and the toxins they contain [19]. The same toxins can cause paralysis of adult nematodes [19].

The following subchapters contain information related to fungal species, but also oomycetes that can be used successfully in the elimination of various animal pathogens.

ELIMINATION OF VECTORS INVOLVED IN THE TRANSMISSION OF VARIOUS DISEASES TO ANIMALS

Amoebae

Amoebae are protozoa that can live freely in very different environments or can be parasitic, surviving in different hosts. Free amoebae are present in the external environment in soil, water, and air, but are also used in various medical fields, such as dialysis centers and dentistry [21]. Parasitic amoebae (*Entamoeba* spp. and *Balantidium* spp.) are found in animals' intestines [22].

In veterinary medicine, only four classes of free amoebae have pathogenic potential: *Acanthamoeba*, *Naegleria*, *Balamuthia,* and *Sappinia* [23]. Each class determines certain clinical manifestations of amoebiasis. *Acanthamoeba* enters the animal body by respiration or skin and through the circulation reaches the central nervous system, causing amoebic granulomatous encephalitis (GAE) [21, 24, 25]. The evolution of the disease is slow, and long-lasting [26]. Certain species of the genus *Balamuthia* (*Balamuthia mandrillaris*) cause similar lesions, respectively: granulomatous *Balamuthia encephalitis* (BAE) [27]. The route of infection is predominantly cutaneous [28]. *Sappiniae* amoebic encephalitis (SAE) is caused by two species, *Sappinia diploidea* and *Sappinia pedata* [29]. From the *Naegleria* class, *Naegleria fowleri* is important. It is found in water and can be accidentally inhaled by animals while swimming [30]. The location is also in the brain, but the migration route is a nerve (olfactory nerve pathway) [18]. The characteristic lesion caused by this class of amoebas is meningoencephalitis, which develops with diffuse cerebral edema [30].

An important role in the circulation of certain pathogens has the amoebas of the *Acanthamoeba* class. Among the pathogens are bacteria (*Listeria monocytogenes*, *Pseudomonas aeruginosa*, *Rickettsia*-like, *Salmonella enterica*, *S. thyphimurium*, *Yersinia enterocolitica*, *Campylobacter jejuni*, *M. avium*, *M. bovis*, *Bacillus anthracis*, *Escherichia coli* O157, *Helicobacter pylori*, *Chlamydia pneumoniae*, *Coxiella burnetii*, *Francisella tularensis*) [31, 32, 33, 34, 35, 36, 37, 38, 39, 40, 41, 42], fungi (*Cryptosporidium parvum*, *Cryptococcus neoformans*) [43, 44, 45] and a limited number of viruses (*Adenoviridae*) [46].

Numerous researchers aim to use amoebophagous fungi in the elimination of vectors and in the prevention of many diseases that can be transmitted to animals. They can act as parasites or predators. Among the fungi with the role of parasites, which invade and multiply inside the amoebae, are found *C. neoformans*, *Blastomyces dermatitidis*, *Sporothrix schenckii*, *Histoplasma capsulatum*, *Aspergillus* spp., *Penicillium* spp. and *Fusarium* spp. [23, 43, 47, 48, 49, 50]. There are species of fungi that multiply in the nucleus (*Nucleophaga* sp.) [51] or others that multiply in the cytoplasm of amoebas (*Sphaerita*, *Pseudosphaerita*) [4]. Species such as *Paramicrosporidium* can cause degeneration and changes in the nuclear and plasma membranes of amoebae [52, 53]. Amoeba trophozoites can be parasitized by *Cochlonema* species [54, 55, 56, 57] or can be captured by hyphae of fungi, such as *Stylopage* [58] and *Acaulopage* [59, 60]. Mycotoxins produced by fungi also have a role in the degeneration and decomposition of trophozoite or cyst forms of amoebae [61]. Thus, ameobophagous fungi can be used in the elimination of pathogens carried by amoebae, by applying and cultivating them in soils and waters.

Insects

Globally, insects can be found in many habitats [62]. They have an important role in all terrestrial ecosystems, intervening in soil fertilization by circulating nutrients and seeds, but also in plant pollination. Thus, they are essential for maintaining optimal qualities in the development of agriculture [63]. Another role with a major impact on the quality of life of animals is the fact that insects are a nutritional basis for them [64]. The larval and adult stages are the most frequently consumed by animals.

In veterinary medicine, the role of insects is very important. Like amoebae, they can transmit various diseases from one animal to another. *Diptera*, insects, flies, and mosquitoes have a major impact on animal health. Culicoids can carry viruses such as BTV (bluetongue virus), AHSV (African horse sickness virus), EHDV (Epizootic hemorrhagic disease virus), and Akabane virus [65]. Newcastle disease [66], certain bacterial agents (*E. coli*, *Salmonella*, *Shigella* spp., *S. aureus*, *Campylobacter*) and parasites (*E. vermicularis*, *S. stercoralis*, *T. canis*, *Trichomonas*, *Diphyllobothrium*, *Taenia*, *Dipylidium*, *Entamoeba histolytica*, *Giardia lamblia*) can be mechanically carried by flies, especially the domestic fly [67, 68, 69]. Mosquitoes, in turn, can carry many pathogens, such as West Nile virus, Rift Valley fever virus, Wesselsbron virus, Middelburg virus, Israel Turkey encephalitis virus, Usutu virus, Batai virus, Sindbis virus, Japanese encephalitis virus, St. Louis encephalitis virus, Eastern equine encephalitis virus, Western equine encephalitis virus, Venezuelan equine encephalitis virus, Tembusu virus, *Wuchereria bancrofti*, *Plasmodium relictum* (avian malaria), *T. corvi* (avian trypanosomiasis), *Chandlerella quiscali* (avian filarial worms), *Dirofilaria repens* and *Dirofilaria immitis* [70, 71, 72, 73, 74, 75, 76, 77, 78, 79].

The use of pyrethroids as insecticides is the most widely used method of control. However, recent research aims to apply fungi, in various forms, as an ecological method of controlling insect populations [80]. Ansari et al. [81] used the conidia of several species of fungi against culicid adults. The species chosen were *Metarhizium anisopliae* V275, *Isaria fumosorosea* PFR 97, *Isaria fumosorosea* CLO 55, *Beauveria bassiana* BG and *Lecanicillium longisporum*. Conidia were applied in the form of dry conidia and wet conidia, the first variant being the most effective, causing the death of all individuals after 5 days. The most virulent strain of the fungus was *Metarhizium anisopliae* V275 [81]. The same fungus was effective against larval forms of culicids, houseflies, horn flies, and mosquitoes [82, 83, 84, 85, 86]. Other authors have reported a larvicidal potential of *Culicinomyces clavisporus* against culicids [87]. Fly larvae, mosquitoes, and culicids have also been eliminated by *Beauveria bassiana*, with many studies reporting this [83, 84, 85, 86]. This fungus has led to the death of culicid larvae of the species *Culex tarsalis*, *Culex pipiens*, *Anopheles albimanus*, *Ochlerotatus sierrensis*, *Ochlerotatus nigromaculis*, and *Aedes aegypti* [88]. Ong'wen et al. [89] tested the simultaneous action of dragonfly nymphs *Pantala favescens* and *B. bassiana* spores against *Anopheles gambiae* mosquitoes. They observed that the larvae exposed to the action of nymphs (predatory role) were much more vulnerable, in the adult stage, to the action of *B. bassiana* spores [89]. Ishii et al. [90] demonstrated the adulticidal action of *B. bassiana* conidia against *An. stephensi* mosquitoes. Seven days after exposure, the insect's body was completely invaded by hyphae [90]. Oomycetes *Lagenidium giganteum*, *Aphanomyces laevis*, *Couchia* spp., *Crypticola* spp., *Leptolegnia caudata* and *Pythium* spp. can kill mosquito larvae through mycelium and oospores [91, 92].

Ticks

Ticks are parasitic mites, which require, for the complete development and completion of the biological cycle, a blood-feed on the vertebrates involved. The tick population is extremely numerous in the warm season, being an important agent for transmitting contagious diseases to animals, but also humans. They can carry bacteria (*Borrelia*, *Ehrlichia*, *Anaplasma*, *Coxiella*, *Brucella*, *Francisella tulacobacteria*, *Rickettsia* spp.) [93, 94, 95], piroplasmas (*Babesia*, *Theileria*), but also protozoa (*Cytauxzoon*, *Hepatozoon*) [76].

Biological control of ticks can be achieved by using entomopathogenic fungi. Currently, many fungi are known with a high potential to eliminate various evolutionary forms of ticks. Among them are: *Beauveria bassiana*, *Beauveria brognardi*, *Metarhizium anisopliae*, *Metarhizium robertsii*, *Metarhizium brunneum*, *Fusarium* sp., *Aspergillus fumigatus*, *Aspergillus ochraceus*, *Aspergillus flavus*, *Aspergillus niger*, *Aspergillus parasiticus*, *Isaria fumosorosea*, *Scopulariopsis brevicaulis*, *Paecilomyces lilacinus*, *Paecilomyces farinosus*, *Paecilomyces fumosoroseus*, *Penicillium insectivorum*, *Conidiobolus coronatus*, *Trichothecium roseum*, *Verticillium aranearum*, *Verticillium lecanii*, *Isaria fumosorosea*, *Isaria farinose*, *Curvularia lunata*, *Rhizopus thailandensis*, and *Rhizopus arrhizus* [96, 97, 98, 99, 100, 101, 102, 103, 104, 105, 106, 107, 108, 109, 110, 111, 112, 113, 114].

Depending on the evolutionary stage, the action of certain fungi is different. Eggs are the most sensitive and nymphs are the most resistant [115, 116]. A high ovicidal action against *Boophilus microplus* eggs were observed in *Verticillium lecanii* (strains LBV-2 and LBV-1) and lower in *Beauveria bassiana* [117]. A decrease in hatching capacity and indirectly the number of larvae formed have been reported by some authors regarding the action of *I. fumosorosea* [112]. The same effect was indicated for *Isaria farinosa* and *Purpureocillium lilacinum* [112]. *Metarhizium anisopliae* Ma-z4 has larvicidal action on the same species of ticks mentioned above [118]. In the case of adult females of *B. microplus*, the isolates E9 and AM of *Metarhizium anisopliae*, applied to the body of animals through spores in a concentration of 7.5×10^8 conidia/ml, determined high mortality and negatively influenced the number of eggs laid by females [119]. A pronounced acaricidal effect on adult females of *Dermanyssus gallinae* was noted in *B. bassiana* CD1123 conidia, applied at a concentration of 10^9/ml [120]. An ovicidal, larvicidal, and adulticidal effect against *Argas reflexus* ticks has been reported in V245, 685, and 715C of *Metarhizium anisopliae*, the first strain being the most pathogenic [121]. High mortality, observed starting one week after application, was also recorded in females of *Rhipicephalus annulatus* exposed to the action of *Metarhizium anisopliae* [122].

Varroa destructor mites are important in veterinary medicine as a consequence of the devastating effects induced in bee populations. Honey is an intense natural product used in various diseases in animals. It helps to heal wounds [123, 124], to treat gastric ulcers, and can be used as an adjunct in the treatment of diabetes, certain bacterial or parasitic infections, and in stopping the growth of tumors [125]. So, protecting bees is undoubtedly fundamental. The scientific research has brought favorable results regarding the use of the following fungi against *V. destructor* mites: *Beauveria bassiana*, *Hirsutella* spp., *Metarhizium* spp., *Paecilomyces* spp., *Tolypocladium* spp., *Verticillium lecanii*, *Clonostachys rosea* and *Lecanicillium lecanii* [126, 127, 128, 129, 130, 131, 132, 133].

ENVIRONMENTAL DETOXIFICATION

Currently, our planet is going through continuous degradation due to the numerous pollutants accumulated in soils, waters, and air. Many of them are difficult to decompose. The current trend in research concerns the concept of bioremediation. It refers to the use of certain microbes in various habitats to metabolize various pollutants [134, 135]. Fungi have been intensively studied, their potential to cleanse the planet being recognized by many researchers. Detoxified soils are more fertile, ensuring rapid growth of plants, their nutritional qualities being better preserved. Indirectly, fungi provide animals with adequate food. The same is true of detoxifying water and air: it improves the quality of life of animals.

Heavy Metals in the Soil

Animals exposed for a long time to the action of heavy metals have developed developmental problems, spermatogenesis, neurological, renal, and liver problems [136]. Their carcinogenic potential has also been reported [137].

The action of fungi on heavy metals in the soil (Pb, Cd, Cu, Zn, Cr, Ni, Ag) is mediated by external temperature, but also by pH, the whole detoxification process being explained by the phenomena of bioabsorption, bioconcentration, and biotransformation [138]. Among the effective fungi are *Beauveria bassiana*, *Aspergillus* sp., *Fusarium* sp., *Penicillium chrysogenum*, *Rhizopus* sp., and *Absidia* [139, 140, 141, 142, 143].

Pesticides in Wastewater

Wastewater is subject to filtration and treatment, as it can be an important source of pesticides, with harmful effects on the environment and animals. Currently, certain fungi capable of eliminating these pollutants have been identified. Hultberg and Bodin [144] used experimentally a combination of *Chlorella vulgaris* (algae) and *Aspergillus niger* and observed a significant reduction in the concentration of pesticides present in water. Piazides based on triazines, dicarboximides, and organophosphates can be successfully degraded by *Verticillium* sp. (H5) and *Metacordyceps* sp. (H12) [145].

Certain residual insecticides, such as endosulfan, can be deteriorated by *Penicillium chrysogenum*, *Bacillus subtilis*, *Aspergillus terreus*, *Aspergillus flavus*, *Aspergillus niger*, *Fusarium ventricosum,* and *Cladosporium oxysporum* [146, 147, 148]. Mohammed and Badawy [149] indicate the use of *A. terreus* YESM3 in the elimination of the insecticide imidacloprid.

Various Pollutants from Soil, Water, and Air

Xenobiotic compounds are chemicals that enter the animal body in numerous ways (digestive, respiratory, parenteral) and are various. Reproductive problems (infertility, abortion) have been reported in animals following exposure [150]. Many plant constituents, various pesticides, medicinal products, feed additives, or industrial chemicals, are considered xenobiotics [151]. They have been successfully degraded by species of white-rot fungi (*Pleurotus* spp., *Agaricus bisporus*, *Bjerkandera adusta*, *Phanerochaete chrysosporium*, *Irpex lacteus*, *Lentinula edodes*, *Trametes versicolor*) [152].

Polycyclic aromatic hydrocarbons are found in the form of aerosol particles and can enter the body through the respiratory tract. Prolonged exposure to these constituents has devastating effects on the body. They can adversely affect the endocrine, reproductive, immune, and nervous systems. It also has a carcinogenic and teratogenic action [153]. *Polyporus* sp. S133, *Hypocrea,* and *Fusarium* can decompose polycyclic aromatic hydrocarbons [10]. Recent studies show that the *Pythium aphanidermatum* oomycete intensifies the action of *Mycobacterium gilvum* VM552 and *Pseudomonas putida* G7 against the pollutants mentioned [154].

BIOCONTROL OF ANIMAL PARASITOSIS

Parasites are pathogens that can survive in the body of animals for long periods, significantly affecting their quality of life. Depending on the class they belong to (Protozoa, Trematodes, Cestodes, Nematodes), they can be diagnosed in different age categories of the hosts [155]. There are many ways to infest animals, with a major impact on the digestive tract. In this way, the hosts can ingest from the external environment eggs or larvae of parasites. Adult forms usually survive in various animal organs. In stopping the evolutionary cycle of parasites, the veterinarian must take several preventive measures. These are undoubtedly necessary, due to the zoonotic potential of certain parasites. To eliminate and kill the adult forms, but also certain larval stages of the parasites, it is well known that various medicinal substances with the antiparasitic role are used. Of the four parasitic classes, nematodes are the most developed, and the main classes of drugs used against them are benzimidazoles, nicotinic receptor agonists, and macrocyclic lactones (avermectins, milbemycins) [156]. Cestodes are sensitive to isoquinolines (praziquantel) and trematodes to thiabendazole (benzimidazole) [157]. We mention only the helminths because they are pentiful in the animal population and the intermediate evolutionary forms resist the most in the external environment. One aspect that must be taken into account when administering the anthelmintics mentioned above is the one related to their use in farm animals. The possibility of eliminating them through milk (ruminants) must be known and indirectly, their remanence in certain secondary products must be mentioned. Macrocyclic lactones also have a long residue in the body of animals [158]. Analyzing this desideratum we can consider the elimination and the complete degradation of parasitic elements from the external environment as the main stage in stopping the biological cycle of parasites. This stage was a basis for current research in the field of biomedical sciences. Disinfectants have been tested and analyzed in numerous studies. Among those discovered so far as having a potential effect on the intermediate elements of nematodes, are those based on alcohols (ethanol, propanol), pentapotassium, and quaternary ammonium compounds [159, 160]. Alcohol-based disinfectants and more can have a corrosive effect if applied to different surfaces and instruments. Also, not enough details are known about the effect they can have on the skin of animals. Here we refer to those kept in paddocks or cages. Considering these aspects, the current research investigates the application of some fungi or oomycetes in the control of the evolutionary cycle of parasites, being an ecological and environmentally friendly method.

Ruminants are frequently parasitized with trichostrongyls. Of these, *Haemonchus* sp. is very important due to the severe anemias, but also to the elaborate clinical symptoms that it can give. Many studies have reported the nematicidal action of some *Pleurotus* species against larval forms (L1, L3, L4), but also of adult *Haemonchus* sp. [161]. This action is due to chemical compounds contained in hyphae (fatty acids, alkaloids, quinones, peptides, polyphenols, and terpenoids) [162]. Vieira et al. [163] associated two fungi (*Pochonia chlamydosporia* VC4 isolate and *Arthrobotrys cladodes* var. macroides CG719 isolate) against the larvae of *Haemonchus* sp. but also of *Cooperia* sp. and *Oesophagostomum* sp. The results were promising, the two fungi potentiating each other's action [163]. Besides the larvicidal action, *P. chlamydosporia* also has an ovicidal action against some helminth eggs [164]. Other researchers have observed that *A. cladodes* used alone against the larvae of *Haemonchus* sp. resulted in high mortality, between 68.7% and 81.73% [165, 166, 167]. Silva et al. [168] do not recommend the associations between the following fungi, in combating the larval forms of *Haemonchus* sp.: *Duddingtonia flagrans*, *Clonostachys rosea*, *Arthrobotrys musiformis,* and *Trichoderma esau*. Other authors propose the use of the following fungi, frequently isolated from the external environment, in the control of gastrointestinal helminthiases of small ruminants: *Arthrobotrys oligospora*, *Candelabrella musiformis*, *Arundo conoides*, *Andropogon dactyloides*, *Trichoderma*, *Beauveria*, *Clonostachys* and *Lecanicillium* [169]. Cai et al. [170] investigated the action of two species of *Arthrobotrys* (*Arthrobotrys musiformis* and *Arthrobotrys robusta*) against the larval forms of trichostrongyls from sheep and goats. The percentages obtained were remarkable, between 97.71% and 99.98% [170]. Similar results regarding the larvicidal action of *Arthrobotrys musiformis* (90.4%) were reported by Silva et al. [171] and much lower percentages of 50% were obtained by Acevedo-Ramírez et al. [172]. The same authors observed a reduction in the number of *Haemonchus* sp. larvae, over 60% in the case of *Trichoderma esau* and *Clonostachys rosea* and 85.7% in the case of *Duddingtonia flagrans* [171]. A larval reduction of over 90% was identified by Chandrawathani et al. after administering *in vivo* to small ruminants *D. flagrans* at a dose of 1×10^6 spores/animal/day for 6 days [173].

Other researchers have investigated the action of fungi (*Arthrobotrys* sp. E1; *A. cladodes* CG719; *A. conoides* I40; *A. musiformis* A1, A2, A3; *A. oligospora* C1, C2; *A. robusta* B1, I31; *Duddingtonia flagrans* CG722, CG768; *Monacrosporium appendiculatum* CGI; *Methanocorpusculum sinense* SF53, SF139; *M. thaumasium* NF34A; *Nematoctonus robustus* D1) on infesting larvae of *Strongyloides papillosus* isolated from cattle. The results were satisfactory, causing a larval reduction between 65.4 and 100% [174]. *D. flagrans* can destroy *Strongyloides* larvae in 2 weeks, and *V. chlamidosporium* (PTCC 5179) in 3 weeks, as reported by Zarrin et al. [175]. The same authors indicate the use of *F. solani* (PTCC 5284) and *T. harzianum* (IBRC-M 30059) in the control of strongyloidiasis in domestic animals [175].

In horses, Araujo et al. [176] investigated the larvicidal action of 3 fungi (*Duddingtonia flagrans* AC001, *Monacrosporium thaumasium* NF34, *Arthrobotrys robusta* I-31) against *Strongyloides westeri*. The results showed a reduction in the larval population between 67.9% and 80.4% [176]. Also in horses, effective against the larvae of *Strongylus equinus*, it is *Arthrobotrys oligospora* [177]. *P. chlamydosporia* is a fungus used in numerous researches against several species of parasites, against which it has shown significant negative effects. Among the species of parasites that have proved sensitive to its action, are found: *Ascaridia galli* [178, 179], *Heterakis gallinarum* [178, 179], *Oxyuris equi* [180], *Ascaris suum* [181], and *Toxocara canis* [182].

A satisfactory larvicidal potential against the gastrointestinal nematode *Ancylostoma caninum*, found in canids, had the fungus *Arthrobotrys oligospora* [177] and the oomycete *Pythium oligandrum* [183]. The same oomycete has an ovicidal action against *Toxocara canis* and *Toxocara cati* eggs, found in dogs and cats [17]. Other authors recommend the use of *Paecilomyces lilacinus*, *Trichoderma virens,* and *Fusarium pallidoroseum* in the biocontrol of ascariasis in dogs [184, 185, 186].

Biocontrol in animal trematodes is still at the beginning of the research, until now the ovicidal effect of *Paecilomyces lilacinus* and *P. variety* against *Fasciola gigantica* [187], but also *P. chlamydosporia* against *Fasciola hepatica* eggs [188] are known.

CONCLUSIONS

Fungi and oomycetes are important agents in the control of animal diseases, which can seriously alter their health. Through the actions they present (insecticide, amoebicide, antiparasitic - ovicidal, larvicidal, nematicidal, and anti-pollution) according to those deduced from the scientific literature, they are key elements in ensuring the welfare of animals and improving their quality of life.

REFERENCES

1. Volk TJ. Fungi. In: Levin SA, editor. Encyclopedia of Biodiversity. Second ed. Cambridge, Massachusetts: Academic Press; 2013. pp. 624-640. DOI: 10. 1016/B978-0-12-384719-5. 00062-9
2. Barr DJS. Evolution and kingdoms of organisms from the perspective of a mycologist. Mycologia. 1992;84:1-11
3. Phillips AJ, Anderson VL, Robertson EJ, Secombes CJ, van West P. New insights into animal pathogenic oomycetes. Trends in Microbiology. 2007;16:13-19. DOI: 10. 1016/j. tim. 2007. 10. 013
4. Sparrow FK. Aquatic Phycomycetes Exclusive of the Saprolegniaceae and Pythium. Ann Arbor: University of Michigan Press; 1943
5. Roberts DW. Toxins of entomopathogenic fungi. In: Burges HD, editor. Microbial Control of Pests and Plant Diseases. 1970-1980. New York, NY: Academic Press; 1981. pp. 441-464
6. Clark TB, Kellen WR, Fukuda T, Lindegren JE. Field and laboratory studies on the pathogenicity of the fungus Beauveria bassiana to three genera of mosquitoes. Journal of Invertebrate Pathology. 1968;11(1):1-7. DOI: 10. 1016/0022-2011(68)90047-5
7. Beys da Silva WO, Santi L, Corrêa AP, Silva LA, Bresciani FR, Schrank A, et al. The entomopathogen Metarhizium anisopliae can modulate the secretion of lipolytic enzymes in response to different substrates including components of arthropod cuticle. Fungal Biology. 2010;114(11-12):911-916. DOI: 10. 1016/j. funbio. 2010. 08. 007
8. Ortiz-Urquiza A, Keyhani NO. Action on the surface: Entomopathogenic fungi versus the insect cuticle. Insects. 2013;4:357-374. DOI: 10. 3390/insects4030357
9. Skinner M, Parker BL, Kim JS. Role of entomopathogenic fungi in integrated pest management. Journal of Integrated Pest Management. 2014;10:169-191. DOI: 10. 1016/B978-0-12-398529-3. 00011-7
10. Deshmukh R, Khardenavis AA, Purohit HJ. Diverse metabolic capacities of Fungi for bioremediation. Indian Journal of Microbiology. 2016;56(3):247-264. DOI: 10. 1007/s12088-016-0584-6
11. Minney SF, Quirk AV. Growth and adaptation of Saccharomyces cerevisiae at different cadmium concentrations. Microbios. 1985;42(167):37-44
12. Betancor L, Johnson GR, Luckarift HR. Stabilized laccases as heterogeneous bioelectrocatalysts. ChemCatChem. 2013;5(1):46-60
13. Ahman J, Ek B, Rask L, Tunlid A. Sequence analysis and regulation of a gene encoding a cuticle-degrading serine protease from the nematophagous fungus Arthrobotrys oligospora. Microbiology (Reading). 1996;142(7):1605-1616. DOI: 10. 1099/13500872-142-7-1605

14. Bonants PJ, Fitters PF, Thijs H, den Belder E, Waalwijk C, Henfling JW. A basic serine protease from Paecilomyces lilacinus with biological activity against Meloidogyne hapla eggs. Microbiology (Reading). 1995;141(4):775-784. DOI: 10. 1099/13500872-141-4-775

15. Ahman J, Johansson T, Olsson M, Punt PJ, van den Hondel CA, Tunlid A. Improving the pathogenicity of a nematode-trapping fungus by genetic engineering of a subtilisin with nematotoxic activity. Applied Environmental Microbiology. 2002;68(7):3408-3415. DOI: 10. 1128/AEM. 68. 7. 3408-3415. 2002

16. Rosén S, Sjollema K, Veenhuis M, Tunlid A. A cytoplasmic lectin produced by the fungus Arthrobotrys oligospora functions as a storage protein during saprophytic and parasitic growth. Microbiology (Reading). 1997;143(8):2593-2604. DOI: 10. 1099/00221287-143-8-2593

17. Luca I, Ilie MS, Florea T, Olariu-Jurca A, Stancu A, Dărăbuş G. The use of Pythium oligandrum in the biological control of roundworm infection in dogs and cats. Pathogens. 2022;11(3):367. DOI: 10. 3390/pathogens11030367

18. Chen TH, Hsu CS, Tsai PJ, Ho YF, Lin NS. Heterotrimeric G-protein and signal transduction in the nematode-trapping fungus Arthrobotrys dactyloides. Planta. 2001;212(5-6):858-863. DOI: 10. 1007/s004250000451

19. Nordbring-Hertz B, Jansson HB, Tunlid A. Nematophagous fungi. Chichester: John Wiley & Sons; 2006. pp. 145-179

20. Zhang Y, Li GH, Zhang KQ. A review on the research of nematophagous fungal species. Mycosystema. 2011;30:836-884

21. Trabelsi H, Dendana F, Sellami A, Sellami H, Cheikhrouhou F, Neji S, et al. Pathogenic free-living amoebae: Epidemiology and clinical review. Pathologie Biologie (Paris). 2012;60(6):399-405. DOI: 10. 1016/j. patbio. 2012. 03. 002

22. Ravdin JI. Pathogenesis of disease caused by Entamoeba histolytica: Studies of adherence, secreted toxins, and contact-dependent cytolysis. Research and Reviews of Infectious Diseases. 1986;8(2):247-260. DOI: 10. 1093/clinids/8. 2. 247

23. Balczun C, Scheid PL. Free-living amoebae as hosts for and vectors of intracellular microorganisms with public health significance. Viruses. 2017;9(4):65. DOI: 10. 3390/ v9040065

24. Qvarnstrom Y, Nerad TA, Visvesvara GS. Characterization of a new pathogenic Acanthamoeba species, A. byersi n. sp. , isolated from a human with fatal amoebic encephalitis. The Journal of Eukaryotic Microbiology. 2013;60(6):626-633. DOI: 10. 1111/ jeu. 12069

25. Walochnik J, Aspöck H. Die Diagnostik von Infektionen mit freilebenden Amöben (FLA). Laboratoriums Medizin. 2005;29:446-456

26. Butt CG. Primary amebic meningoencephalitis. The New England Journal of Medicine. 1966;274(26):1473-1476. DOI: 10. 1056/NEJM196606302742605

27. Scheid P. Balamuthiose. In: Hofmann F, editor. Handbuch der Infektionskrankheiten. Hamburg, Germany: ecomed Verlag; 2012

28. Siddiqui R, Khan NA. Balamuthia amoebic encephalitis: An emerging disease with fatal consequences. Microbial Pathogenesis. 2008;44(2):89-97. DOI: 10. 1016/j. micpath. 2007. 06. 008

29. Qvarnstrom Y, da Silva AJ, Schuster FL, Gelman BB, Visvesvara GS. Molecular confirmation of Sappinia pedata as a causative agent of amoebic encephalitis. The Journal of Infectious Diseases. 2009;199(8):1139-1142. DOI: 10. 1086/597473

30. Marciano-Cabral F, Cabral GA. The immune response to Naegleria fowleriamebae and pathogenesis of infection. FEMS Immunology and Medical Microbiology. 2007;51(2):243-259. DOI: 10. 1111/j. 1574-695X. 2007. 00332. x

31. Akya A, Pointon A, Thomas C. Mechanism involved in phagocytosis and killing of listeria monocytogenes by Acanthamoeba polyphaga. Parasitology Research. 2009;105(5):1375-1383. DOI: 10. 1007/s00436-009-1565-z

32. Cirillo JD, Falkow S, Tompkins LS, Bermudez LE. Interaction of Mycobacterium avium with environmental amoebae enhances virulence. Infection and Immunity. 1997;65(9):3759-3767. DOI: 10. 1128/iai. 65. 9. 3759-3767. 1997

33. Samba-Louaka A, Robino E, Cochard T, Branger M, Delafont V, Aucher W, et al. Environmental Mycobacterium avium subsp. paratuberculosis hosted by free-living amoebae. Frontiers in Cellular and Infection Microbiology. 2018;8:28. DOI: 10. 3389/fcimb. 2018. 00028

34. Michel R. Freilebende Amöben als Wirte und Vehikel von Mikroorganismen. Mitteilungen der Österreichischen Gesellschaft für Tropenmedizin und Parasitologie. 1997;19:11-20

35. Fritsche TR, Sobek D, Gautom RK. Enhancement of in vitro cytopathogenicity by Acanthamoeba spp. following acquisition of bacterial endosymbionts. FEMS Microbiology Letters. 1998;166(2):231-236. DOI: 10. 1111/j. 1574-6968. 1998. tb13895. x

36. Gaze WH, Burroughs N, Gallagher MP, Wellington EM. Interactions between Salmonella typhimurium and Acanthamoeba polyphaga, and observation of a new mode of intracellular growth within contractile vacuoles. Microbial Ecology. 2003;46(3):358-369. DOI: 10. 1007/s00248-003-1001-3

37. Snelling WJ, McKenna JP, Lecky DM, Dooley JS. Survival of Campylobacter jejuni in waterborne protozoa. Applied and Environmental Microbiology. 2005;71(9):5560-5571. DOI: 10. 1128/AEM. 71. 9. 5560-5571. 2005

38. Steinert M, Birkness K, White E, Fields B, Quinn F. Mycobacterium avium bacilli grow saprozoically in coculture with Acanthamoeba polyphaga and survive within cyst walls. Applied and Environmental Microbiology. 1998;64(6):2256-2261. DOI: 10. 1128/AEM. 64. 6. 2256-2261. 1998

39. Dey R, Hoffman PS, Glomski IJ. Germination and amplification of anthrax spores by soil-dwelling amoebas. Applied and Environmental Microbiology Journal. 2012;78:8075-8081

40. Winiecka-Krusnell J, Wreiber K, von Euler A, Engstrand L, Linder E. Free-living amoebae promote growth and survival of helicobacter pylori. Scandinavian Journal of Infectious Diseases. 2002;34(4):253-256. DOI: 10. 1080/00365540110080052

41. La Scola B, Raoult D. Survival of Coxiella burnetii within free-living amoeba Acanthamoeba castellanii. Clinical Microbiology and Infection. 2001;7(2):75-79. DOI: 10. 1046/j. 1469-0691. 2001. 00193. x

42. Abd H, Johansson T, Golovliov I, Sandström G, Forsman M. Survival and growth of Francisella tularensis in Acanthamoeba castellanii. Applied and Environmental Microbiology Journal. 2003;69(1):600-606. DOI: 10. 1128/AEM. 69. 1. 600-606. 2003

43. Steenbergen JN, Shuman HA, Casadevall A. Cryptococcus neoformansinteractions with amoebae suggest an explanation for its virulence and intracellular pathogenic strategy in macrophages. Proceedings of the National Academy of Sciences of the United States of America. 2001;98(26):15245-15250. DOI: 10. 1073/pnas. 261418798

44. Scheid PL, Schwarzenberger R. Free-living amoebae as vectors of cryptosporidia. Parasitology Research. 2011;109(2):499-504. DOI: 10. 1007/s00436-011-2287-6

45. Ryan U, Zahedi A, Paparini A. Cryptosporidium in humans and animals-a one health approach to prophylaxis. Parasite Immunology. 2016;38(9):535-457. DOI: 10. 1111/pim. 12350

46. Lorenzo-Morales J, Coronado-Alvarez N, Martinez-Carretero E, Maciver SK, Valladares B. Detection of four adenovirus serotypes within water-isolated strains of Acanthamoeba in the Canary Islands, Spain. American Journal of Tropical Medicine and Hygiene. 2007;77:753-756

47. Van Waeyenberghe L, Baré J, Pasmans F, Claeys M, Bert W, Haesebrouck F, et al. Interaction of aspergillus fumigatus conidia with Acanthamoeba castellanii parallels macrophage-fungus interactions. Environmental Microbiology Reports. 2013;5(6):819-824. DOI: 10. 1111/1758-2229. 12082

48. Hillmann F, Novohradská S, Mattern DJ, Forberger T, Heinekamp T, Westermann M, et al. Virulence determinants of the human pathogenic fungus aspergillus fumigatus protect against soil amoeba predation. Environmental Microbiology. 2015;17(8):2858-2869. DOI: 10. 1111/1462-2920

49. Nunes T, Brazil N, Fuentefria A, Rott M. Acanthamoeba and fusarium interactions: A possible problem in keratitis. Acta Tropica. 2016;157:102-107. DOI: 10. 1016/j. actatropica. 2016. 02. 001

50. Bullock JD, Warwar RE. Contact lens solution-associated Acanthamoeba and fusarium keratitis. Emerging Infectious Diseases. 2010;16(9):1501-1502. DOI: 10. 3201/eid1609. 091381

51. Sassuchin D. Hyperparasitism in Protozoa. The Quarterly Review of Biology. 1934;9(2):215-224. DOI: 10. 1086/394461

52. Scheid P. Mechanism of intrusion of a microspordian-like organism into the nucleus of host amoebae (Vannella sp.) isolated from a keratitis patient. Parasitology Research. 2007;101:1097-1102. DOI: 10. 1007/s00436-007-0590-z

53. Kurek R, Scheid P, Michel R. Darstellung von pilzartigen Endoparasiten bei freilebenden Amöben nach spezifischer Fluoreszenzanfärbung. Mikrokosmos. 2010;99:327-330

54. Drechsler C. Five new Zoopagaceae destructive to Rhizopods and nematodes. Mycologia. 1939;31(4):388-415. DOI: 10. 1080/00275514. 1939. 12017354

55. Drechsler C. Three new Zoopagaceae subsisting on soil amoebae. Mycologia. 1946;38(2):120-143

56. Saikawa M, Sato H. Ultrastructure of Cochlonema odontosperma, an endoparasite in amoebae. Mycologia. 1991;83(4):403-408. DOI: 10. 1080/00275514. 1991. 12026029

57. Koehsler M, Michel R, Lugauer J, Wylezisch C. Molecular identification and classification of Cochlonema euryblastum, a zoopagalean parasite of Thecamoeba quadrilineata. Mycologia. 2007;99:215-221. DOI: 10. 1080/15572536. 2007. 11832580

58. Drechsler C. Some non-catenulate conidial phycomycetes preying on terriculous amoebae. Mycologia. 1935;27:176-205. DOI: 10. 1080/00275514. 1935. 12017070

59. Michel R, Walochnik J, Scheid P. Isolation and characterisation of various amoebophagous fungi and evaluation of their spectrum. Experimental Parasitology. 2014;145:131-136. DOI: 10. 1016/j. exppara. 2014. 10. 005

60. Saikawa M, Kadowaki T. Sudies on Acaulopage dichotoma and A. tetraceros (Zoopagales, Zygomycota) capturing amoebae. Nova Hedwigia. 2002;74:365-371. DOI: 10. 1127/0029-5035/2002/0074-0365

61. Michel R, Scheid P, Köhsler M, Walochnik J. Acaulopage tetraceros DRECHSLER 1935 (Zoopagales): Cultivation, prey pattern and molecular characterization. Endocytobiosis and Cell Research. 2015;26:76-82

62. Grimaldi D, Engel MS. Evolution of the Insects. New York: Cambridge University Press; 2005. p. 755

63. Cock MJW, Biesmeijer JC, Cannon RJC, Gerard PJ, Gillespie D, Jiménez JJ, et al. The positive contribution of invertebrates to sustainable agriculture and food security. CAB Reviews. 2012;7:1-27

64. Carpenter GH. The Biology of Insects. London: Sidgwick and Jackson; 1928. p. 473

65. Mellor PS, Boorman J, Baylis M. Culicoides biting midges: Their role as arbovirus vectors. Annual Review of Entomology. 2000;45:307-340. DOI: 10. 1146/annurev. ento. 45. 1. 307

66. Barin A, Arabkhazaeli F, Rahbari S, Madani SA. The housefly, Musca domestica, as a possible mechanical vector of Newcastle disease virus in the laboratory and field. Medical and Veterinary Entomology. 2010;24(1):88-90. DOI: 10. 1111/j. 1365-2915. 2009. 00859. x

67. Goraichuk IV, Arefiev V, Stegniy BT, Gerilovych AP. Zoonotic and reverse zoonotic transmissibility of SARS-CoV-2. Virus Research. 2021;302:198473. DOI: 10. 1016/j. virusres. 2021. 198473

68. Shane SM, Montrose MS, Harrington KS. Transmission of Campylobacter jejuni by the housefly (Musca domestica). Avian Diseases. 1985;29(2):384-391

69. Barreiro C, Albano H, Silva J, Teixeira P. Role of flies as vectors of foodborne pathogens in rural areas. International Scholarly Research Notices. 2013;2013:718780. DOI: 10. 1155/2013/718780

70. Bamou R, Mayi MPA, Djiappi-Tchamen B, Nana-Ndjangwo SM, Nchoutpouen E, Cornel AJ, et al. An update on the mosquito fauna and mosquito-borne diseases distribution in Cameroon. Parasites Vectors. 2021;14:527. DOI: 10. 1186/s13071-021-04950-9

71. Komarov A, Kalmar E. A hitherto undescribed disease–Turkey meningo-encephalitis. Veterinary Record. 1960;72:257-621

72. Rijks JM, Kik ML, Slaterus R, Foppen RPB, Stroo A, IJzer J, et al. Widespread Usutu virus outbreak in birds in the Netherlands, 2016. Euro Surveillance. 2016;21(45):30391. DOI: 10. 2807/1560-7917. ES. 2016. 21. 45. 30391

73. Huhtamo E, Lambert AJ, Costantino S, Servino L, Krizmancic L, Boldorini R, et al. Isolation and full genomic characterization of Batai virus from mosquitoes, Italy 2009. Journal of General Virology. 2013;94(6):1242-1248. DOI: 10. 1099/vir. 0. 051359-0

74. Eiden M, Ziegler U, Keller M, Müller K, Granzow H, Jöst H, et al. Isolation of sindbis virus from a hooded crow in Germany. Vector Borne Zoonotic Diseases. 2014;14(3):220-222. DOI: 10. 1089/vbz. 2013. 1354

75. Genchi C, Kramer L. Subcutaneous dirofilariosis (Dirofilaria repens): An infection spreading throughout the old world. Parasitology & Vectors. 2017;10(2):517. DOI: 10. 1186/s13071-017-2434-8

76. Lytra I, Emmanouel N. Study of Culex tritaeniorhynchus and species composition of mosquitoes in a rice field in Greece. Acta Tropica. 2014;134:66-71. DOI: 10. 1016/j. actatropica. 2014. 02. 018

77. Kopp A, Gillespie TR, Hobelsberger D, Estrada A, Harper JM, Miller RA, et al. Provenance and geographic spread of St. Louis encephalitis virus. MBio. 2013;4(3):e00322-13. DOI: 10. 1128/mBio. 00322-13

78. Folly AJ, Dorey-Robinson D, Hernández-Triana LM, Phipps LP, Johnson N. Emerging threats to animals in the United Kingdom by arthropod-borne diseases. Frontiers in Veterinary Science. 2020;7:20. DOI: 10. 3389/fvets. 2020. 00020

79. Kono Y, Tsukamoto K, Abd Hamid M, Darus A, Lian TC, Sam LS, et al. Encephalitis and retarded growth of chicks caused by Sitiawan virus, a new isolate belonging to the genus

Flavivirus. American Journal of Tropical Medicine and Hygiene. 2000;63(1-2):94-101. DOI: 10. 4269/ajtmh. 2000. 63. 94

80. Papadopoulos E, Bartram D, Carpenter S, Mellor P, Wall R. Efficacy of alphacypermethrin applied to cattle and sheep against the biting midge Culicoides nubeculosus. Veterinary Parasitology. 2009;163(1-2):110-114. DOI: 10. 1016/j. vetpar. 2009. 03. 041

81. Ansari MA, Pope EC, Carpenter S, Scholte EJ, Butt TM. Entomopathogenic fungus as a biological control for an important vector of livestock disease: The Culicoides biting midge. PLoS One. 2011;6(1):e16108. DOI: 10. 1371/journal. pone. 0016108

82. Ansari MA, Carpenter S, Butt TM. Susceptibility of Culicoides biting midges larvae to the entomopathogenic fungus, Metarhizium anisopliae: Prospects for bluetongue vector control. Acta Tropica. 2010;113:1-6

83. Mishra S, Kumar P, Malik A, Satya S. Adulticidal and larvicidal activity of Beauveria bassiana and Metarhizium anisopliae against housefly, Musca domestica (Diptera: Muscidae), in laboratory and simulated field bioassays. Parasitology Research. 2011;108(6):1483-1492. DOI: 10. 1007/s00436-010-2203-5

84. Sharififard M, Mossadegh MS, Vazirianzadeh B, Mahmoudabadi AZ. Laboratory evaluation of pathogenecity of entomopathogenic fungi Beauveria bassiana (Bals) and Metarhizium anisopliae (Metech) Sorok to larvae and adults of the housefly, Musca domestica L (Diptera: Muscidae). Asian Journal of Biological Sciences. 2011;4(2):128-137

85. Mwamburi LA, Laing MD, Miller RM. Laboratory screening of insecticidal activities of Beauveria bassiana and Paecilomyces lilacinus against larval and adult house fly (Musca domestica L.). African Entomology. 2010;18:38-46

86. Lohmeyer KH, Miller JA. Pathogenicity of three formulations of entomopathogenic fungi for control of adult Haematobia irritans (Diptera: Muscidae). Journal of Economic Entomology. 2006;99(6):1943-1947. DOI: 10. 1603/0022-0493-99. 6. 1943

87. Unkles SE, Marriott C, Kinghorn JR, Panter C, Blackwell A. Efficacy of the entomopathogenic fungus, Culicinomyces clavisporus against larvae of the biting midges, Culicoides nubeculosus (Diptera: Ceratopogonidae). Biocontrol Science and Technology. 2004;14:397-401

88. Narladkar BW, Shivpuje PR, Harke PC. Fungal biological control agents for integrated management of Culicoides spp. (Diptera: Ceratopogonidae) of livestock. Veterinary World. 2015;8(2):156-163. DOI: 10. 14202/vetworld. 2015. 156-163

89. Ong'wen F, Onyango PO, Bukhari T. Direct and indirect effects of predation and parasitism on the Anopheles gambiae mosquito. Parasites Vectors. 2020;13:43. DOI: 10. 1186/s13071-020-3915-8

90. Ishii M, Kanuka H, Badolo A, Sagnon NF, Guelbeogo WM, Koike M, et al. Proboscis infection route of Beauveria bassiana triggers early death of Anopheles mosquito. Scientific Reports. 2017;7:3476. DOI: 10. 1038/s41598-017-03720-x

91. Kerwin JL. Oomycetes: Lagenidium giganteum. Journal of the American Mosquito Control Association. 2007;23(2):50-57. DOI: 10. 2987/8756-971X(2007)23[50,OLG]2. 0. CO;2

92. Kaczmarek A, Boguś MI. Fungi of entomopathogenic potential in Chytridiomycota and Blastocladiomycota, and in fungal allies of the Oomycota and microsporidia. IMA Fungus. 2021;12:29. DOI: 10. 1186/s43008-021-00074-y

93. Wang Q, Zhao S, Wureli H, Xie S, Chen C, Wei Q, et al. Brucella melitensis and B. abortus in eggs, larvae and engorged females of Dermacentor marginatus. Ticks and Tick Borne Diseases. 2018;9(4):1045-1048. DOI: 10. 1016/j. ttbdis. 2018. 03. 021

94. Li S, Wang Y, Qv G, Sun C, Yang L, Lin C, et al. Epidemiological investigation of Francisella tularensis transmitted by rabbits and ticks in some provinces of China. China Animal Husbandry & Veterinary Medicine. 2020;47:4069-4075

95. Fang LQ, Liu K, Li XL, Liang S, Yang Y, Yao HW, et al. Emerging tick-borne infections in mainland China: An increasing public health threat. The Lancet Infectious Diseases. 2015;15(12):1467-1479. DOI: 10. 1016/S1473-3099(15)00177-2

96. Cradock KR, Needham GR. Beauveria bassiana (Ascomycota: Hypocreales) as a management agent for free-living Amblyomma americanum (Acari: Ixodidae) in Ohio. Experimental and Applied Acarology. 2011;53(1):57-62. DOI: 10. 1007/s10493-010-9381-9

97. Garcia MV, Rodrigues VDS, Monteiro AC, Simi LD, Higa LDOS, Martins MM, et al. In vitro efficacy of Metarhizium anisopliae sensu lato against unfed Amblyomma parvum (Acari: Ixodidae). Experimental and Applied Acarology. 2018;76:507-512

98. Kaaya GP, Mwangi EN, Ouna EA. Prospects for biological control of livestock ticks, Rhipicephalus appendiculatus and Amblyomma variegatum, using the entomogenous fungi Beauveria bassiana and Metarhizium anisopliae. Journal of Invertebrate Pathology. 1996;67(1):15-20. DOI: 10. 1006/jipa. 1996. 0003

99. Sullivan CF, Parker BL, Davari A, Lee MR, Kim JS, Skinner M. Evaluation of spray applications of Metarhizium anisopliae, Metarhizium brunneum and Beauveria bassiana against larval winter ticks, Dermacentor albipictus. Experimental and Applied Acarology. 2020;82(4):559-570. DOI: 10. 1007/s10493-020-00547-6

100. Maranga RO, Kaaya GP, Mueke JM, Hassanali A. Effects of combining the fungi Beauveria bassiana and Metarhiziumanisopliae on the mortality of the tick Amblyomma variegatum (ixodidae) in relation to seasonal changes. Mycopathologia. 2005;159:527-532

101. Frazzon AP, da Silva Vaz Junior I, Masuda A, Schrank A, Vainstein MH. In vitro assessment of Metarhizium anisopliae isolates to control the cattle tick Boophilus microplus. Veterinary Parasitology. 2000;94(1-2):117-125. DOI: 10. 1016/s0304-4017(00)00368-x

102. Szczepańska A, Kiewra D, Plewa-Tutaj K, Dyczko D, Guz-Regner K. Sensitivity of Ixodes ricinus (L. , 1758) and Dermacentor reticulatus (Fabr. , 1794) ticks to entomopathogenic fungi isolates: Preliminary study. Parasitology Research. 2020;119(11):3857-3861. DOI: 10. 1007/s00436-020-06805-1

103. Samsináková A, Kálalová S, Daniel M, Dusbábek F, Honzáková E, Cerný V. Entomogenous fungi associated with the tick Ixodes ricinus (L.). Folia Parasitologica (Praha). 1974;21(1):39-48

104. Kirkland BH, Westwood GS, Keyhani NO. Pathogenicity of entomopathogenic fungi Beauveria bassiana and Metarhizium anisopliae to Ixodidae tick species Dermacentor variabilis, Rhipicephalus sanguineus, and Ixodes scapularis. Journal of Medical Entomology. 2004;41(4):705-711. DOI: 10. 1603/0022-2585-41. 4. 705

105. Yoder JA, Rodell BM, Klever LA, Dobrotka CJ, Pekins PJ. Vertical transmission of the entomopathogenic soil fungus Scopulariopsis brevicaulis as a contaminant of eggs in the winter tick, Dermacentor albipictus, collected from calf moose (New Hampshire, USA). Mycology. 2019;10(3):174-181. DOI: 10. 1080/21501203. 2019. 1600062

106. Zhendong H, Guangfu Y, Zhong Z, Ruiling Z. Phylogenetic relationships and effectiveness of four Beauveria bassiana sensu lato strains for control of Haemaphysalis longicornis (Acari: Ixodidae). Experimental and Applied Acarology. 2019;77(1):83-92. DOI: 10. 1007/s10493-018-0329-9

107. Ren Q, Chen Z, Luo J, Liu G, Guan G, Liu Z, et al. Laboratory evaluation of Beauveria bassiana and Metarhizium anisopliae in the control of Haemaphysalis qinghaiensis in China. Experimental and Applied Acarology. 2016;69(2):233-238. DOI: 10. 1007/s10493-016-0033-6

108. Lipa JJ. Microbial control of mites and ticks. In: Burges HD, Hussey NW, editors. Microbial Control of Insects and Mites. London, UK: Academic Press; 1971. pp. 357-373

109. Kaay GP, Hassan S. Entomogenous fungi as promising biopesticides for tick control. Experimental and Applied Acarology. 2000;24(12):913-926. DOI: 10. 1023/a:1010722914299

110. Campos RA, Boldo JT, Pimentel IC, Dalfovo V, Araújo WL, Azevedo JL, et al. Endophytic and entomopathogenic strains of Beauveria sp to control the bovine tick Rhipicephalus (Boophilus) microplus. Genetics and Molecular Research. 2010;9(3):1421-1430. DOI: 10. 4238/vol9-3gmr884

111. Fernández-Salas A, Alonso-Díaz MA, Alonso-Morales RA, Lezama-Gutiérrez R, Rodríguez-Rodríguez JC, Cervantes-Chávez JA. Acaricidal activity of Metarhizium anisopliae isolated from paddocks in the Mexican tropics against two populations of the cattle tick Rhipicephalus microplus. Medical and Veterinary Entomology. 2017;31(1):36-43. DOI: 10. 1111/mve. 12203

112. Angelo IC, Fernandes ÉK, Bahiense TC, Perinotto WM, Golo PS, Moraes AP, et al. Virulence of Isaria sp. and Purpureocillium lilacinum to Rhipicephalus microplus tick under laboratory conditions. Parasitology Research. 2012;111(4):1473-1480. DOI: 10. 1007/s00436-012-2982-y

113. Casasolas-Oliver A, Estrada-Pena A, Gonzalez-Cabo J. Activity of Rhizopus thailandensis, Rhizopus arrhizus and Curvularia lunata on reproductive efficacy of Rhipicephalus sanguineus (Ixodidae). In: Dusbadek E, Bukva V, editors. Modern Acaralogy. Prague, Czech Republic: Academia Prague and SPB Academic Publishing BV; 1991. pp. 633-637

114. Samish M, Gindin G, Alekseev E, Glazer I. Pathogenicity of entomopathogenic fungi to different developmental stages of Rhipicephalus sanguineus (Acari: Ixodidae). The Journal of Parasitology. 2001;87(6):1355-1359. DOI: 10. 1645/0022-3395(2001)087[1355,POEFTD]2. 0. CO;2 PMID: 11780821

115. Fernandes ÉK, Bittencourt VR, Roberts DW. Perspectives on the potential of entomopathogenic fungi in biological control of ticks. Experimental Parasitology. 2012;130(3):300-305. DOI: 10. 1016/j. exppara. 2011. 11. 004

116. Aboelhadid SM, Ibrahium SM, Arafa WM, Maahrous LN, Abdel-Baki AAS, Wahba AA. In vitro efficacy of Verticillium lecanii and Beauveria bassiana of commercial source against cattle tick, Rhipicephalus (Boophilus) annulatus. Advances in Animal and Veterinary Sciences. 2018;6(3):139-147

117. Abdigoudarzi M, Esmaeilnia K, Shariat N. Laboratory study on biological control of ticks (Acari: Ixodidae) by Entomopathogenic indigenous Fungi (Beauveria bassiana). Iranian Journal of Arthropod-Borne Diseases. 2009;3(2):36-43

118. da Costa GL, Sarquis MI, de Moraes AM, Bittencourt VR. Isolation of Beauveria bassiana and Metarhizium anisopliae var. anisopliae from Boophilus microplus tick (Canestrini, 1887), in Rio de Janeiro state, Brazil. Mycopathologia. 2002;154(4):207-209. DOI: 10. 1023/a:1016388618842

119. do Carmo Barcelos Correia A, Fiorin AC, Monteiro AC, Veríssimo CJ. Effects of Metarhizium anisopliae on the tick Boophilus microplus (Acari: Ixodidae) in stabled cattle. Journal of Invertebrate Pathology. 1998;71(2):189-191. DOI: 10. 1006/jipa. 1997. 4719 PMID: 9500942

120. Immediato D, Camarda A, Iatta R, Puttilli MR, Ramos RA, Di Paola G, et al. Laboratory evaluation of a native strain of Beauveria bassiana for controlling Dermanyssus gallinae (De Geer, 1778) (Acari: Dermanyssidae). Veterinary Parasitology. 2015;212(3-4):478-482. DOI: 10. 1016/j. vetpar. 2015. 07. 004

121. Tavassoli M, Pourseyed SH, Ownagh A, Bernousi I, Mardani K. Biocontrol of pigeon tick Argas reflexus (Acari: Argasidae) by entomopathogenic fungus Metarhizium

anisopliae (Ascomycota: Hypocreales). Brazilian Journal of Microbiology. 2011;42(4):1445-1452. DOI: 10. 1590/S1517-83822011000400030

122. Pirali-Kheirabadi K, Haddadzadeh H, Razzaghi-Abyaneh M, Bokaie S, Zare R, Ghazavi M, et al. Biological control of Rhipicephalus (Boophilus) annulatus by different strains of Metarhizium anisopliae, Beauveria bassiana and Lecanicillium psalliotae fungi. Parasitology Research. 2007;100(6):1297-1302. DOI: 10. 1007/s00436-006-0410-x

123. Molan PC. Potential of honey in the treatment of wounds and burns. American Journal of Clinical Dermatology. 2001;2:13-19. DOI: 10. 2165/00128071-200102010-00003

124. Ahmed S, Othman NH. Honey as a potential natural anticancer agent: A review of its mechanisms. Evidence-Based Complementary and Alternative Medicine. 2013;2013:829070. DOI: 10. 1155/2013/829070

125. Vogt NA, Vriezen E, Nwosu A, Sargeant JM. A scoping review of the evidence for the medicinal use of natural honey in animals. Frontiers in Veterinary Sciences. 2021;7:618301. DOI: 10. 3389/fvets. 2020. 618301

126. Shaw KE, Davidson G, Clark SJ, Bal BV, Pell JK, Chandler D, et al. Laboratory bioassays to assess the pathogenicity of mitosporic fungi to Varroa destructor (Acari: Mesostigmata), an ectoparasitic mite of the honeybee, Apis mellifera. Biological Control. 2002,24.266-276

127. Kanga LH, James RR, Boucias DG. Hirsutella thompsonii and Metarhizium anisopliae as potential microbial control agents of Varroa destructor, a honey bee parasite. Journal of Invertebrate Pathology. 2002;81(3):175-184. DOI: 10. 1016/s0022-2011(02)00177-5

128. Steenberg T, Kryger P, Holst N. A scientific note on the fungus Beauveria bassiana infecting Varroa destructor in worker brood cells in honey bee hives. Apidologie. 2010;41:127-128. DOI: 10. 1051/apido/2009057

129. Peng CY, Zhou X, Kaya HK. Virulence and site of infection of the fungus, Hirsutella thompsonii, to the honey bee ectoparasitic mite, Varroa destructor. Journal of Invertebrate Pathology. 2002;81(3):185-195. DOI: 10. 1016/s0022-2011(02)00188-x

130. García-Fernández P, Santiago-Álvarez C, Quesada-Moraga E. Pathogenicity and thermal biology of mitosporic fungi as potential microbial control agents of Varroa destructor (Acari: Mesostigmata), an ectoparasitic mite of honey bee, Apis mellifera (Hymenoptera: Apidae). Apidologie. 2008;39:662-673. DOI: 10. 1051/apido:2008049

131. Hamiduzzaman MM, Sinia A, Guzman-Novoa E, Goodwin PH. Entomopathogenic fungi as potential biocontrol agents of the ecto-parasitic mite, Varroa destructor, and their effect on the immune response of honey bees (Apis mellifera L.). Journal of Invertebrate Pathology. 2012;111(3):237-243. DOI: 10. 1016/j. jip. 2012. 09. 001

132. Ahmed AA, Abd-Elhady HK. Efficacy of two fungus-based biopesticide against the honeybee ectoparasitic mite, Varroa destructor. Pakistan Journal of Biological Sciences. 2013;16(16):819-825. DOI: 10. 3923/pjbs. 2013. 819. 825

133. Voigt K, Rademacher E. Effect of the Propolis components, Cinnamic acid and pinocembrin, on Apis Mellifera and Ascosphaera Apis. Journal of Apicultural Science. 2015;59(1):89-95. DOI: 10. 1515/jas-2015-0010

134. Gillespie IMM, Philip JC. Bioremediation, an environmental remediation technology for the bioeconomy. Trends in Biotechnology. 2013;31:329-332. DOI: 10. 1016/j. tibtech. 2013. 01. 015

135. Mishra A, Malik A. Novel fungal consortium for bioremediation of metals and dyes from mixed waste stream. Bioresource Technology. 2014;171:217-226. DOI: 10. 1016/j. biortech. 2014. 08. 047

136. Chałabis-Mazurek A, Valverde Piedra JL, Muszyński S, Tomaszewska E, Szymańczyk S, Kowalik S, et al. The concentration of selected heavy metals in muscles, liver and kidneys of pigs fed standard diets and diets containing 60% of new Rye varieties. Animals. 2021;11(5):1377. DOI: 10. 3390/ani11051377

137. Hejna M, Gottardo D, Baldi A, Dell'Orto V, Cheli F, Zaninelli M, et al. Review: Nutritional ecology of heavy metals. Animal. 2018;12(10):2156-2170. DOI: 10. 1017/S175173111700355X

138. Liu SH, Zeng GM, Niu QY, Liu Y, Zhou L, Jiang LH, et al. Bioremediation mechanisms of combined pollution of PAHs and heavy metals by bacteria and fungi: A mini review. Bioresource Technology. 2017;224:25-33. DOI: 10. 1016/j. biortech. 2016. 11. 095

139. Gola D, Dey P, Bhattacharya A, Mishra A, Malik A, Namburath M. Shaikh Ziauddin Ahammad. Multiple heavy metal removal using an entomopathogenic fungi Beauveria bassiana. Bioresource Technology. 2016;218:388-396. DOI: 10. 1016/j. biortech. 2016. 06. 096

140. Iram S, Zaman A, Iqbal Z, Shabbir R. Heavy metal tolerance of fungus isolated from the soil contaminated with sewage and industrial waste- water. Polish Journal of Environmental Studies. 2013;22:691-697

141. Volesky B. Advances in biosorption of metals: Selection of biomass types. FEMS Microbiology Reviews. 1994;14(4):291-302. DOI: 10. 1111/j. 1574-6976. 1994. tb00102. x

142. Maheswari S, Murugesan AG. Removal of arsenic (III) ions from aqueous solution using aspergillus favus isolated from arsenic contaminated site. Indian Journal of Chemical Technology. 2011;18:45-52

143. Park D, Yun YS, Park JM. Use of dead fungal biomass for the detoxifcation of hexavalent chromium: Screening and kinetics. Process Biochemistry. 2015;40:2559-2565. DOI: 10. 1016/j. procbio. 2004. 12. 002

144. Hultberg M, Bodin H. Effects of fungal-assisted algal harvesting through biopellet formation on pesticides in water. Biodegradation. 2018;29:557-565. DOI: 10. 1007/s10532-018-9852-y

145. Levio-Raiman M, Briceño G, Leiva B, López S, Schalchli H, Lamilla C, et al. Treatment of pesticide-contaminated water using a selected fungal consortium: Study in a batch and packed-bed bioreactor. Agronomy. 2021;11(4):743. DOI: 10. 3390/agronomy11040743

146. Ahmad KS. Remedial potential of bacterial and fungal strains (Bacillus subtilis, aspergillus Niger, aspergillus flavus and Penicillium chrysogenum) against organochlorine insecticide Endosulfan. Folia Microbiologica (Praha). 2020;65(5):801-810. DOI: 10. 1007/s12223-020-00792-7

147. Supreeth M, Raju NS. Biotransformation of chlorpyrifos and endosulfan by bacteria and fungi. Applied Microbiology and Biotechnology. 2017;101(15):5961-5971. DOI: 10. 1007/s00253-017-8401-7

148. Siddique T, Okeke BC, Arshad M, Frankenberger WT Jr. Biodegradation kinetics of endosulfan by fusarium ventricosum and a Pandoraea species. Journal of Agricultural and Food Chemistry. 2003;51(27):8015-8019. DOI: 10. 1021/jf030503z

149. Mohammed YMM, Badawy MEI. Biodegradation of imidacloprid in liquid media by an isolated wastewater fungus aspergillus terreus YESM3. Journal of Environmental Science and Health. 2017;52(10):752-761. DOI: 10. 1080/03601234. 2017

150. Panter KE, Stegelmeier BL. Effects of xenobiotics and phytotoxins on reproduction in food animals. Veterinary Clinics of North America: Food Animal Practice. 2011;27(2):429-446. DOI: 10. 1016/j. cvfa. 2011. 02. 010

151. Idle JR, Gonzalez FJ. Metabolomics. Cell Metabolism. 2007;6(5):348-351. DOI: 10. 1016/j. cmet. 2007. 10. 005

152. Adenipekun CO, Lawal R. Uses of mushrooms in bioremediation: A review. Biotechnology and Molecular Biology Review. 2012;7(3):62-68

153. Sun K, Song Y, He F, Jing M, Tang J, Liu R. A review of human and animals exposure to polycyclic aromatic hydrocarbons: Health risk and adverse effects, photo-induced toxicity and regulating effect of microplastics. Science of the Total Environment. 2021;773:145403. DOI: 10. 1016/j. scitotenv. 2021. 145403

154. Sungthong R, van West P, Heyman F, Funck Jensen D, Ortega-Calvo JJ. Mobilization of pollutant-degrading Bacteria by eukaryotic zoospores. Environmental Science & Technology. 2016;50(14):7633-7640. DOI: 10. 1021/acs. est. 6b00994

155. Dhaliwal BBS, Juyal PD. Parasitic Zoonoses. New Delhi: Springer; 2013. pp. 1-14. DOI: 10. 1007/978-81-322-1551-6_1

156. Romero-Gonzalez R, Garrido Frenich A, Martınez Vida JL. Anthelmintics. In: Motarjemi Y, Moy G, Todd E, editors. Encyclopedia of Food Safety. Cambridge, Massachusetts: Academic Press; 2013. pp. 45-54

157. Chai JY. Praziquantel treatment in trematode and cestode infections: An update. Infection & Chemotherapy. 2013;45(1):32-43. DOI: 10. 3947/ic. 2013. 45. 1. 32

158. Moreno L, Lanusse C. Chapter 24 - specific veterinary drug residues of concern in meat production. In: Purslow PP, editor. Food Science, Technology and Nutrition, New Aspects of Meat Quality. Sawston, Cambridge: Woodhead Publishing Series; 2017. pp. 605-627. DOI: 10. 1016/B978-0-08-100593-4. 00025-4

159. Luca I, Oprescu I, Morariu S, Mederle N, Ilie MS, Dărăbuş G. Effects of some disinfectants on Toxocara spp. eggs viability of dogs and cats. Turkish Journal of Veterinary & Animal Sciences. 2020;44(3):734-739. DOI: 10. 3906/vet-1905-92

160. Luca I, Iancu TG, Oprescu I, Dărăbuş G. The in vitro effect of 1% pentapotassium solution on Toxocara canis eggs. Scientia Parasitologica. 2018;19(1-2):66-69

161. Cuevas-Padilla EJ, Aguilar-Marcelino L, Sánchez JE, González-Cortázar M, Zamilpa-Álvarez A, Huicochea-Medina M, et al. A Pleurotus spp. hydroalcoholic fraction possess a potent in vitro ovicidal activity against the sheep parasitic nematode Haemonchus contortus. In: Sánchez JE, Mata G, Royse DJ, editors. Updates on Tropical Mushrooms. Basic and Applied Research. 1st. ed. San Cristóbal de las Casas, Mexico: El Colegio de la Frontera Sur, San Cristóbal de Las Casas; 2018. pp. 193-211

162. Li S, Shah NP. Antioxidant and antibacterial activities of sulphated polysaccharides from Pleurotus eryngii and Streptococcus thermophilus ASCC 1275. Food Chemistry. 2014;165:262-270. DOI: 10. 1016/j. foodchem. 2014. 05. 110

163. Vieira ÍS, Oliveira IC, Campos AK, Araújo JV. Association and predatory capacity of fungi Pochonia chlamydosporia and Arthrobotrys cladodes in the biological control of parasitic helminths of bovines. Parasitology. 2019;146(10):1347-1351. DOI: 10. 1017/ S003118201900060X

164. Araújo JV, Braga FR, Silva AR, Araujo JM, Tavela AO. In vitro evaluation of the effect of the nematophagous fungi Duddingtonia flagrans, Monacrosporium sinense, and Pochonia chlamydosporia on Ascaris suum eggs. Parasitology Research. 2008;102(4):787-790. DOI: 10. 1007/s00436-007-0852-9

165. Ranjbar-Bahadori S, Rhazzagi-Abyaneh M, Baya M, Eslami A, Pirali K, Shams-Ghahfarokhi M, et al. Studies on the effect of temperature, incubation time and in vivo gut passage on survival and Nematophagous activity Arthrobotrys oligospora var. oligospora and A. cladodes var. macroides. Global Veterinaria. 2010;4:112-117

166. Braga FR, Araújo JV, Tavela A de O, Vilela VL, Soares FE, Araujo JM, et al. First report of interaction of nematophagous fungi on Libyostrongylus douglassii (Nematoda: Trichostrongylidae).

Revista Brasileira de Parasitologia Veterinaria. 2013;22(1):147-151. DOI: 10. 1590/s1984-29612013000100027

167. de Castro OI, de Carvalho LM, Vieira ÍS, Campos AK, Freitas SG, de Araujo JM, et al. Using the fungus Arthrobotrys cladodes var. macroides as a sustainable strategy to reduce numbers of infective larvae of bovine gastrointestinal parasitic nematodes. Journal of Invertebrate Pathology. 2018;158:46-51. DOI: 10. 1016/j. jip. 2018. 09. 004

168. Silva ME, Braga FR, de Gives PM, Millán-Orozco J, Uriostegui MA, Marcelino LA, et al. Fungal antagonism assessment of predatory species and producers metabolites and their effectiveness on Haemonchus contortus infective larvae. Biomed Research International. 2015;2015:241582. DOI: 10. 1155/2015/241582

169. Soto-Barrientos N, de Oliveira J, Vega-Obando R, Montero-Caballero D, Vargas B, Hernández-Gamboa J, et al. In-vitro predatory activity of nematophagous fungi from Costa Rica with potential use for controlling sheep and goat parasitic nematodes. Revista de Biologia Tropical. 2011;59(1):37-52. DOI: 10. 15517/rbt. v59i1. 3177

170. Cai KZ, Wang BB, Xu Q, Liu JL, Wang KY, Xue YJ, et al. In vitro and in vivo studies of nematophagous fungi Arthrobotrys musiformis and Arthrobotrys robusta against the larvae of the trichostrongylides. Acta Parasitologica. 2017;62(3):666-674. DOI: 10. 1515/ap-2017-0080

171. Silva ME, Uriostegui MA, Millán-Orozco J, Gives PM, Hernández EL, Braga FR, et al. Predatory activity of Butlerius nematodes and nematophagous fungi against Haemonchus contortus infective larvae. Revista Brasileira de Parasitologia Veterinaria. 2017;26(1):92-95. DOI: 10. 1590/S1984-29612016091

172. Acevedo-Ramírez PMC, Quiroz-Romero H, Valero-Coss RO, Mendozade-Gives P, Gómez JL. Nematophagous fungi from Mexico with activity against the sheep nematode Haemonchus contortus. Revista Ibero-Latinoamericana de Parasitologia. 2011;70(1):101-108

173. Chandrawathani P, Jamnah O, Waller PJ, Höglund J, Larsen M, Zahari WM. Nematophagous fungi as a biological control agent for nematode parasites of small ruminants in Malaysia: A special emphasis on Duddingtonia flagrans. Veterinary Research. 2002;33(6):685-696. DOI: 10. 1051/vetres:2002049

174. Kanadani Campos A, Caixeta Valadão M, de Carvalho LM, de Araújo JV, Pezzi GM. In vitro nematophagous activity of predatory fungi on infective larvae of Strongyloides papillosus. Acta Veterinaria Brasilica. 2017;11(4):213-218. DOI: 10. 21708/avb. 2017. 11. 4. 7261

175. Zarrin M, Rahdar M, Poormohamadi F, Rezaei-Matehkolaei A. In vitro Nematophagous activity of predatory Fungi on infective nematodes larval stage of Strongyloidae family. Open Access Macedonian Journal of Medical Sciences. 2017;5(3):281-284. DOI: 10. 3889/oamjms. 2017. 064

176. Araujo JM, Araújo JV, Braga FR, Carvalho RO. In vitro predatory activity of nematophagous fungi and after passing through gastrointestinal tract of equine on infective larvae of Strongyloides westeri. Parasitology Research. 2010;107(1):103-108. DOI: 10. 1007/s00436-010-1841-y

177. Zhong W, Chen Y, Gong S, Qiao J, Meng Q, Zhang X, et al. Enzymological properties and nematode-degrading activity of recombinant chitinase AO-379 of Arthrobotrys oligospora. Kafkas Üniversitesi Veteriner Fakültesi Dergisi. 2019;25:435-444

178. Lozano J, Almeida C, Oliveira M, Paz-Silva A, Madeira de Carvalho L. Biocontrol of avian gastrointestinal parasites using predatory Fungi: Current status, challenges, and opportunities. Parasitologia. 2022;2(1):37-44. DOI: 10. 3390/parasitologia2010004

179. Thapa S, Thamsborg SM, Wang R, Meyling NV, Dalgaard TS, Petersen HH, et al. Effect of the nematophagous fungus Pochonia chlamydosporia on soil content of ascarid eggs and infection levels in exposed hens. Parasites & Vectors. 2018;11:319. DOI: 10. 1186/s13071-018-2898-1

180. Braga FR, Araújo JV, Silva AR, Carvalho RO, Araujo JM, Ferreira SR, et al. Viability of the nematophagous fungus Pochonia chlamydosporia after passage through the gastrointestinal tract of horses. Veterinary Parasitology. 2010;168(3-4):264-268. DOI: 10. 1016/j. vetpar. 2009. 11. 020

181. Ferreira SR, de Araújo JV, Braga FR, Araujo JM, Frassy LN, Ferreira AS. Biological control of Ascaris suum eggs by Pochonia chlamydosporia fungus. Veterinary Research Communications. 2011;35(8):553-558. DOI: 10. 1007/s11259-011-9494-6

182. Araujo JM, Araújo JV, Braga FR, Ferreira SR, Tavela AO. Predatory activity of chlamydospores of the fungus Pochonia chlamydosporia on Toxocara canis eggs under laboratory conditions. Revista Brasileira de Parasitologia Veterinaria. 2013;22(1):171-174. DOI: 10. 1590/s1984-29612013000100033

183. Luca I, Imre M, Ilie MS, Oprescu I, Dărăbuş G. The biological potential of a product containing Pythium oligandrum against Uncinaria stenocephala (Railliet, 1884) larvae. Journal of the Hellenic Veterinary Medical Society. 2022;73(1):3651-3656. DOI: 10. 12681/jhvms. 25380

184. de Souza Maia Filho F, da Silva Fonseca AO, Persici BM, de Souza SJ, Braga CQ, Pötter L, et al. Trichoderma virens as a biocontrol of Toxocara canis: In vivo evaluation. Revista Iberoamericana de Micologia. 2017;34(1):32-35. DOI: 10. 1016/j. riam. 2016. 06. 004

185. Carvalho RO, Araújo JV, Braga FR, Araujo JM, Alves CD. Ovicidal activity of Pochonia chlamydosporia and Paecilomyces lilacinus on Toxocara canis eggs. Veterinary Parasitology. 2010;169(1-2):123-127. DOI: 10. 1016/j. vetpar. 2009. 12. 037

186. Ciarmela ML, Minvielle MC, Lori G, Basualdo JA. Biological interaction between soil fungi and Toxocara canis eggs. Veterinary Parasitology. 2002;103(3):251-257. DOI: 10. 1016/s0304-4017(01)00598-2

187. Manzanilla-López RH, Esteves I, Finetti-Sialer MM, Hirsch PR, Ward E, Devonshire J, et al. Pochonia chlamydosporia: Advances and challenges to improve its performance as a biological control agent of sedentary Endo-parasitic nematodes. Journal of Nematology. 2013;45(1):1-7

188. Dias AS, Araújo JV, Braga FR, Araujo JM, Puppin AC, Fernandes FM, et al. Biological control of Fasciola hepatica eggs with the Pochonia chlamydosporia fungus after passing through the cattle gastrointestinal tract. Parasitology Research. 2012;110(2):663-667. DOI: 10. 1007/s00436-011-2538-6

9 Biological Control of Parasites

Tebit Emmanuel Kwenti

Faculty of Health Sciences, University of Buea, Buea, Cameroon

ABSTRACT

Parasites (ectoparasites or endoparasites) are a major cause of diseases in man, his livestock and crops, leading to poor yield and great economic loss. To overcome some of the major limitations of chemical control methods such as rising resistance, environmental and health risks, and the adverse effect on non-target organisms, biological control (biocontrol) is now at the forefront of parasite (pests) control. Biocontrol is now a core component of the integrated pest management. Biocontrol is defined as "the study and uses of parasites, predators and pathogens for the regulation of host (pest) densities". Considerable successes have been achieved in the implementation of biocontrol strategies in the past. This chapter presents a review of the history of biocontrol, its advantages and disadvantages; the different types of biological control agents (BCAs) including predators, parasites (parasitoids) and pathogens (fungi, bacteria, viruses and virus-like particles, protozoa and nematodes); the effect of biocontrol on native biodiversity; a few case studies of the successful implementation of biocontrol methods and the challenges encountered with the implementation of biocontrol and future perspectives.

Keywords: *Biological Control, Biological Control Agents, Parasites, Humans, Plants, Livestock, Case Study, Challenges*

INTRODUCTION

In nature, the population size of every species is regulated by natural environmental factors. These factors are responsible for the "checks and balances" of a population of living organisms. The event where living organisms live and die a natural death unaided by man is termed "natural control". Weather (abiotic or non-living factors) is an important factor in natural control; temperature and humidity are determinants of the survival of living organisms. Availability of competition (biotic factors) is also an important determinant for the survival of living organisms [1]. Many organisms are killed by pathogens (disease-causing agents) such as bacteria, viruses, fungi, parasites (parasitoids) and predators [1].

Living organisms, which are considered undesirable, are generally referred to as pests. Environmental factors (such as weather, geography and soil conditions) which affect pest populations generally vary from one location to another and changes through time. A combination of these factors may substantially reduce the pest population in one geographical area and make it more abundant in another. Pests sometimes outwit their natural enemies and grow to very high population density. To keep their population in check will necessitate the manipulation of the population of their natural enemies by man. This is termed biological control or simply biocontrol. Biocontrol is therefore defined as "any activity of one species that reduces the adverse effect of another" [1]. Biocontrol can also be defined as "the study and uses of parasites, predators and pathogens for the regulation of host (pest) densities" [2]. Biological control differs from natural control in that the latter does not involve human manipulation. The organism that suppresses the pest population is generally referred to as a biological control agent (BCA).

A parasite is an organism that lives and feeds in or on a host [3]. Parasites that invade and live within the host are referred to as endoparasites; meanwhile, those that live on the surface without invading the host are referred to as ectoparasites. Endoparasites include helminths and protozoa, and ectoparasites are fleas, ticks, mites, insects and so on. Parasites are a major cause of disease in man, his livestock and crops, leading to poor yield and economic loss. The biocontrol of parasites therefore entails the use of BCAs to suppress the population of the parasites.

This chapter focuses on the biological control of parasites, providing a brief history of biocontrol; their advantages and disadvantages; types of BCAs including predators, parasites (parasitoids) and pathogens (fungi, bacteria, viruses and virus-like particles, protozoa and nematodes); their effect on the native biodiversity; a few case studies of successful implementation of biocontrol; challenges encountered with the implementation of biocontrol strategies and finally their future perspectives.

HISTORY OF BIOLOGICAL CONTROL

The concept of biological control is not entirely new. The ancient Egyptians were probably the first to employ biocontrol dating some 4000 years ago, when they observed that cats fed on rodents, which damaged their crops. This most likely led to the domestication of the house cat [4]. However, the first record of biocontrol is from China. As early as the third century, a nest of the ants *Oecophylla smaragdina* were sold near Canton (today known as Guangzhou in China) for use in control of the citrus insect pests such as *Tesseratoma papillosa* (Lepidoptera). By 1200 A.D., the usefulness of the ladybird beetles as biological control agents of aphids and scales had been recognized. Between 1300 and 1799 A.D., the importance of biological control tools was recognized. Van Leeuwenhoek was probably the first to describe insect parasitism, which he illustrated in his publication in 1701. In 1726, de Reaumur recognized the first insect pathogen, a Cordyceps fungus that infects noctuid. The mynah bird, *Acridotheres tristis*, was successfully introduced from India to Mauritius by the British and the French for the control of the red locust, *Nomadacris septemfasciata,* in 1762 (see Figure 1). In 1776, in Europe, the control of the bedbug, *Cimex lectularius*, was successfully accomplished by the release of the predatory pentatomid, *Picromerus bidens*. Koller was the first to put forth the concept of "natural control" in 1837 [5].

Between 1850 and 1887, the concept of biological control switched to the United States. In 1870, Charles V. Riley was the first person to conduct the successful movement of parasitoids for biological control when parasitoids were moved from Kirkwood, Missouri, to other parts of the United States for the control of the weevil (*Conotrachelus menuphar*). In 1883, the US Department of Agriculture (USDA) imported *Apanteles glomeratus* from

England to control *Pieris rapea* (the imported cabbageworm) parasites that were distributed in DC, Iowa, Nebraska and Missouri.

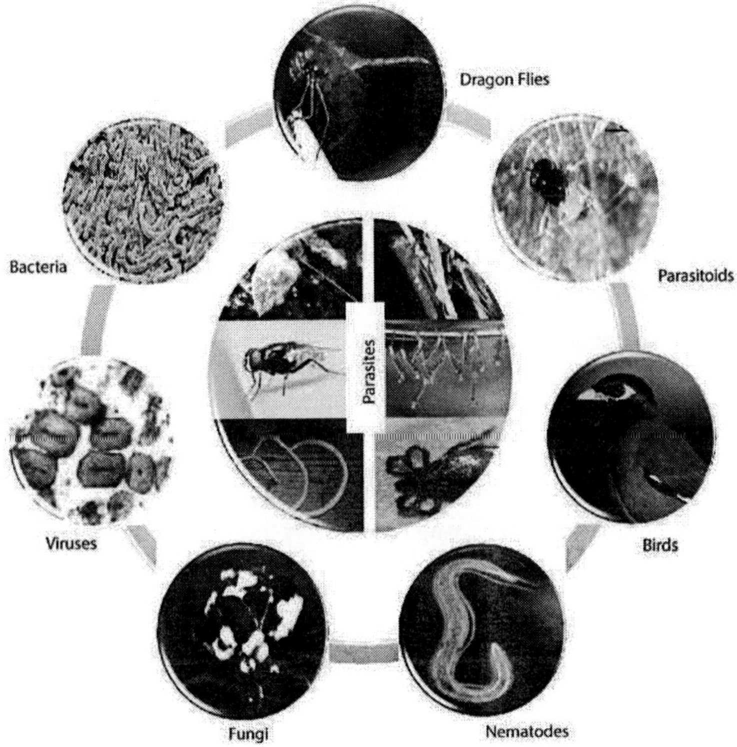

Figure 1. Images of some common parasites/pests (centre cycle) and biological control agents (external cycles) used in the biocontrol of parasites.

This marked the first intercontinental shipment of parasites. It was not until the 1800s that well-thought-out biological control projects were implemented across Europe. In 1888, the cottony cushion scale project was launched to control the cottony cushion scale, *Icerya purchase*, which was threatening to destroy the infant citrus industry. This was the first project to be launched. Since then, many projects have been launched including the gypsy moth project in New England (1905–1911) [5].

Between 1930 and 1940, there was a peak in biological control activity in the world with 57 different biological control agents established at various places. During World War II, there was a sharp drop in biological control activity and after the war, biological control did not regain popularity due to the production of relatively inexpensive synthetic pesticides. It was not until the late 1960s that the concept of integrated pest management (IPM) was implemented, and biological control was seen as a core component of IPM by some [5]. The other components of IPM are habitat manipulation, modification of cultural practices and the use of resistant varieties.

IMPORTANCE OF THE BIOLOGICAL CONTROL OF PARASITES

Control of parasites nowadays is mainly by the use of chemicals (pesticides), but the commonly used chemicals are fast losing their effectiveness as a result of resistance arising from indiscriminate use. Moreover, pesticides present a danger to people, the environment, their residual build-up and their effect on non-target organisms such as beneficial insects, birds, domestic animals and sometimes the crop itself. A suitable alternative to the growing problem is biological (natural) control. Under ideal conditions, biocontrol has sustainability, which is lacking in the other methods of parasite control. There are several methods through which biological control of parasites could be achieved, including the use of predators (such as arthropods, mites, flies, beetles, amphibians, fish, birds, rodents, etc.), parasites (parasitoids) and pathogens (such as fungi, bacteria, viruses and virus-like particles, protozoa and nematodes).

ADVANTAGES AND DISADVANTAGES OF BIOCONTROL

Advantages of Biocontrol

Biocontrol offers some advantages over other pest-control strategies, particularly chemical pesticides. These advantages include as follows:

- It is environmentally friendly and safe to the applicator.
- There are no residues.
- Biocontrol could be very economical in some cases.
- Biocontrol is easy to apply; in many cases, we are merely manipulating something to favour naturally occurring controls.
- Biological control is sometimes lasting, thereby eliminating the needs for continuous reapplication as is necessary with pesticides.
- Biocontrol is easily established
- BCAs are frequently very host specific.
- Unlike chemical methods, pests do not become resistant against BCAs.

Disadvantages of Biocontrol

The disadvantages of biocontrol include as follows:

- Biocontrol is often slow. In biocontrol of pests, there is often a lag time between build-up of the pest population and build-up of the biocontrol agent. If a pest population is already at or above economically damaging levels, pesticides are the only alternative.
- BCAs do not completely eliminate their host [6]. If they do, they would also die. However, biological control may be integrated with other pest control strategies to achieve complete eradication.
- With biocontrol, there is the possibility that the BCA may tend to feed on the desired plants or insect, that is, crossovers [7–9]. Careful selection of the BCA will minimize this problem.
- BCAs are frequently ineffective in multiple weed complexes when used in biocontrol of weeds. This may be because the weed and the crop are so closely related that the control agent affects both the pest and the crop.
- The shipping, storage and application techniques of BCA can be relatively complex. Production of the BCA is also costly in some cases.
- Biocontrol sometimes may be costly compared to conventional methods. The high cost is usually attributed to the research that has to be done prior to implementation of the biocontrol strategy.

- Biocontrol if not well conceived may lead to dramatic changes in native biodiversity.

TYPES OF BIOLOGICAL CONTROL AGENTS

Biocontrol of insects may include predators (e.g. spiders), parasites (parasitoids) or pathogens like viruses, bacteria, fungi, protozoa and nematodes (see Figure 1).

Predators

Predators can be vertebrates or invertebrates, some of which are arachnids, but deployment of insects is most common. The efficiency of predators in controlling populations of some ticks in different habitats varies and may reach up to 100% [10, 11]. For example, predation has been observed to be lower in tall grass areas than in short grass areas [12]. Likewise, predation has been observed to be two to eight times higher in open areas than in thick pasture areas and non-intensive pasture or agricultural areas [13]. The different types of predators can be classified as invertebrates and vertebrates.

Invertebrates

Spiders and insect herbivores

Spiders prey on many insects. Spiders have a defined habitat; a change in the habitat such as mulching may increase their population by as much as 60% [14, 15]. River prawns have been observed to prey on snails [16]. Insect herbivores including the cell-content feeder *Liothrips ludwigi* (Thysanoptera), the stem borers *Merocnemus binotatus* (Boheman) and *Tyloderma* spp. (Coleoptera) have shown promise in the control of weeds [17]. Both the adult and larval stages of the predatory thrips, *Scolothrips sexmaculatus,* are known to feed on spider mites and other thrips [18]. *S. sexmaculatus* prefers spider mite eggs but adult females will consume other mite stages as well [18].

Mites

Some mites are nematode predators. For example, some mites (*Phytoseiid* spp.) are capable of consuming *Ascaris* ova in the soil [19]. There are also a few mite species that are voracious predators of eggs and larvae of houseflies and other filth flies that develop in manure and faeces of livestock; for example, *Macrocheles muscaedomesticae* can eat up to 10 housefly eggs per day [20].

Flies

Use of the predatory fly, *Hydrotaea (Ophyra) aenescens*, which is commercially available in several northern European countries, presents a breakthrough in the indoor control of the housefly, *Musca domestica* [21]. Small flies such as *Mutilla glossinae* are important parasites of tsetse and are promising BCAs against the tsetse fly [22].

Ants

Around 27 species of ants from 16 genera mainly *Aphaenogaster*, *Iridomyrmex*, *Monomorium*, *Pheidol* and *Solenopsis* are known to prey on ticks, horn flies and different agricultural pests [23]. Application of the fire ant, *Solenopsis inucta,* in Louisiana in the USA markedly reduced the population of ticks (*Ixodes* spp.) transmitting anaplasmosis in cattle [23]. However, a wide applicability of fire ants may pose a challenge because of their painful sting.

Beetles

Dung beetles of the family Scarabaeidae (Scarabaeinae, Geotropinae and Aphodiinae) are useful in the control of pasture livestock flies since they breed primarily in cow pats. In addition, dung beetles such as *Onthophagus ganelle* and *Euniticellus intermedius*, introduced from Africa to Australia, are regarded as useful in the biocontrol of *Musca vetustissima* and the buffalo fly *Haematobia exigua*. The African dung beetles are well adapted to cattle faeces and compete with fly larvae for food. Furthermore, the rapid burial of dung by the beetles reduces the breeding habitats for the flies [21]. The scarab beetle (*Scarabaeus sacer*), also referred to as sacred scarab among ancient Egyptians, was famous for its habit of rolling balls of dung along the ground depositing them in its burrows. The female would lay her eggs in the ball of dung. When they hatched, the larvae would use the ball for food. When the dung was consumed, the young beetles would emerge from the hole [24]. Dung beetles have been reported to reduce horn flies by as much as 95%, bush flies by 80–100% and result in nine times of fewer parasites produced [25, 26]. Dung beetles can also play a role in the biocontrol of bovine gastrointestinal nematodes (Trichostrongylidae). The spotted lady beetle (*Coleomegilla maculata*) is also able to feed on the eggs and larvae of the Colorado potato beetle *Leptinotarsa decemlineata* [27] and can be used in its control. The larvae of Coccinellids (ladybird or ladybug) are voracious predators of aphids and also consume mites, scale insects and small caterpillars.

Dragonflies and water bugs

Dragonflies (see Figure 1) may look like scary biters, but they are only dangerous to mosquitoes. Dragonfly larvae, “nymphs”, feed on mosquito larvae, and adult dragonflies feed on adult mosquitoes [28]. On the other hand, water bugs, *Diplonychus indicus,* are also known to prey on mosquito larvae [29].

Vertebrates

Amphibians and fishes

The water tortoise *Pelomedusa subrufa* has been reported to be able to remove ticks from black rhinos in a streambed [30]. Also in some areas, the mosquito larvae may be controlled biologically by predatory fish such as *Gambusia affinis* and *Guppy poecilia* [31]. One study showed that introducing *Gambusia affinis* into water wells resulted in 98% reduction in the larval density of *Anopheles stephensi* [32]. Other predatory fishes such as the *Cyprinus carpio*, *Ctenopharyngodon idella*, *Aphanius dispar*, *Aplocheilus blocki*, *Tilapia* spp., *Catla catla*, *Labeo rohita* and *Cirrhinus mrigala* have also shown promise in the control of mosquitoes [33]. In China, for example, the presence of carp fish in certain rice fields reduced the number of malaria cases [34]. Another predatory fish, the black carp (*Mylopharyngodon piceus*), has shown promise in the biocontrol of the intermediate host snails of fish-borne zoonotic trematodes [35]. Snails (some of which are intermediate hosts of fascioliasis, paramphistomes and schistosomes) are eaten by some fishes as well.

Reptilians

Some lizards can eat arthropods. The lizard stomach may contain as many as 2.5–15 ticks/stomach. However, because there are few lizards near the bird nest, their effect on the tick population may be limited [21]. The Australian gecko *Gehydra dubia* and the exotic

Asian house gecko *Hemidactylus frenatus* have been observed to prey on mosquitoes; in the laboratory, they have been observed to prey more on female mosquitoes and are therefore a promising tool for the biological control of malaria [28].

Birds

Birds are generally thought to be the main predators of insects. Some bird species are known to pick off ticks from the host during flight or collect them from the ground. Birds also eat the larvae of dung flies. One approach for biocontrol of trematodes is the control of the snail intermediate host. Domestic fowls and birds are predators of snails. Scrub jays have been observed to spend 89% of their time searching deer for ectoparasites [36]. In Africa, chickens are natural predators of ticks and actually pick ticks from the bodies of cattle as they lie down as well as from the vegetation [37].

Rodents and mammals

Some mammals are insectivorous. As an example, *Sorex araneus* preys on ticks and at times prefers them to alternative foods [12, 38]. Shrews seem to locate hidden ticks by their smell. Mice and rats are often cited as preying on ticks [39]. However, it is worth to mention here that it is not advisable to use rodents for controlling insects as they are more harmful and transmit more diseases than insects.

Parasites (Parasitoids)

Parasites that attack other parasites are generally referred to as parasitoids. Parasitoids are very diverse in appearance, biology and the hosts they attack. Parasitoids lay their eggs on or in the body of an insect host, which is then used as food for the developing larvae. The host is ultimately killed. Most insect parasitoids are wasps or flies and may have a very narrow host range. The most important groups are the ichneumonid wasps, which prey mainly on caterpillars of butterflies and moths; braconid wasps, which attack caterpillars and a wide range of other insects including greenfly; chalcid wasps, which parasitize eggs and larvae of greenfly, whitefly [40], cabbage caterpillars and scale insects and tachinid flies, which parasitize a wide range of insects including caterpillars, adult and larval beetles and true bugs [37, 41–44].

Pathogens

Fungi

Pathogenic fungi can be classified into two: entomopathogenic fungi and nematopathogenic fungi.

Entomopathogenic fungi

Fungi that infect and kill arthropod (insects, ticks or mites) pests are referred to as "entomopathogenic fungi". Over 750 species of entomopathogenic fungi have been identified, a majority of them belong to the phylum Ascomycota and a few to the phylum Zygomycota and Ascomycotina [45]. Unlike the other BCAs, some fungi do not need to be ingested by the host [33]; entomopathogenic fungi produce spores as the insect comes in contact with these spores either on the body of dead insects or surfaces or in the air as airborne particles; the spores germinate in the presence of high humidity and produce germ tubes that allow them to penetrate the cuticle of the insect, usually at joints or creases where the insect's protective covering is thinner [46]. Death usually follows between 4 and 10 days, depending on the type of fungus and the number of infecting spores. Other fungi cause death by the production of toxins (mycotoxin). After death, the fungus produces thousands of new spores on the dead body, which disperse and continue their life cycle on new hosts. Some species go into a resting stage, which survive periods of adverse conditions before forming or releasing spores. The ascomycetes together with the mitosporic fungi are most widely used for biocontrol of pests.

The most commonly investigated entomopathogenic fungi belong to the genera *Metarhizium* and *Beauveria* and are increasingly being used in commercial formulation against arthropods. The Hyphomycetes, *Beauveria bassiana* and *Metarhizium anisopliae* (formerly known as *Enthomphthora anisopliae*) are the most common species known to cause natural outbreaks to a wide range of insect hosts, on their own under favourable conditions. These fungi provide a long-term strategy for larvae and puparia control since they may survive in the soil through recycling in insects or roots [47, 48]. *Metarhizium anisopliae* and *Beauveria bassiana* are also effective in the control of mosquitoes [49]. They infect mosquitoes early in life and kill them, depending on the exposure dose and fungus isolate after 3–14 days [50]. Fungal spores can be applied in outdoor attracting odour traps, on indoor house surfaces and on cotton pieces hanging from ceilings, bed nets and curtains [51, 52] to control adult mosquitoes. Commercially available products based on *B. bassiana* are Mycotrol O (Emerald BioAgriculture), Naturalis Home and Garden (H&G), Naturalis L (Troy BioSciences, Inc.) and Biosect® (Kafr El Zayat—KZ Chemicals, Egypt) [44]. For example, Khater [53] used Biosect® to control larvae of both *Musca domestica* and *Culex pepiens* in-vitro and observed that the total larval mortalities of mosquitoes were almost 100%.

Hyphomycetes of the genera *Fusarium* also contain some important pathogens. For example, Ghannam et al. [54] observed that certain species of *Fusarium* (*F. solani, F. oxysporum and F. arthrosporioides* strain E4a) were able to increase the dead spikes of the obligate holoparasitic weed, broomrape (*Orobanche* spp.), by 33.6–72.7%, thereby making it promising for broomrape control.

Other fungi species that are increasingly being used as BCAs include the Oomycetes, *Lagenidium giganteum (*formerly*: L. culicidum)*, which are known to be pathogenic to the larvae of several mosquito genera [55]. Unfortunately, the fungus is not effective for mosquitoes in brackish or organically rich aquatic habitats. In contrast, *Lagenidium* spp. was isolated from Egypt for the first time from *Culex pipiens* larvae infesting a polluted creak in Miet El-Attar, Benha, Egypt, and it was observed to effectively control *Culex pipiens* [53]. As the fungi has the ability of self-propagation, it could be used for effective control of the vector of bancroftian filariasis and rift valley fever virus [46].

The entomophthorales are another group of fungi that are able to cause natural outbreaks in insect populations and are also promising as good BCAs [56]. Several different *Entomophthora muscae* sensu stricto genotypes have been documented, and each type has demonstrated a high degree of host specificity [56]. All available literature deal with *E. muscae* as a pathogenic fungi of adult *Musca domestica*, but Khater [53] isolated, for the first time in Egypt, from Moshtohor, Toukh and Qlubia governorate a strain that has the unique ability to infect larvae of the house flies. Fungi such as *Leptolegnia* spp., *Coelomomyces* spp., *Hirsutella thomsonii*, *Nomuraea rileyi* and *Vericillum lecanii* are also being used in the control of insects [46].

The ascomycetes, *Trichoderma harzianum* and *T. viride,* have been shown to antagonize the fungi causing damping-off and wilt in bean plants [57].

Nematopathogenic fungi

Fungi that infect and kill nematodes (worms) are referred to as nematopathogenic fungi. Over 150 species of fungi are known to invade nematodes. Nematode-destroying fungi can be grouped into three: nematode-trapping fungi, the endoparasitic fungi and the fungal parasites of cyst and root-knot nematodes. Most nematopathogenic fungi fall in the group of nematode trapping; they use constricting (active) or non-constricting (inactive) rings, sticky hyphae, sticky knobs, sticky branches or sticky networks at intervals along the length of a widely distributed vegetative hyphal system to trap and kill nematodes by penetration and growth of hyphal elements within the host, for example, *Arthrobotrys candida, A. oligospora, Drechmeria coniospora* [58], *Harposporium anguillulae* [59] *and Monacrosporium* spp. [60]. The nematode-trapping fungi, *Duddingtonia flagrans*, which have demonstrated considerable superiority in the reduction of gastrointestinal nematodes parasitizing animals, produce thick-walled clamydospores that enable it to survive the passage through the gastrointestinal tract and is therefore effective in destroying the larval stages of parasitic nematodes in livestock [61, 62]. Feeding or field trials have clearly demonstrated that dosing with a few hundred thousand spores per kilogram of live birth weight (BW) of *D. flagrans* not only reduced the number of infective larvae but also increased the BW of the lambs compared with controls [63]. In another example, Araujo et al. [64] tested the nematode-trapping fungus *Arthrobotrys robusta* against *Cooperia punctate* larvae (L3) and observed a 53.81% reduction in the helminths eggs (EPG) in treated calves compared to non-treated calves as well as a 70.45% reduction in the number of recovered worms at necropsy in the treated calves compared to the control. Endoparasitic fungi infect nematodes by spores, which then develop and absorb the body contents, for example, *Harposporium anguillulae* [65]; meanwhile, the fungal parasites of cysts and root-knot nematodes exert their effect by invading eggs or females by ingrowth of vegetative hyphae, for example, *Verticillium chlamydosporum* [66–69]. Nematode-trapping fungi have increasingly been tested in the management of parasitic nematode infections of ruminants [70].

Bacteria

The most important entomopathogenic bacteria belong to the genera of *Bacillus* (see Figure 1). *B. thuringiensis* (Bt) is among the most widely used antagonist in the biological control of insects. After ingestion, target insects are killed by an enterotoxin released from a crystal protein in the bacterial spores. The mode of action of the toxin has been fully described [46]. Various subspecies of Bt has been used in biocontrol: *Bacillus thuringiensis* var *israelensis* (Bti), with activity against mosquito larvae, blackfly (Simuliid), sand fly, fungus gnats and related dipterans species; *B. thuringiensis* var *kurstaki* (Btk) and *B. thuringiensis* var *aizawai* (Bta) with activity against lepidopteran larval species; *B. thuringiensis* var *tenebrionis*(Btt) with activity against coleopteran adults and larvae and *B. thuringiensis* var *japonensis* (Btj) strain buibui, with activity against soil-inhabiting beetles [46]. In some countries, commercial formulation of *B. thuringiensis var israelensis* is available for the control of mosquito larvae and the blackfly *Simulium damnosum* [71]. A study performed in Egypt comparing the activity of three *Bacillus thuringiensin* products in controlling ticks shows that Btk was more potent compared to Bti and *Bacillus thuringiensin* var *thuringiensin* in the control of ticks [72]. Several products of *Bacillus thuringiensin* are available in the market; a few examples of products include Dipel 2x (*B. thuringiensis* var. *kurstaki*), VectoBac (*B. thuringiensis* var. *israeliensis*) and HD

703 (*B. thuringiensis* var. *thuringiensis*) [72]. VectoBac, Bti (12 AS, Wady El Niel for agricultural development Co. Egypt) has been shown to be highly effective against *C. pipence* than *M. domestica* [53].

Mosquito larvae are also susceptible to *B. sphaericus*. *B. sphaericus* is effective in killing larvae of *Culex* spp. and *Anopheles* spp., especially those breeding in polluted water. Bti and *B. sphaericus* have been reported to successfully control certain species of sand fly (vector for the protozoa *Leshmania*) [73]. *B. penetrans* is also a well-known nematopathogenic bacterium of plant parasitic root-knot nematodes.

The bacterial pathogen, *Paenibacillus glabratella,* recently discovered by Duval et al. [74] has been observed to infect and cause high mortality in snails, therefore, making a promising BCA for the control of snails.

Another bacterium, *Streptomyces avermitilis*, produces toxins collectively called "avermectins" which are highly effective against several invertebrates from the classes Insecta, Arachnida and Nematodes [21]. *Streptomyces griseolus* has been shown in the laboratory to be able to control the trematode liver fluke, *Fasciola gigantica*, the causative agent of Fasciolosis [75]. Streptomyces are believed to kill parasites by the production of lytic enzymes such as α and β-glucanases, proteases, peptidases, cellulases, chitinases and lipases [75].

Bacteria belonging to the following genera have been tested for the control of plant parasitic nematodes including *Pasteuria* which are parasites of many plant-parasitic nematodes and water fleas [76]; *Brevibacillus laterosporus* strain G4 which is parasitic on *Heterodera glycines*, *Trichostrongylus columbriformis* and *Bursaphelenchus xylophilys* and the saprophytic nematode *Panagrellus redivius* [77, 78]; rhizobacteria (mainly *Bacillus* spp. and *Pseudomonas* spp.) are able to antagonize nematodes [79, 80] and the well-studied *Bacillus thuringiensis* (Bt) are also able to kill plant-parasitic nematodes [81]. More information about using bacteria as biocontrol agents has been extensively reviewed by Khater [46] and Tian et al. [82].

Nota bene: The Rickettsiae are a diverse group of bacteria, which cause diseases to humans and warm-blooded animals, and are transmitted by a number of arthropods such as ticks, fleas and so on. Some of these bacteria tend to parasitize these arthropods [83]. For example, ticks have become adapted as vectors, reservoirs and/or propagation sites of Rickettsiae [84] and often harbour generalized asymptomatic infections. Rickettsial infection may lead to alterations in tick behaviour, interfere with their development and cause pathological changes in salivary glands and ovarian tissues. In severe cases, infection may lead to death [85]. However, the use of Rickettsiae in biocontrol is not a reliable method.

Viruses and virus-like particles

Thousands of entomopathogenic viruses have been described but only a few, belonging to the families Entomopoxviridae (Entomopoxviruses, EPVs), Reoviridae (Cypoviruses, CPVs) and Baculoviridae (Baculoviruses, BVs), have been used successfully in controlling pest population [86]. The mode of pathogenesis and replication of entomopathogenic viruses varies according to the family, but infection nearly always occurs by ingestion [46]. The baculovirus (see Figure 1) is the most widely exploited virus group for biocontrol [87, 88]; they are very different from viruses that infect vertebrates and are considered very safe to use. The family Baculoviridae contains four genera: Alphabaculovirus (lepidopteran-specific NPVs), Betabaculovirus (lepidopteran-specific GVs), Gammabaculovirus (hymenopteran-specific NPVs) and Deltabaculovirus (dipteran-specific NPVs) [89]. At present, there are approximately 16 biopesticides based on baculoviruses available for use or are under development. The majority of these products are targeted against Lepidoptera. For example, codling moth granulovirus, CpGV (Cydia pomonella Granulovirus), is an effective biopesticide of codling moth caterpillar pests of apples, Gemstar LC (NPV of *Heliothis/Helicoverpa* spp. e.g. corn earworm, tobacco budworm and cotton bollworm); Spod-X LC (NPV of *Spodoptera* spp. e.g. beet armyworm); CYD-X and Virosoft CP4 (GV of *Cydia pomonella*, the codling moth) and CLV LC (NPV of *Anagrapha falcipera*, the celery looper) [46].

The leafhopper-infecting virus, Homalodisca coagulate virus-1 (HoCV-1, Dicistroviridae), has been shown to increase leafhopper mortality [90, 91]. The virus occurs in nature and spreads most readily at high population densities through contact among infected individuals, contact with virus-contaminated surfaces and/or as an aerosol in leafhopper excreta.

Protozoa

Very little attention has been given to entomopathogenic protozoans. Some protozoa such as *haemogregarina*, *Nosema*, *Babesia* and *Theileria* are pathogenic to some arthropods like ticks. Although there are no examples of effective direct biocontrol of protozoans, however, indirectly, some protozoans such as *Plasmodium* spp. and *Onchocerca volvulus* may indirectly be controlled by their intermediate hosts or vectors. The predatory soil amoeba *Theratromyxa weberi* is capable of ingesting nematodes. It flows over the nematode body and assimilates it within 24 h. This and other amoebae can be expected to have limited biocontrol capacities because they are slow-moving, as compared to nematodes. Other protozoa including *Nosema locustae* are pathogenic to grasshoppers and crickets; *Nosema pyrausta* (also known as *Perexia pyraustae*) is pathogenic to the European corn borer and *Vairimorpha necatrix* occurs naturally and infects corn earworm, European corn borer, armyworms, fall webworm and cabbage looper [92].

Nematodes

Numerous nematodes belonging to the genera *Steinernema* and *Heterorhabditis* are either obligate or facultative parasites of insects (including houseflies, fleas and other non-biting flies) and have been proven as effective BCAs [86] to control a wide range of insect pests including filth flies, German cockroaches, cat fleas, armyworms, carpenter worms, crown borers, cutworms, flea beetles, leaf miners, mole crickets, plume moths, sciarid flies, root weevils, stem borers, webworms and so on [93]. They infect through penetration of the cuticle; invasion through the spiracles or anus or after ingestion by the host insect. The symbiotic bacteria contained within the nematode, when released into the body of the insect, cause septicaemia and death of the host. The bacteria then break down the insect body, which provides food for the nematodes. The nematode-bacterium relationship is highly specific; only *Xenorhabdus* spp. coexists with Steinermatids and only Photorhabdus bacteria coexist with heterorhabditids [46]. *Steinemema carpocapsae* (see Figure 1) has demonstrated effectiveness in the control of mosquitoes [49]. The host-specific entomoparasitic nematode, *Heterlylenchus autumnalis,* has been observed to parasitize *Musca autumnalis,* resulting in sterile female flies as nematode development occurs at the expense of egg production [94]. Entomopathogenic nematodes have been used commercially against insects during the last decades [95]. Seven species of nematodes have been commercialized worldwide and seven are currently available in the USA: *Steinernema carpocapsea*, *S. feltiae*, *S. glaseri*, *S. riobraus*, *Heterorhabditis bacteriophora*, *H. megidis* and *H. marelatus* [96]. There are two commercial nematode products available for termite control, Spear® and Saf T-Shield® [46].

The nematode *Paraiotonchium muscadomesticae* is also known to infect housefly larvae, but mortality is usually low except at high nematode concentrations. *P. muscadomesticae* infects housefly larvae and its descendants invade and damage the ovaries of adult female flies and are deposited in the larval habitat when the flies attempt to oviposit [46]. Furthermore, it has been observed that infected adults lived only about half as long as uninfected adults [97]. All these indirectly reduce housefly population.

Steinernema carpocapsae and *S. glaseri* have also been proven to be effective against *Teladorsagia* spp. and *Trichonstrongylus* spp. These nematodes are particularly useful on ground-inhabiting stages of fleas [98] and engorged females of numerous other ticks that fall to the ground [99–101]. Entomopathogenic nematodes are not harmful to humans, animals or plants and are generally regarded as remarkably safe to the environment [46].

Chaetogaster limnaei (Oligochaeta: Naididae) has long been observed to infect freshwater snails and protect the host from infection with various species of trematodes by eating both the miracidia and the cercaria. *C. limnaei* therefore has potentials in the biocontrol of parasitic diseases vectored by the freshwater snail (such as fascioliasis, schistosomiasis and related trematode infections) [102].

Earthworms

Earthworm population consume a large volume of soil and organic matter such as animal faeces. During feeding, they consume nematodes present in the soil and faeces. In different parts of the world, earthworms are responsible for natural biological control of trichostrongyle nematodes. For example, in northern Europe, earthworms play an important and often dominating role in removal of cattle dung from pastures and can be responsible for significant reduction of infective larvae of trichostrongyle nematodes on the pasture [103].

For more information about the life cycle, safety, production and genetically modified organisms (GMOs) of biological control agents, see Khater [46].

EFFECT OF BIOLOGICAL CONTROL ON THE NATIVE BIODIVERSITY

Biocontrol may have potential positive or negative effects on the diversity of native species. One of the major problems with biocontrol is the effect of the BCA on non-target species; the purpose of introduction of a BCA is to reduce the competitive advantage of exotic species that has previously invaded or been introduced there over the native species. However, the introduced BCA does not always target only the intended species; it can also target native species. Therefore, when introducing a BCA to a new area, a primary concern is its host specificity. BCA not targeting one species or a narrow range of species often makes for poor BCA and may become invasive species themselves. For this reason, potential BCA should be subject to extensive testing and quarantine before release to any environment. If an introduced species attacks the native species, this can lead to widespread changes in the biodiversity in that area. A classic example of biocontrol gone wrong is the cane toad that was introduced in Australia to control the introduced French's cane beetle and the Greyback cane beetle [104]. The toad instead was feeding on the native insect and soon took over native amphibian habitat and brought foreign disease to native toads and frogs, dramatically reducing their population.

Another notable example where biocontrol has gone wrong is in the introduction of the small Asian mongoose (*Herpestus javanicus*) found in the wild in South and Southeast Asia to Hawaii [105, 106]. *H. javanicus* was introduced to Hawaii over 100 years ago to control the rat population that were destroying the sugarcane plantations. Mongooses are entirely diurnal [107] meanwhile rats are nocturnal. The mongoose preyed on the endemic birds, especially their eggs, more often that it preyed on the rats. Both the mongoose and the rats now constitute a major threat to the bird's population in Hawaii. A few attempts have been made to eradicate these invasive mongooses but with limited success [108], and now the small Asian mongoose is regarded as one of the world's 100 worst invasive species [108, 109].

Furthermore, the sturdy and prolific eastern mosquitofish (*Gambusia holbrooki*), native to the eastern and southern United States, was introduced around the world in the 1930s and 1940s to feed on mosquito larvae and thus combat malaria. Unfortunately, it has thrived at the expense of local species, causing a decline of endemic fish and frogs through competition for food resources as well as through eating their eggs and larvae [110]. Many characteristics have been identified in Gambusia that contribute to their invasiveness: mosquitofish have short breeding periods and high fecundity [111], they exhibit higher feeding rates than their non-invasive relatives [112] and also show evidence of plastic responses to salinity-related stress; they produce more offsprings in higher salinities [113].

On the other hand, the replacement of the target species with another species which constitute more of a nuisance and for which the BCA does not normally attack is another challenge of biocontrol. This has happened in the past, for example in Douglas county, Oregon, USA, where Klamath weed populations were sharply reduced by biocontrol agents only to be replaced by tansy ragwort *(Senecio jacobaea*), which was in turn sharply reduced by BCAs only to be replaced by the Italian thistles (*Carduus pycnocepahalus*) [114].

APPROACHES TO BIOCONTROL

There are three broad approaches to biocontrol.

Importation

Importation involves the importation, screening and release of natural enemies to permanently establish effective natural enemies in a new area. Importation (also referred to as "classical biological control") usually targets introduced (non-native) pests in an area where their natural enemies normally do not exist. Native pests that are not adequately controlled by existing natural enemies may also be the target of classical biocontrol. The introduction of natural enemies to control the population of a pest is usually tightly regulated and is conducted solely by the federal or state agencies compared to the following two approaches that can be done by anyone [115]. This is necessary so that we do not import "solutions" that become more serious than the "problems" themselves.

Augmentation

Augmentative biological control typically involves the purchase and release of natural enemies that are already present in an area but not in quantity, enough to adequately keep in check the pest population in a particular location. The goal of this approach is simply to increase the number of natural enemies temporarily and therefore decrease the pest population in the area [115].

Release of natural enemies may take one of these forms: inundation or inoculation. With inundation, the target area is flooded with a large number of the natural enemies. Ideally, such a release will bring the pest(s) under control quickly, and it is hoped that the natural enemies will become permanently established in the area. Meanwhile, inoculation of an area usually involves much lower numbers. It is designed to allow establishment of a biological control agent in an area. Or such a release may be used merely to improve the natural enemy/pest ratio [116].

Conservation

This involves practices to conserve the population of natural enemies, thereby improving their effectiveness in the control of pests. Such practices include farming and gardening that provide the necessary resources for their survival and protect them from toxins and other adverse conditions. These conservative practices will benefit all natural enemies, whether native or imported or released through augmentation. This approach is frequently overlooked, yet it is just as important as the other two approaches [115].

CASE STUDIES OF BIOCONTROL

One of the most foretold stories of the success of biocontrol on a large scale is the eradication of the cottony cushion scale (origin: Australia) which was a serious threat to the citrus industry. The cottony cushion scale (*Icerya purchasi* Maskell) was introduced into North America and India and it rapidly spread, threatening the citrus crop. Chemical methods were either ineffective or too expensive to control the pest. The coccinellid beetle, *Rodolia cardinalis*, which is the natural enemy of the scale in its native Australia was introduced into the areas affected by the scale in North America and India, and it successfully controlled the cottony cushion scale [5]. Since then, other successes on a similar scale have been recorded, most in the biocontrol of parasites (pests) of plants. Biocontrol of parasites of medical and veterinary importance is still at its infancy, that is at the level of research, and as such no success story has been described. A few success stories in the biocontrol of parasites of agricultural importance are described below.

Case Study 1: Biocontrol of Water Hyacinth (*Eichhornia crassipes*)

Water hyacinth is a free-floating aquatic weed of South American origin and ranks among the top 10 weeds worldwide. It is one of the most noxious weeds known to man and has spread to at least 50 countries around the globe. The weed grows and occupies water surfaces of ponds, tanks, lakes, reservoirs, streams, rivers and irrigation channels. It was also a menace in flooded rice fields, considerably reducing yield. It interferes with the production of hydroelectricity, blocks water flow in irrigation channels, prevents the free movement of navigation vessels, interferes with fishing and fish culture and facilitates breeding of mosquitoes as well as fostering waterborne diseases [117]. Furthermore, water loss due to evapo-transpiration was a major concern especially in areas where freshwater shortage was common. Under ideal conditions, water hyacinth plants can propagate vegetatively and double their number in 10 days; the seeds can remain dormant for as long as 20 years before germinating [117]. The weed was indeed a major problem in India [117]. With this high growth rate, the weed defied most control methods.

Three exotic natural enemies were introduced in India, that is hydrophilic weevils—*Neochetina bruchi* (from Argentina) and *N. eichhorniae* (from Argentina)—and galumnid mite *Orthogalumna terebrantis* (from South America) in 1982 for the biological suppression of water hyacinth. Starting from October 1983, field releases of mass-bred weevils *N. eichhorniae* and *N. bruchi* in different water tanks in Karnataka, located at Byramangala (500 ha), Bellandur (344 ha), Varthuru (40 ha), Hebbal (20 ha), Nagavara (20 ha), Agram (20 ha) and others from October 1983 to December 1986; in an 8-ha tank at Nacharam in Hyderabad (Andhra Pradesh) in 1987; Ramgarh lake near Gorakhpur (Uttar Pradesh) in 1988; in 43-km-peripheral Surha lake, Balia, (Uttar Pradesh) in 1990 and Lakhaibill (Alengmore) and Assam in 2000, resulted in suppression of water hyacinth within 4 years. The weevils have cleared the Tocklai River and were proving very effective in most of the water bodies. Releases of the water hyacinth mites, like *O. terebrantis,* which are specific to water hyacinth were initiated in 1986 at Bangalore, Karnataka. About 25,000 adults were released in Agram, Kengeri and Byramangala tanks. Establishment was obtained within 6 months in all the tanks. The mite was more efficient in water in which *N. eichhorniae* was also present [117]. Many other successes have been recorded in the biocontrol of weeds which can be found in the review by Cork et al. [118].

Case Study 2: Biocontrol of the Glassy-winged Sharpshooter (*Homalodisca vire-pennis* Formerly known as *H. coagulata*)

The glassy-winged sharpshooter (*Homalodisca vitripennis*) is a large leafhopper insect from the family Cicadellidae. It is native to North America (northeastern Mexico) but has spread into the USA, where it has become an agricultural pest [119]. It is thought that the glassy-winged sharpshooter invaded and was established in the southern California sometimes around 1990 [120]. The glassy-winged sharpshooter usually lays a mass of eggs on the underside of leaves and covers them with the "brochosomes", a powdery white protective secretion kept in dry form. After hatching, the nymphs feed within the vascular system of small stems, molt several times and become adults which continue to feed on a wide variety of plants including grapes, citrus trees, almonds, stone fruit and oleanders resulting in enormous damage. Their feeding method along with their voracious appetite for so many different hosts makes them an effective vector for the bacterium *Xylella fastidiosa*, which causes plant disease. *X. fastidiosa* has been linked to many plant diseases including phoney peach disease in the southern USA; oleander leaf scorch and Pierce's disease in California and citrus X disease in Brazil. Plants not affected by the bacterium become a reservoir for other sharpshooters to pick up and carry to other plants [121].

The glassy-winged sharpshooter has a number of natural enemies, in particular egg parasitoids. Female parasitoids lay their eggs inside glassy-winged sharpshooter eggs and the developing parasitoid larvae kill glassy-winged sharpshooter eggs by feeding inside the egg. The parasitoid larvae pupate inside the glassy-winged sharpshooter egg and then chew a circular exit hole through which they emerge. The winged parasitoids can fly and after mating, they look out for more glassy-winged sharpshooter eggs to parasitize. In this manner, the egg parasitoids help keep the glassy-winged sharpshooter population in check [121]. In the southeastern USA and northeastern Mexico, glassy-winged sharpshooter eggs are parasitized by several species of mymarid and trichogrammatid parasitoids, including *Gonatocerus ashmeadi* Girault, *G. triguttatus* Girault, *G. morrilli* Howard and *G. fasciatus* Girault. Virtually, all species of parasitoid in the family Mymaridae (order: Hymenoptera) are the most common natural enemies associated with *H. vitripennis* eggs in the southeastern United States [122]. *Gonatocerus tuberculifemur* and *G. deleoni* are other species of parasitoids that attack the glassy-winged sharpshooter eggs and were introduced into California from Argentina [123, 124].

The glassy-winged sharpshooter has also successfully invaded French Polynesia (the Society Islands, Marquesas and Austral Island groups) where it became established in 1999 [125], Hawaii where it became established in 2004 [126], Easter Island and the Cook Islands. Glassy-winged sharpshooter became established in Tahiti French Polynesia in 1999 and was likely introduced accidentally on ornamental plants imported from California [121]. In contrast to California, no natural enemies for the glassy-winged sharpshooter existed there, and no obvious competitors existed in urban or natural settings. The glassy-winged sharpshooter populations underwent an exponential growth and were a complete nuisance to the population; watery excreta known as sharpshooter rain literally rained from infested trees because there were so many glassy-winged sharpshooters feeding on trees, their noisy wings, their dead bodies littered in houses and their high populations retarded plant growth and reduced local fruit production [121]. Due to intense population movement, the glassy-winged sharpshooter spread to other areas in the region such as Raiatea (Leeward Islands) Moorea, Leeward Islands of Huahine, Bora Bora, Tahaa and Maupiti. At the end of 2004 and the beginning of 2005, the glassy-winged sharpshooter populations were discovered outside of the Society Islands in two other archipelagos of French Polynesia substantially distant from Tahiti: the Australs, where two islands were infested (Rurutu and Tubuai) and the Marquesas, where one island, Nuku Hiva, was found infested [121].

To combat the glassy-winged sharpshooter infestation in French Polynesia, the mymarid egg parasitoid *Gonatocerus ashmeadi* was imported from California, mass bred and released. Between May and October 2005, 13,786 parasitoids were released at 27 sites in Tahiti. The parasitoid established readily, and within 7 months of release, the glassy-winged sharpshooter had been completely controlled in Tahiti, and glassy-winged sharpshooter populations were reduced by over 95% [127]. The parasitoid also spread unassisted to every other island infested by the glassy-winged sharpshooter and parasitized their eggs [121], which led to a successful control of the glassy-winged sharpshooter in the area.

CASE STUDY 3: BIOCONTROL OF THE VELVET BEAN CATERPILLAR (*ANTICARSIA GEMMATALIS*)

One of the most successful uses of baculoviruses in biological control has been in Brazil. The baculovirus AgMNPV has been successfully used in the control of the velvet bean caterpillar (*Anticarsia gemmatalis*), a pest of soybeans. Plots of soybeans that were naturally infested with *A. gemmatalis* were sprayed with the virus. The AgMNPV is highly virulent for *A. gemmatalis* and only needs to be applied once, which makes it a good BCA for the control of the velvet bean caterpillar. Furthermore, the virus can be spread by insect predators and survive passage through the digestive tract of beetles and hemipteran. In Brazil, virus preparations were applied at 1.5×10^{11} occlusion bodies per ha, that is, about 20 g or 50 larval equivalents. The programme, which was initiated in the early 1980s, by 2005, had seen the treatment of area of over 2 m ha [128].

In other examples, the granulovirus of the codling moth *Cydia pomonella* (CpGV) has been used in a number of countries in North America and Europe for the control of the insect on pear and apple crops [128]. In China, the baculovirus HearNPV has also been successfully used to control the cotton bollworm, *Helicoverpa armigera*, which was a major pest of cotton and had developed resistance to the chemical insecticides in many parts of the world [129].

CHALLENGES IN THE BIOLOGICAL CONTROL OF PARASITES

Some challenges in the implementation of biocontrol strategies are listed below.

The introduction of exotic natural enemies raises concern regarding the effect it may have on non-target native species as mentioned above. Conservation biologists are typically concerned with the health and growth of a wide variety of organisms. If a BCA does in fact attack any native non-target species, its persistence and ability to spread to areas far from the site of release become a serious liability [130–132].

There are also concerns among conservation biologists about the release of BCA precisely because the agents themselves which are non-native may carry non-native parasites and commensal species [114].

BCAs are easily influenced by environmental factors such as temperature, humidity and oxygen extremes, which determine the success of the biological control strategy. BCA if applied when conditions are not favourable is bound to fail.

There are also challenges in the distribution of BCAs product, especially those containing living organisms. Most industries producing BCA products are often situated a considerable distance away from where the BCA is to be used. Before the BCA reaches its destination, most of the organisms are dead. There is therefore the need to develop a sizeable distribution network comprising a group of producers that will safeguard the quality of the products and provide advice for the users [133].

Another challenge, which may be faced with the implementation of a biocontrol strategy in pest control, is the lukewarm attitude among agriculturalists, who find it difficult to forego their fast-acting chemical pesticides over the sluggish BCA [134, 135].

FUTURE PERSPECTIVE

Biotechnology

With the advances in biotechnology, there is the potential of identifying and manipulating "biocontrol genes" particularly in microbial agents to produce more effective BCAs. Furthermore, genes in BCAs responsible for their antagonistic effects will also be used to screen for more effective BCAs. Biotechnologists in many countries are experimenting with fungi, viruses, bacteria, nematodes and insects genetically modified to express toxins (scorpion toxin, mite toxin and trypsin inhibitor), hormones (eclosion hormone and diuretic hormone) or metabolic enzymes (juvenile hormone esterase) to increase the speed of killing, enhance virulent and extend host specificity of these organisms. The so-called third-generation genetically modified organisms (GMOs) have been engineered to control pests in agriculture, pathogens in human health and invasive species in the environment [136].

In one approach, to improve the efficacy of *Bacillus thuringiensis* var *israelensis* (Bti), genes encoding the potent insecticidal proteins from Bti, Btj and *B. sphaericus* have been spliced into new bacteria strains that are 10-fold more toxic than wild types species of Bti and *B. sphaericus* used in current commercial formulations. These new GMOs are safe to humans, animals and the environment and can be used as components in the integrated vector control programmes aimed at reducing malaria, filariasis and other diseases of medical importance [137]. These recombinant bacterial larvicides are much more efficient than the wild-type strains from which they are derived, their costs are similar to the new chemical insecticides and they are much more environmentally compatible than most chemical insecticides [46].

In another approach, biotechnologists are trying to develop new biopesticides based on fungi. Fungi tend to be host specific, can be mass produced on inexpensive media and are thought to be harmless to animals, humans and the environment. Unfortunately, naturally occurring fungi tend to kill insects slowly. Genetic technology holds the promise of producing biopesticides based on hypervirulent insect-specific fungi that kill quickly; for example, laboratory experiments have been performed where scorpion toxin gene has been spliced into the fungus that infect mosquitoes to enhance the killing efficiency of the fungus [138].

In yet another approach, biotechnologists are studying baculoviruses, a large variety of viruses that act specifically on hundreds of arthropods, including many agricultural pests, but appear to be safe to plants and vertebrates. But because baculoviruses typically kill much more slowly than chemical pesticides, their use is limited. Biotechnologists are experimenting to increase the killing efficiency of baculoviruses by splicing into them toxin-expressing genes isolated from mites, scorpions and spiders [139]. Baculovirus recombinants that produce occlusion bodies incorporating Bt toxin have also been constructed by making a fusion protein consisting of a polyhedron and Bt toxin [140]. Other constructs have been tested with varying success [141]. This new biopesticide is highly pathogenic than the wild-type baculovirus as it combines the advantages of the virus and the bacteria toxin.

However, the use of biotechnology raises some questions regarding the potential impact of those GMOs or plants to human, animal and the environment and other non-target species. This has presented a major hurdle to research and field testing and the introduction of these recombinant BCAs to users. Fortunately, the use of genetically engineered microbial pathogen products for control is increasingly being accepted by the society, and commercial production is gradually gaining grounds. In the near future, genetically engineered microbial BCAs will soon be the most common biocontrol products available in the market to circumvent the problem of growing resistance to chemical pesticides and the threats posed to public health and the environment by the chemical pesticides.

Nanotechnology

Nanotechnology is another field that holds wide applicability in biological control in the near future. Nanotechnology for control has been applied mostly in the control of agricultural pests. Its application in the control of agriculture pest offers some advantages over traditional methods by providing green and highly efficient alternatives for the management of insect pests without harming nature [142]. Nanoparticles are known to be effective against plant pathogens, insects and pests. Hence, nanoparticles can be used in the preparation of new formulations like pesticides, insecticides and insect repellents [143–146]. Nanomaterials come in many forms—porous hollow silica nanoparticles (PHSNs) loaded with validamycin (pesticide) [147], nano-silica prepared from silica, polyethylene glycol-coated nanoparticles loaded with garlic essential oil, silver nanoparticles synthesized from various plant extracts and so on.

One of the most studied nanomaterials for the control of agricultural pests is nano-silica. Nano-silica formulated as nano-pesticide can effectively be used in the control of insect pests. The mechanism of control of insect pests using nano-silica is based on the fact that insect pests use a variety of cuticular lipids to protect their water barrier and thereby prevent death from desiccation. But nano-silica gets absorbed into the cuticular lipids by physiosorption and thereby causes death of insects purely by physical means when applied on leaves and stem surfaces [142]. It has also been shown that in addition to agricultural insect pests, surface-charged modified hydrophobic nano-silica (~3–5 nm) could be successfully used to control animal ectoparasites of veterinary importance [148].

Silver nanoparticles (AgNPs) have been synthesized using various plant extracts as reducing and stabilizing agents. These AgNPs have been tested and shown to be of higher toxicity against the mosquito vectors of parasites of medical and veterinary importance. For example, an AgNP synthesized using extracts of *Artemisia vulgaris* leaves has been observed to be highly toxic to *Aedes aegypti* larval instars (I–IV) and pupae, with LC_{50} ranging from 4.4 (for the first instar) to 13.1 ppm (for the pupae) and was also observed to increase the predatory efficiency of the Asian bullfrog tadpole, *Hoplobatrachus tigerinus*, a natural predator on mosquito larvae [149]. AgNP synthesized using other plant extracts has also demonstrated similar or higher efficacy: AgNP synthesized using the aqueous leaf extract of the seaweed, *Hypnea musciformis*, has shown larvicidal and pupicidal toxicity against *Aedes aegypti* and the cabbage pest, *Plutella xylostella* [150]; AgNP synthesized using *Nicondra physalodes* has shown larvicidal toxicity against *Anopheles stephensi*, *Aedes aegypti* and *Culex quinquefasciatus*, with the maximum efficacy detected against *An. Stephensi* (LC_{50} = 12.39 μg/ml) [151] and AgNPs synthesized using *Zornia diphylla* have shown higher toxicity against *Anopheles subpictus*, *Aedes albopictus* and *Culex tritaniorhynchus* with LC_{50} values of 12.53, 13.42 and 14.61 μg/ml, respectively [152]. AgNPs are promising for the development of eco-friendly larvicides against mosquito vectors, with negligible effect against non-target species.

Yang et al. [153] have demonstrated that the efficacy of the insecticidal activity of polytherlene glycol-coated nanoparticles loaded with garlic essential oil against adult red flour beetle (*Tribolium castaneum*) insects found in store products was as high as 80%. In another example, Sabbour [154] tested two nanomaterials Aluminium oxide (Al_2O_3) and Titanium dioxide (TiO_2) against rice weevil *Sitophilus oryzae* and observed that under laboratory conditions, the mortality increased significantly to 50.6 ± 3.6 as compared to 3.0 ± 3.4 for the control and under store condition, the mortality increased significantly to 67.3 ± 1.4 after 45 days of storage as compared to 3.8 ± 3.8 in the control. Furthermore, accumulative mortality (%) of *S. oryzae* beetles increased gradually by increasing the period of exposure.

Nanotechnology has also been applied on BCAs. Nanoparticles as various formulations of essential oils, silica gels, powders and so on applied on BCAs have been shown to increase the effectiveness of BCAs in neutralizing some agricultural pests. For example, Sabbour [155] showed that in the laboratory, the nano-entomopathogenic fungi, nano-*Beauveria bassiana* and nano-*Metarhizium anisopliae,* formulated using dust carriers, were more effective in the killing of the insect pest of stored rice *Sitophilus oryzae* (L.) compared to control. The LC_{50} obtained were 45 x 10^4 and 57 x 10^4 conidia/ml for nano-*B. bassiana* and nano-*M. anisopliae,* respectively, lower than 66 x 10^4 and 77 x 10^4 conidia/ml for *B. bassiana* and *M. anisopliae,* respectively. There was a significant reduction of the number eggs laid/female as well as the number of emerged adults in stored bags that were treated with nano-entomopathogenic fungi nano-*B. bassiana* and nano-*M. anisopliae* compared to control. On the other hand, some BCAs are capable of producing nanoparticles. For example, there are a large volume of research reports that suggest that actinobacteria are capable of producing metal oxide nanoparticles. These can be exploited in the green synthesis of nanomaterials and utilized in biological systems [156]. Sabbour [157] tested the efficacy of nano-extracted destruxin from *Metarhizium anisopliae* against the Indian meal moth *Plodia interpunctella* (which is one of the most serious stored grain pest worldwide), and the LC_{50} obtained was 77×10^4 for nano-destruxin compared to 103×10^4 for destruxin. Under laboratory conditions, the number of eggs laid/female significantly decreased to 17.4 ± 3.8 and 10.6 ± 9.5 eggs/female after treatment with destruxin and nano-destruxin as compared to 99.9 ± 7.9 eggs/female for the control after 120 days. And under store conditions, the number of eggs laid/female decreased significantly to 13.1 ± 9.2 after nano-destruxin treatments after 120 days. Furthermore, the emerged adults decreased to 2% after nano-destruxin treatments after 120 days [157].

Nanotechnology also has promising applications in nanoparticle-mediated gene (DNA) transfer. It can be used to deliver DNA and other desired chemicals into plant tissue for protection of host plants against insect pests [158]. There is evidence that nanotechnology will revolutionize agriculture including pest management in the near future [159].

Microencapsulation

Microencapsulation is another new field that holds promise in biological control. Microencapsulation is a process in which active substances are coated by extremely small capsules [160]. Microencapsulation has numerous applications in areas such as the pharmaceutical, agricultural, medical and food industries, being widely used in the encapsulation of essential oils, colourings, flavourings, sweeteners and microorganisms, among others [161]. Microencapsulation in biological control can be used for the enhancement of the activity of BCAs in biocontrol, especially pathogens. The coating may impact stability, protection from UV radiation and/or other environmental conditions, enhance the attractiveness of the pesticide to the pest and/or serve to separate two different biologically incompatible pesticides within a mixture. For example, *Bacillus subtilis* has been widely used as a BCA in agriculture but their short shelf life limits their use. In a study in which *Bacillus subtilis* was microencapsulated using maltodextrin, it was observed that the mean survival rate of *B. subtilis* was more than 90%, when spray drying was performed at 145°C, with a feed flow rate of 550 mL h−1 and a spray pressure of 0.15 MPa. The shelf life was also significantly prolonged compared to wettable powders. Moreover, the biocontrol efficacy of the *B. subtilis* microcapsule reached 79.91% when a dosage of 300 g hm^{-2} was used; the microcapsule showed higher control efficacy than thiram wettable powder against the plant pathogenic fungus *Rhizoctonia solani* in tomato under field conditions [162]. This approach can be applied to other BCAs, especially pathogenic microorganisms, to enhance their effectiveness.

CONCLUSION

To date, many strategies have been used in the control of parasites including the use of chemicals. The chemical methods are limited in their application, partly as a result of the rising resistance, environmental and health risks and the potential effect to non-target organisms. In addition to the previously mentioned biological control agents, parasites could also be controlled naturally through botanicals [163–167], photosensitizers [168, 169], symbiotic [170], organic [171] and short-chain fatty acids [172]. Biological control approaches hold promise as the most suitable alternative to the chemical pesticides and are now a core component of IPM. A good number of promising BCAs including predators, parasites (parasitoids) and pathogens (fungi, bacteria, viruses and virus-like particles, protozoa and nematodes) have been identified and proven to be efficacious against many parasites of medical, veterinary and agricultural importance, as highlighted in the chapter [25, 49, 85]. In the past, biological control has been applied successfully to control parasites especially in the agricultural sector [120]. However, there are still many challenges in the implementation of biological control strategies including their potential effects on native biodiversity [133–135], the unwillingness to ditch the chemical methods for BCAs by farmers [129] and challenges in the production and distribution of the BCAs [136]. With the recent advances in biotechnology and the application of most recent technologies such as nanotechnology [145] and microencapsulation [162], there are many opportunities for the continued use and expanded role of natural enemies in biological control; newer BCAs are being identified and older ones are being genetically engineered to make them more efficacious in their antagonism of parasites. There is, therefore, optimism that in the future, biological control will develop to overcome many of the challenges, and BCAs will become the mainstay for the control of parasites.

REFERENCES

1. Alston DG. General Concepts of Biological Control. Utah State University Extension and Utah Plant Pest Diagnostic Laboratory. Logan, Utah, US. IPM-015-11. 2011.
2. DeBach P. Biological Control of Insect Pests and Weeds. London, UK: Chapman and Hall; 1964. p. 844
3. Dreistadt SH. Biological control and natural enemies of invertebrates: Integrated pest management for home gardeners and landscape professionals. Statewide Integrated Pest Management Program. University of California, Davis, California, US; 2014; Pest Notes Publication 74140:1-6
4. Du Roi IPM. Integrated Pest Management: The Concept [Internet]. Available from: http:// www. duroibugs. co. za/about. htm [Accessed: 17 October 2016]
5. van den Bosch R, Messenger PS, Gutierrez AP. The history and development of biological control. In: An Introduction to Biological Control. US: Springer; 1982. pp. 21-36. DOI: 10. 1007/978-1-4757-9162-4_3
6. Greathead DJ. Benefits and risks of classical biocontrol. In: Hokkanen HM, Lynch JM, editors. Biological Control: Benefits and Risks. Cambridge, UK: Cambridge University Press; 1995. pp. 53-63
7. Lockwood JA. Environmental issues involved in biological control of rangeland grasshoppers (Orthoptera: Acrididae) with exotic agents. Environmental Entomology. 1993;22:503-518
8. Lockwood JA. Nontarget effects of biological control: What are we trying to miss? In: Follett PA, Duan JJ, editors. Nontarget Effects of Biological Control. Boston, Massachusetts: Kluwer Academic Publishers; 2000. pp. 15-30
9. McEvoy PB, Coombs EM. Why things bite back: Unintended consequences of biological weed control. In: Follett PA, Duan JJ, editors. Nontarget Effects of Biological Control. Boston, Massachusetts: Kluwer Academic Publishers; 2000. pp. 167-194
10. Wilkinson PR. A preliminary note on predation on free-living engorged female rocky mountainwood ticks. Journal of Medical Entomology. 1970;7:493-496
11. Wilkinson PR. Factors affecting the distribution and abundance of the cattle tick in Australia: Observations and hypotheses. Acarologia. 1970;12:492-507
12. Mwangi EN, Dipeolu OO, Newson RM, Kaaya GP, Hassan SM. Predators, parasitoids and pathogens of ticks: A review. Biocontrol Science and Technology. 1991;1:147-156

13. Krivolutsky DA. Eradication of larvae and nymphs of the tick Ixodes persulcatus by predators. In: Proceedings of the Conference on Ticks Encephalitis Hemorrhagic Fever viruses; December 10-13, 1963; Omsk, Izd. Minzdrav RSFSR. Omsk NII POI, Omsk: Otd. San. epidemiol. kontr. ; 1963. p. 187-188

14. Jackson RR, Pollard SD. Predatory behavior of jumping spiders. Annual Review of Entomology. 1996;41:287-308

15. Riechert SE, Bishop L. Prey control by an assemblage of generalist predators: Spiders in garden test systems. Ecology. 1990;71:441-1450

16. Sokolow SH, Lafferty KD, Kuris AM. Regulation of laboratory populations of snails (Biomphalaria and Bulinus spp.) by river prawns, Macrobrachium spp. (Decapoda, Palaemonidae): Implications for control of schistosomiasis. Acta Tropica. 2014;132:64-74

17. Hernández MC, Walsh GC. Insect herbivores associated with Ludwigia species, Oligospermum section, in their Argentine distribution. Journal of Insect Science. 2014;14(1):201. DOI: 10. 1093/jisesa/ieu063

18. Mahr SER, Cloyd RA, Mahr DL, Sadof CS. Biological control of insects and other pests of greenhouse crops. University of Wisconsin Cooperative Extension. Lake street, Madison, Wisconsin, US. North Central Regional Publication 581; 2001

19. Lysek H. Effect of certain soil organisms on the eggs of parasitic roundworms. Nature. 1963;199:925

20. Safaa, Abo-Taka M, Heikal HM, Abd El-Raheem AM. Macrochelid mite, Macrocheles muscaedomesticae (Acarina: Macrochelidae) as a biological control agent against house fly, Musca domestica (Diptera: Muscidae) in Egypt. International Journal of Zoological Research. 2014;10:30-36

21. Pirali-Kheirabadi K. Biological control of parasites. In: Shah MM, editor. Parasitology. Rijeka, Croatia: Intech; 2012. p. 54-66.

22. Oluwafemi R. Biological Control of Tsetse Fly Project (BICOT) in Lafia local government area of Nasarawa State, Nigeria, 1984-2000. The Internet Journal of Veterinary Medicine. 2008;7(1):1-5

23. Jemal A, Hugh-Jones M. A review of the red imported fire ant (Solenopsis invicta Buren) and its impacts on plant, animal, and human health. Preventive Veterinary Medicine. 1993;17:19-32

24. Egyptian Myths. Ancient Egypt: The Mythology [Internet]. 2014. Available from: http://www. egyptianmyths. net/scarab. htm [Accessed: 26 November 2016]

25. Bornemissza GF. Insectary studies on the control of dung breeding flies by the activity of the dung beetle, Onthophagus gazelle F. (Coleoptera: Scarabaeidae). Australian Journal of Entomology. 1970;9(1):31-41

26. Bornemissza GF. The Australian dung beetle project, 1965-1975. Australian Meat Research Committee Reviews. 1976;30:1-30

27. Acorn J. Ladybugs of Alberta: Finding the Spots and Connecting the Dots. Edmonton, Alberta, Canada: University of Alberta; 2007. p. 15

28. Canyon DV, Hii JL. The gecko: An environmentally friendly biological agent for mosquito control. Medical and Veterinary Entomology. 1997;11(4):319-323

29. Sankaralingam A, Venkatesan P. Larvicidal properties of water bug Diplonychus indicus Venkatesan & Rao and its use in mosquito control. Indian Journal of Experimental Biology. 1989;27(2):174-176

30. Mwangi EN, Newson RM, Kaaya GP. Predation of free-living engorged female Rhipicephalus appendiculatus. Experimental and Applied Acarology. 1991;12:153-162

31. Walker K. A review of control methods for African malaria vectors: Activity Report 108 [thesis]. Washington DC, USA: Agency for International Development; 2002. p. 54. Available from: http://www. ehproject. org/PDF/Activity_Reports/AR108MalRevArch. pdf

32. Menon PKB, Rajagopalan PK. Control of mosquito breeding in wells by using Gambusia affinis and Aplocheilus blocki in Pondicherry town. Indian Journal of Medical Research. 1978;68:927-933

33. Kamareddine L. The biological control of the malaria vector. Toxins. 2012;4:748-767. DOI: 10. 3390/toxins4090748

34. World Health Organization. Manual on Environmental Management for Mosquito Control with Special Emphasis on Malaria Vectors. WHO Offset Publication No. 66. Geneva, Switzerland: World Health Organization; 1982. pp. 1-276

35. Hung NM, Duc NV, Stauffer JR, Madsen H. Use of black carp (Mylopharyngodon piceus) in biological control of intermediate host snails of fish-borne zoonotic trematodes in nursery ponds in the Red River Delta, Vietnam. Parasites & Vectors. 2013;6:142. DOI: 10. 1186/1756-3305-6-142

36. Isenhart FR, DeSante DF. Observations of scrub jays cleaning ectoparasites from black-tailed deer. Condor. 1985;87:145-147

37. Hassan SM, Dipeolu OO, Amoo AO, Odhiambo TR. Predation on livestock ticks by chickens. Veterinary Parasitology. 1991;38(2-3):199-204

38. Short NJ, Norval RAI. Tick predation by shrews in Zimbabwe. Journal of Parasitology. 1982;68:1052

39. Samish M. Pathogens and predators of ticks and their potential in biological control. Annual Review of Entomology. 1999;44:159-182

40. Hoddle MS, Van Driesche RG, Sanderson JP. Biology and use of the whitefly parasitoid Encarsia formosa. Annual Review of Entomology. 1998;43:645-669

41. Smith SM. Biological control with Trichogramma: Advances, successes, and potential of their use. Annual Review of Entomology. 1996;41:375-406. DOI: 10. 1146/annurev. en. 41. 010196. 002111

42. Wajnberg E, Hassan SA. Biological Control with Egg Parasitoids. Wallingford, Oxfordshire, England: CABI Publishing; 1994

43. Gullan PJ, Cranston PS. The Insects: An Outline of Entomology. 4th ed. Oxford, U. K. : Wiley-Blackwell; 2010

44. Jian L, Dakshina RS. Parasitoids of Dipteran leafminers, Diglyphus spp. (Insecta: Hymenoptera: Eulophidae). EENY-484 (IN877). Entomology and Nematology Department, Florida Cooperative Extension Service, Institute of Food and Agricultural Sciences, University of Florida, Gainesville, Florida, US; 2010

45. McCoy CW, Samson RA, Boucias DG. Entomogenous fungi. In: Ignoffo CM, editor. CRC Handbook of Natural Pesticides: Microbial Insecticides, Part A; Entomogenous Protozoa and Fungi. Florida, USA: CRCPress; 1988. pp. 151-236

46. Khater HF. Ecosmart biorational insecticides: Alternative insect control strategies. In: Perveen F, editor. Insecticides—Advances in Integrated Pest Management. Rijeka, Croatia: InTech; 2012. pp. 18-61

47. Leger RJS. Studies on adaptations of Metarhizium anisopliae to life in the soil. Journal of Invertebrate Pathology. 2008;96:271-276

48. Quesada-Moraga E, Ruiz-Garcia A, Santiago-Alvarez C. Laboratory evaluation of entomopathogenic fungi Beauveria bassiana and Metarhizium anisopliae against puparia

and adults of Ceratitis capitata (Diptera: Tephritidae). Journal of Economic Entomology. 2006;99:1955-1966

49. Ebrahim AY. Biological control of vector born protozoan parasites of veterinary importance. Applied Scientific Reports. 2015;10(3):122-127. DOI: 10. 15192/PSCP. ASR. 2015. 10. 3. 122127

50. Knols BGJ, Bukhari T, Farenhorst M. Entomopathogenic fungi as the next-generation control agents against malaria mosquitoes. Future Microbiology. 2010;5(3):339-341

51. Scholte EJ, Ng'habi K, Kihonda J, Takken W, Paaijmans K, Abdulla S, Killeen GF. An entomopathogenic fungus for control of adult African malaria mosquitoes. Science. 2005;308:1641-1642

52. Okumu FO, Madumla EP, John AN, Lwetoijera DW, Sumaye RD. Attracting, trapping, and killing disease-transmitting mosquitoes using odor-baited stations—the Ifakara odor-baited stations. Parasites & Vectors. 2010;3:1-10

53. Khater HF. Biocontrol of some insects [thesis]. Benha Branch, Egypt: Zagazig University; 2003

54. Ghannam I, Barakat R, Al-Masri M. Biological control of Egyptian broomrape (Orobanche aegyptiaca) using Fusarium spp. Phytopathologia Mediterranea. 2007;46:177-184

55. Sur B, Bihari V, Sharma A, Joshi AK. Studies on physiology, zoospore morphology and entomopathogenic potential of the aquatic oomycete: Coelomomyces giganteum. Mycopathologia. 2001;154:51-54

56. Jensen AB, Thomsen L, Eilenberg J. Intraspecific variation and host specificity of Entomophthora muscae sensu stricto isolates revealed by random amplified polymorphic DNA, universal primed PCR, PCR-restriction fragment length polymorphism, and conidial morphology. Journal of Invertebrate Pathology. 2001;78(4):251-259

57. Sallam NMA, Abo-Elyousr KAM, Hassan MAE. Evaluation of Trichoderma Species as biocontrol agents for damping-off and wilt diseases of Phaseolus vulgaris L. and efficacy of suggested formula. Egypt Journal of Phytopathology. 2008;36(1-2):81-93

58. Santos CP, Charles TP. Effetio da aplicacao de conidios de Drechmeria coniospora em cultivos de fezes contendo ovos de Haemonchus contortus [Effect of an endo-parasitic fungus, Drechmeria coniospora, in faecal cultures containing eggs of Haemonchus contortus]. Arquivo Brasileiro de Medicina Veterinária e Zootecnia. 1995;47:123-128

59. Charles TP, Rouque MVC, Santos CD. Reduction of Haemonchus contortus infective larvae by Harposporium anguillulae in sheep faecal cultures. International Journal for Parasitology. 1996;26:509-510

60. Gronvold J, Korsholm H, Wolstrup J, Nansen P, Henriksen SA. Laboratory experiments to evaluate the ability of Arthobotrys oligospora to destroy infective larvae of Cooperia species and to investigate the effect of physical factors on the growth of the fungus. Journal of Helminthology. 1985;59:119-126

61. Mendoza de Gives P, Crespo JF, Rodriguez DH, Prats VV, Hernandez EL, Fernandez GEO. Biological control of Haemonchus contortus infective larvae in ovine faeces by administering an oral suspension of Duddingtonia flagrans chlamydospores to sheep. Journal of Helminthology. 1998;72:343-347

62. Vilela VLR, Feitosa TF, Bragab FR, de Araújo JV, de Oliveira Souto DV, da Silva Santos HE, da Silva GLL, Athayde ACR. Biological control of goat gastrointestinal helminthiasis by Duddingtonia flagrans in a semi-arid region of the Northeastern Brazil. Veterinary Parasitology. 2012;188:127-133. DOI: 10. 1016/j. vetpar. 2012. 02. 018

63. Larsen M. Biological control of nematode parasites in sheep. Journal of Animal Science. 2006;84:E133-E139

64. Araujo JV, Gomes APS, Guimaraes MP. Biological control of bovine gastrointestinal nematode parasites in Southeastern Brazil by the nematode-trapping fungus Arthrobotrys robusta. Revista Brasileira de Parasitologia Veterinária. 1998;7(2):117-122
65. De S, Sanyal PK. Biological control of helminth parasites by predatory fungi. VetScan. 2009;4(1): 387-395
66. Tribe HT. Pathology of cystnematodes. Biological Reviews of the Cambridge Philosophical Society. 1977;52:447-508
67. Lysek H, krajci D. Penetration of ovicidal fungus Verticillium chlamydosporium through the Ascaris lumbricoides egg-shells. Folia Parasitologica. 1987;34:57-60
68. Lysek H, Sterba J. Colonization of Ascaris lumbricoides eggs by the fungus Verticillium chlamydosporium Goddard. Folia Parasitologica. 1991;38:255-259
69. Kunert J. On the mechanism of penetration of ovicidal fungi through egg shells of parasitic nematodes, decomposition of chitinous and ascaroside layers. Folia Parasitologica. 1992;39:61-66
70. Ranjbar-Bahadori SH, Razzaghi-Abyaneh M, Bayat M, Eslami A, Pirali-Kheirabadi KH, Shams-Ghahfarokhi M, Lotfollahzadeh S. Studies on the effect of temperature, incubation time and in vivo gut passage on survival and nematophagous activity Arthrobotrys oligospora var. oligospora and A. cladodes var. macroides. Global Veterinaria. 2010;4:112-117
71. Ravensberg WJ. Biological control of pests: Current trends and future prospects. In: Brighton Crop Protection Conference-Pest and Diseases. Thornton Heath, UK: British Crop Protection Council; 1994. pp. 591-600
72. Hassanain MA, el Garhy MF, Abdel-Ghaffar FA, el-Sharaby A, Abdel Megeed KN. Biological control studies of soft and hard ticks in Egypt. I. The effect of Bacillus thuringiensis varieties on soft and hard ticks (ixodidae). Parasitology Research. 1997;83(3):209-213
73. Robert LL, Perich MJ, Schlein Y. Phlebotomine sand fly control using bait-fed adults to carry the larvicide Bacillus sphaericus to the larval habitat. Journal of the American Mosquito Control Association. 1997;13:140-144
74. Duval D, Galinier R, Mouahid G, Toulza E, Allienne JF, Portela J, Calvayrac C, Rognon A, Arancibia N, Mitta G, Théron A, Gourbal B. A novel bacterial pathogen of Biomphalaria glabrata: A potential weapon for schistosomiasis control? PLoS Neglected Tropical Diseases. 2015;9(2):e0003489. DOI: 10. 1371/journal. pntd. 0003489
75. El-Gammal EW, Shalaby HA, Ashry HM, El-Diwany AI. In vitro action of Streptomyces griseolus proteases as bio-control on Fasciola gigantica eggs. Journal of Bacteriology & Parasitology. 2014;5:1000192. DOI: 10. 4172/2155-9597. 1000192
76. Bekal S, Borneman J, Springer MS, Giblin-Davis RM, Becker JO. Phenotypic and molecular analysis of a Pasteuria strain parasitic to the sting nematode. Journal of Nematology. 2001;33:110-115
77. Oliveira EJ, Rabinovitch L, Monnerat RG, Passos LKJ, Zahner V. Molecular characterization of Brevibacillus laterosporus and its potential use in biological control. Applied and Environmental Microbiology. 2004;70:6657-6664
78. Huang XW, Tian BY, Niu QH, Yang JK, Zhang LM, Zhang KQ. An extracellular protease from Brevibacillus laterosporus G4 without parasporal crystal can serve as a pathogenic factor in infection of nematodes. Research in Microbiology. 2005;156:719-727
79. Rovira AD, Sands DC. Fluorescent pseudomonas—a residual component in the soil microflora. Journal of Applied Microbiology. 1977;34:253-259
80. Krebs B, Hoeding B, Kuebart S, Workie MA, Junge H, Schmiedeknecht G, Grosch R, Bochow H, Hevesi M. Use of Bacillus subtilis as biocontrol agent. I. Activities and characterization

of Bacillus subtilis strains. Zeitschrift für Pflanzenkrankheiten und Pflanzenschutz. 1998;105:181-197

81. Feitelson JS, Payne J, Kim L. Bacillus thuringiensis: Insects and beyond. Bio/Technology. 1992;10:271-275. DOI: 10. 1038/nbt0392-271

82. Tian B, Yang J, Zhang K-Q. Bacteria used in the biological control of plant-parasitic nematodes: Populations, mechanisms of action, and future prospects. FEMS Microbiology Ecology. 2007;61:197-213

83. Hsiao C, Hsiao TH. Rickettsia as the cause of cytoplasmic incompatibility in the alfalfa weevil, Hypera postica. Journal of Invertebrate Pathology. 1985;45:244-246

84. Raoult D, Roux V. Rickettsioses as paradigms of newer emerging infectious diseases. Clinical Microbiology Reviews. 1997;10:694-719

85. Sidorov VE. Some features of Coxiella burnetii interaction with argasid ticks (experimental morphological study). In: Grochovskaia IM, Melejaeva MA, editors. Razvitie Parazitologicheskoi Nauki v Turkmenistane. Ashchabad: Yilim; 1979. pp. 112-128

86. Lacey LA, Kaya HK. Field Manual of Techniques in Invertebrate Pathology. 2nd ed. Dordrecht, The Netherlands: Springer; 2007

87. Szewczyk B, Rabalski L, Krol E, Sihler W, Lobo de Souza M. Baculovirus biopesticides—a safe alternative to chemical protection of plants. Journal of Biopesticides. 2009;2(2):209-216

88. Szewczyk B, Lobo de Souza M, Batista de Castro ME, Moscardi ML, Moscardi F. Baculovirus biopesticides. In: Stoytcheva M, editor. Pesticides—Formulations, Effects, Fate. Rijeka, Croatia: InTech; 2011. pp. 25-36

89. Jehle JA, Blissard GW, Bonning BC, Cory JS, Herniou EA, Rohrmann GF, Theilmann DA, Thiem SA, Vlak JM. On the classification and nomenclature of baculoviruses: A proposal for revision. Archives of Virology. 2006;151:1257-1266

90. Hunter WB, Katsar CS, Chaparro J. Molecular analysis of capsid protein of Homalodisca coagulata virus-1, a new leafhopper-infecting virus from the glassy-winged sharpshooter, Homalodisca coagulata. Journal of Insect Science. 2006;6:28

91. Hunnicutt LE, Hunter WB, Cave RD, Powell CA, Mozoruk JJ. Genome sequence and molecular characterization of Homalodisca coagulata virus-1, a novel virus discovered in the glassy-winged sharpshooter (Hemiptera: Cicadellidae). Virology. 2006;350(1):67-78

92. Olson DM, Dinerstein E, Powell GVN, Wikramanayake ED. Conservation biology for the biodiversity crisis. Conservation Biology. 2002;16(1):1-3. DOI: 10. 1046/j. 1523-1739. 2002. 01612. x

93. Smart GC Jr. Entomopathogenic nematodes for the biological control of insects. Journal of Nematology. 1995;27(4S):529-534

94. Krafsur ES, Moon RD. Bionomics of the face fly, Musca autumnalis. Annual Review of Entomology. 1997;42:503-523

95. Martin WRJ. Using entomopathogenic nematodes to control insects during stand establishment. Horticultural Science. 1997;32:196-200

96. Kaya HK, Koppenhöfer AM. Biology and ecology of insecticidal nematodes. In: Polavarapu S, editor. Workshop Proceedings: Optimal Use of Insecticidal Nematodes in Pest Management. New Brunswick, NJ, United States: Rutgers University; 1991. pp. 1-8

97. Geden CJ. Evaluation of Paraiotonchium muscadomesticae (Nematoda: Tylenchida: Iotonchiidae), a potential biological control agent of the housefly (Diptera: Muscidae). Biological Control. 1997;10:42-47

98. Henderson G, Manweiler SA, Lawrence WJ, Templeman RJ, Foil LD. The effects of Steinernema carpocapsae (Weiser) application to different life stages on adult emergence of the cat flea Ctenocephalides felis (Bouche). Veterinary Dermatology. 1995;6:159-163

99. Zhioua E, Lebrun RA, Ginsberg HS, Aeschlimann A. Pathogenicity of Steinernema carpocapsae and S. glaseri (Nematoda: Steinernematidae) to Ixodes scapularis (Acari: Ixodidae). Journal of Medical Entomology. 1995;32:900-905

100. Samish M, Glazer I, Alekseev EA. The susceptibility of the development stages of ticks (Ixodidae) to entomopathogenic nematodes. In: Rodger M, Horn DJ, Needham GR, Welbourn WC, editors. Acarology IX. Columbus, Ohio: Ohio Biological Survey; 1996. pp. 121-123

101. Kocan KM, Pidherney MS, Blouin EF, Claypool PL, Samish M, Glazer I. Interaction of entomopathogenic nematodes (Steinernematidae) with selected species of ixodid ticks (Acari: Ixodidae). Journal of Medical Entomology. 1998;35(4):514-520

102. Ibrahim MM. Population dynamics of Chaetogaster limnaei (Oligochaeta: Naididae) in the field populations of freshwater snails and its implications as a potential regulator of trematode larvae community. Parasitology Research. 2007;101(1):25-33. DOI: 10. 1007/ s00436-006-0436-0

103. Gronvold J. Field experiment on the ability of earthworms (Lumbricidae) to reduce the transmission of infective larvae of Cooperra oncopnora (Trichostrongylidae: Nematoda). Journal of Parasitology. 1987;73:1133-1137

104. Clarke GM, Gross S, Matthews M, Catling PC, Baker B, Hewitt CL, Crowther D, Saddler SR. Environmental pest species in Australia. In: Australia: State of the Environment, Second Technical Paper Series (Biodiversity). Canberra: Department of the Environment and Heritage; 2000

105. Hoagland DB, Horst GR, Kilpatrick CW. Biogeography and population biology of the mongoose in the West Indies. In: Woods CA, editor. Biogeography of the West Indies. Gainesville, Florida, USA: Sand Hill Crane Press; 1989. pp. 611-634

106. Simberloff D, Dayan T, Jones C, Ogura G. Character displacement and release in the small Indian mongoose, Herpestes javanicus. Ecology. 2000;81(8):2086-2099

107. Nellis DW, Everard COR. The biology of the mongoose in the Caribbean. Studies on the Fauna of Curaçao and Other Caribbean Islands. 1983;1:1-162

108. Barun A, Hanson CC, Campbell KJ, Simberloff D. A review of small Indian mongoose management and eradications on islands. In: Veitch CR, Clout MN, Towns DR, editors. Island Invasives: Eradication and Management. Gland, Switzerland: IUCN; 2011. pp. 17-25

109. IUCN. IUCN guidelines for the prevention of biodiversity loss caused by alien invasive species. In: Fifth Meeting of the Conference of the Parties to the Convention on Biological Diversity; Species Survival Commission of IUCN; Gland, Switzerland. 2000

110. National Research Council (U. S.). Incorporating science, economics, and sociology in developing sanitary and phytosanitary standards in international trade. In: Proceedings of a Conference; June 2000. Washington DC, US: National Academies Press; 2000. p. 97

111. Vila-Gispert A, Alcaraz C, Garcia-Berthou E. Life-history traits of invasive fish in small Mediterranean streams. Biological Invasions. 2005;7:107-116

112. Rehage JS, Barnett BK, Sih A. Foraging behaviour and invasiveness: Do invasive Gambusia exhibit higher feeding rates and broader diets than their noninvasive relatives? Ecology of Freshwater Fish. 2005;14:352-360

113. Alcaraz C, Garcia-Berthou E. Life history variation of an invasive fish (Gambusia holbrooki) along a salinity gradient. Biological Conservations. 2007;139:83-92

114. Randall JM, Tu M. Biological control. In: Weed Control Methods Handbook. Virginia, US: The Nature Conservancy; 2001. pp. 1-24

115. Mahr DL, Whitaker P, Ridgway NM. Biological Control of Insects and Mites: An Introduction to Beneficial Natural Enemies and Their Use in Pest Management. University of Wisconsin Cooperative Extension. Lake street, Madison, Wisconsin, US; 2008; No. A3842

116. El-Ghany TMA, editor. Entomopathogenic Fungi and their Role in Biological Control. Foster City, CA, USA: OMICS Group eBooks; 2015. p. 46. DOI: 10. 4172/978-1-63278-065-2-66

117. Singh SP. Some Success Stories in Classical Biological Control of Agricultural Pest in India [Internet]. 2004. Available from: http://www. apaari. org/wp-content/uploads/2009/05/ ss_2004_02. pdf [Accessed: 30 August 2016]

118. Cock MJW, Day RK, Hinz HL, Pollard KM, Thomas SE, Williams FE, Witt ABR, Shaw RH. The impacts of some classical biological control successes. CAB Reviews. 2015;10(42):1-58

119. Takiya DM, McKamey SH, Cavichioli RR. Validity of Homalodisca and of H. vitripennis as the name for glassywinged sharpshooter (Hemiptera: Cicadellidae: Cicadellinae). Annals of the Entomological Society of America. 2006;99(4):648-655

120. Sorensen JT, Gill RJ. A range extension of Homalodisca coagulata (Say) (Hemiptera: Clypeorrhyncha: Cicadellidae) to Southern California. The Pan-Pacific Entomologist. 1996;72(3):160-161

121. University of California, Riverside. Biological Control of the Glassy-winged Sharpshooter [Internet]. 2013. Available from: http://biocontrol. ucr. edu/irvin/gwssbiocontrol. html [Accessed: 19 October 2016]

122. Triapitsyn SV, Phillips PA. First record of Gonatocerus triguttatus (Hymenoptera: Mymaridae) from eggs of Homalodisca coagulata (Homoptera: Cicadellidae) with notes on the distribution of the host. Florida Entomologist. 2000;83(2):200-203

123. Triapitsyn SV, Logarzo GA, De León JH, Virla EG. A new Gonatocerus (Hymenoptera: Mymaridae) from Argentina, with taxonomic notes and molecular data on the G. tuberculifemur species complex. Zootaxa. 2008;1949:1-29

124. Irvin NA, Hoddle MS. Comparative assessments of Gonatocerus ashmeadi and the "new association" parasitoid Gonatocerus tuberculifemur (Hymenoptera: Mymaridae) as biological control agents of Homalodisca vitripennis (Hemiptera: Cicadellidae). Biological Control. 2010;55(3):186-196

125. Cheou D. Incursion of glassy-winged sharpshooter Homalodisca coagulata in French Polynesia. International Plant Protection Convention. Plant Protection Service Pest Alert No. 24; 2002

126. Hoover W. New Invader may Threaten Crops. Honolulu: The Honolulu Advertiser; 14 May 2004

127. Hoddle MS, Grandgirard J, Petit J, Roderick GK, Davies N. Glassy-winged sharpshooter Ko'ed—first round—in French Polynesia. Biocontrol News and Information. 2006;27(3):47N-62N

128. Szewczyk B, Hoyos-Carvajal L, Paluszek M, Skrzecz I, Lobo de Souza M. Baculoviruses—re-emerging biopesticides. Biotechnology Advances. 2006;24(2):143-160. DOI: 10. 1016/j. biotechadv. 2005. 09. 001

129. Sun X, Peng H. Recent advances in biological control of pest insects by using viruses in China. Virologica Sinica. 2007;22:158-162

130. Follett PA, Duan JJ. Nontarget Effects of Biological Control. Norwell, MA: Kluwer Academic Publishers; 2000. p. 316

131. Bigler F, Babendreier D, Kuhlmann U, editors. Environmental Impact of Invertebrates for Biological Control of Arthropods: Methods and Risk Assessment. Wallingford: CABI Publishing; 2006

132. van Lenteren JC, Bale JS, Bigler F, Hokkanen HMT, Loomans AJM. Assessing risks of releasing exotic biological control agents of arthropod pests. Annual Review of Entomology. 2006;51:609-634

133. Nicot PC, Blum B, Köhl J, Ruocco M. Conclusions and perspectives for future research-and-development projects on biological control of plant pests and diseases. Classical and augmentative biological control against diseases and pests: critical status analysis and review of factors. 2011;45:68

134. Heong KL, Escalada MM. Changing rice farmers' pest management practices through participation in a small-scale experiment. International Journal of Pest Management. 1998;44:191-197

135. Thacker JRM. An Introduction to Arthropod Pest Control. Cambridge, England: Cambridge University Press; 2002

136. Sagoff M. Third-generation biotechnology: A first look. Issues in Science and Technology. 2008;25(1): 70-74

137. Federici BA. Recombinant bacterial larvicides for control of important mosquito vectors of disease. In: Atkinson PW, editor. Vector Biology, Ecology and Control. US: Springer; 2010. pp. 163-176

138. Wang C, St. Leger RJ. A scorpion neurotoxin increases the potency of a fungal insecticide. Nature Biotech. 2007;25:1455-1456

139. Bonning BC. Insect viruses: Biotechnological applications. In: Bonning BC, editor. Advances in Virus Research. New York: Academic Press; 2006. p. 68

140. Chang JH, Choi JY, Jin BR, Roh JY, Olszewski JA, Seo SJ, O'Reilly DR, Je YH. An improved baculovirus insecticide producing occlusion bodies that contain Bacillus thuringiensis insect toxin. Journal of Invertebrate Pathology. 2003;84(1):30-37

141. El-Menofy W, Osman G, Assaeedi A, Salama M. A novel recombinant baculovirus overexpressing a Bacillus thuringiensis Cry1Ab toxin enhances insecticidal activity. Biological Procedures Online. 2014;16:7. DOI: 10. 1186/1480-9222-16-7

142. Rai M, Ingle A. Role of nanotechnology in agriculture with special reference to management of insect pests. Applied Microbiology and Biotechnology. 2012;94:287

143. Barik TK, Sahu B, Swain V. Nano-silica—from medicine to pest control. Parasitology Research. 2008;103:253-258

144. Gajbhiye M, Kesharwani J, Ingle A, Gade A, Rai M. Fungus mediated synthesis of silver nanoparticles and its activity against pathogenic fungi in combination of fluconazole. Nanomedicine. 2009;5(4):282-286

145. Goswami A, Roy I, Sengupta S, Debnath N. Novel applications of solid and liquid formulations of nanoparticles against insect pests and pathogens. Thin Solid Films. 2010;519:1252-1257

146. Owolade OF, Ogunleti DO, Adenekan MO. Titanium dioxide affects disease development and yield of edible cowpea. The Electronic Journal of Environmental, Agricultural and Food Chemistry. 2008;7(50):2942-2947

147. Liu F, Wen LX, Li ZZ, Yu W, Sun HY, Chen JF. Porous hollow silica nanoparticles as controlled delivery system for water-soluble pesticide. Materials Research Bulletin. 2006;41:2268-2275

148. Ulrichs C, Mewis I, Goswami A. Crop diversification aiming nutritional security in West Bengal: Biotechnology of stinging capsules in nature's water-blooms. SATSA Annual Technical Issue. 2006;10:1-18

149. Murugan K, Priyanka V, Dinesh D, Madhiyazhagan P, Panneerselvam C, Subramaniam J, Suresh U, Chandramohan B, Roni M, Nicoletti M, Alarfaj AA, Higuchi A, Munusamy MA, Khater HF, Messing RH, Benelli G. Predation by Asian bullfrog tadpoles, Hoplobatrachus tigerinus, against the dengue vector, Aedes aegypti, in an aquatic environment treated with mosquitocidal nanoparticles. Parasitology Research. 2015;114(10):3601-3610

150. Ronia M, Murugana K, Panneerselvama C, Subramaniama J, Nicolettib M, Madhiyazhagana P, Dinesha D, Suresha U, Khater HF, Weid H, Canalee A, Alarfaj AA, Munusamy MA, Higuchig A, Benellie G. Characterization and biotoxicity of Hypnea musciformis-synthesized silver nanoparticles as potential eco-friendly control tool against Aedes aegypti and Plutella xylostella. Ecotoxicology and Environmental Safety. 2015;121:31-38

151. Govindarajan M, Khater HF, Panneerselvam C, Benelli G. One-pot fabrication of silver nanocrystals using Nicandra physalodes: A novel route for mosquito vector control with moderate toxicity on non-target water bugs. Research in Veterinary Science. 2016;107:95-101

152. Govindarajana M, Rajeswary M, Muthukumaran U, Hoti SL, Khater HF, Benelli G. Single-step biosynthesis and characterization of silver nanoparticles using Zornia diphylla leaves: A potent eco-friendly tool against malaria and arbovirus vectors. Journal of Photochemistry and Photobiology B. 2016;161:482-489

153. Yang FL, Li XG, Zhu F, Lei CL. Structural characterization of nanoparticles loaded with garlic essential oil and their insecticidal activity against Tribolium castaneum (Herbst) (Coleoptera: Tenebrionidae). Journal of Agricultural and Food Chemistry. 2009;57(21):10156-10162

154. Sabbour MM. Entomotoxicity assay of two nanoparticle materials 1-(Al_2O_3 and TiO_2) against Sitophilus oryzae under laboratory and store conditions in Egypt. Journal of Applied Sciences. 2012;1(4):103-108

155. Sabbour M. A novel pathogenicity of nano-Beauveria bassiana and Metarihizium anisopliae against Sitophilus oryzae (L.) (Coleoptera: Curculiondae) under laboratory and store conditions. International Journal of Scientific and Engineering Research. 2015;6(12):938-945

156. Subramanian KS, Muniraj I, Uthandi S. Role of actinomycete-mediated nanosystem in agriculture. In: Subramaniam G, Arumugam S, Rajendran V, editors. Plant Growth Promoting Actinobacteria. Singapore: Springer; 2016. pp. 233-247. DOI: 10. 1007/978-981-10-0707-1_15

157. Sabbour MM. Laboratory and store efficacy of nano-extracted destruxin from Metarhizium anisopliae against Indian meal moth Plodia interpunctella (Lepidoptera-Pyralidae). Journal of Nanoscience and Nanoengineering. 2015;1(3):142-147

158. Torney F. Nanoparticle mediated plant transformation. In: Emerging Technologies in Plant Science Research. Interdepartmental Plant Physiology Major. Fall Seminar Series (Phys 696). Iowa, US: Iowa State University; 2009

159. Bhattacharyya A, Bhaumik A, Usha Rani P, Mandal S, Epidi TT. Nano-particles: A recent approach to insect pest control. African Journal of Biotechnology. 2010;9(24):3489-3493

160. da Silva PT, Fries LLM, de Menezes CR, Holkem AT, Schwan CL, Wigmann EF, de Oliveira Bastos J, da Silva CB. Microencapsulation: Concepts, mechanisms, methods and some applications in food technology. Ciência Rural. 2014;44(7):1304-1311

161. Azeredo HMC. Encapsulação: aplicação à tecnologia de alimentos. Alimentos e Nutrição. 2005;16(1):89-97

162. Ma X, Wang X, Cheng J, Nie X, Yu X, Zhao Y, Wang W. Microencapsulation of Bacillus subtilis B99-2 and its biocontrol efficiency against Rhizoctonia solani in tomato. Biological Control. 2015;90:34-41

163. Seddiek SA, Ali MM, Khater HF, El-Shorbagy MM. Anthelmintic activity of the white wormwood, Artemisia herba-alba against Heterakis gallinarum infecting turkey poults. Journal of Medicinal Plants Research. 2011;5(16):946-3957

164. Seddiek SA, Khater HF, El-Shorbagy MM, Ali AM. The acaricidal efficacy of aqueous neem extract and ivermectin against Sarcoptes scabiei var. cuniculi in experimentally infested rabbits. Parasitology Research. 2013;112:2319-2330. DOI: 10. 1007/s00436-013-3395-2

165. Seddiek SA, El-Shorbagy MM, Khater HF, Ali AM. The antitrichomonal efficacy of garlic and metronidazole against Trichomonas gallinae infecting domestic pigeons. Parasitology Research. 2014;113:1319-1329. DOI: 10. 1007/s00436-014-3771-6

166. Khater HF. Bioactivities of some essential oils against the camel nasal botfly, Cephalopina titillator. Parasitology Research. 2014;113:593-605. DOI: 10. 1007/s00436-013-3688-5

167. Khatera HF, El-Shorbagy MM, Seddiek SA. Lousicidal efficacy of camphor oil, d-phenothrin, and deltamethrin against the slender pigeon louse, Columbicola columbae. International Journal of Veterinary Sciences and Medicine. 2014;2(1):7-13

168. Khater HF, Hendawy NI. Photoxicity of Rose Bengal against the camel tick, Hyalomma dromedarii. International Journal of Veterinary Science. 2014;3(2):78-86

169. Khater H, Hendawy N, Govindarajan M, Murugan K, Benelli G. Photosensitizers in the fight against ticks: Safranin as a novel photodynamic fluorescent acaricide to control the camel tick Hyalomma dromedarii (Ixodidae). Parasitology Research. 2016;115:3747-3758. DOI: 10. 1007/s00436-016-5136-9

170. Ali AM, Khater HF, Seddiek SA, Nada MO. Comparative efficacy of synbiotic and diclazuril on broilers experimentally infected with Eimeria acervulina. Assiut Veterinary Medical Journal. 2015;61(146):24-33

171. Khater HF, Seddiek SA, El-Shorbagy MM, Ali AM. The acaricidal efficacy of peracetic acid and deltamethrin against the fowl tick, Argas persicus, infesting laying hens. Parasitology Research. 2013;112(1):259-269. DOI: 10. 1007/s00436-012-3133-1

172. Ali AM, Seddiek ShA, Khater HF. Effect of butyrate, clopidol and their combination on the performance of broilers infected with Eimeria maxima. British Poultry Science. 2014;55(4):474-482. DOI: http://dx. doi. org/10. 1080/00071668. 2014. 920488

10

The Impact of Plant-Parasitic Nematodes on Agriculture and Methods of Control

Gregory C. Bernard, Marceline Egnin and Conrad Bonsi

Tuskegee University, Tuskegee, Alabama, United States

ABSTRACT

Plant-parasitic nematodes are costly burdens of crop production. Ubiquitous in nature, phytoparasitic nematodes are associated with nearly every important agricultural crop and represent a significant constraint on global food security. Root-knot nematodes (Meloidogyne spp.) cyst nematodes (Heterodera and Globodera spp.) and lesion nematodes (Pratylenchus spp.) rank at the top of list of the most economically and scientifically important species due to their intricate relationship with the host plants, wide host range, and the level of damage ensued by infection. Limitations on the use of chemical pesticides have brought increasing interest in studies on alternative methods of nematode control. Among these strategies of nonchemical nematode management is the identification and implementation of host resistance. In addition, nematode genes involved in parasitism represent key targets for the development of control through gene silencing methods such as RNA interference. Recently, transcriptome profiling analyses has been used to distinguish nematode resistant and susceptible genotypes and identify the specific molecular components and pathways triggered during the plant immune response to nematode invasion. This summary highlights the importance of plant-parasitic nematodes in agriculture and the molecular events involved in plant-nematode interactions.

Keywords: *Plant-Parasitic Nematodes, Agriculture,Crops, Genetics, Resistance, Meloidogyne*

INTRODUCTION

Over millions of years, the association of plants and nematodes has resulted in the evolution of the plant-parasitic nematode. Widely distributed pathogens of vascular plants, enormous losses in yields have been attributed to the presence of nematodes. The intricate relationship between the parasitic nematode and plant has culminated in an "evolutionary arms race". Phyto-parasitic nematodes have evolved strategies to suppress host immune responses for the development of feeding sites. In turn, plants have developed specific molecules to recognize pathogens signaling the activation of immune responses. Declining use of chemical pesticides has brought great attention to research in alternative methods of nematode control. An effective strategy for nematode management involves the utilization and implementation of nematode-resistant cultivars into crop breeding programs. Currently, genetic sequencing analyses are widely utilized in the identification of molecular components of nematode parasitism and is also used to distinguish nematode-resistant and susceptible plant genotypes. These detailed analyses have significantly contributed to our overall understanding of the dynamic and complex nature of plant-nematode interactions.

NEMATODE MORPHOLOGY

Nematodes are a fascinating, biologically diverse group of organisms. Their ability to adapt to a wide variety of habitats including; marine, soil and aquatic, provides an evolutionary advantage for species longevity. Phylum Nematoda is largely distinguished by three major monophyletic groups including: Enoplia (marine), Dorylaimia (parasitic trichinellids and mermithids and Chromadoria (nematodes of various environments). Nematodes belong to the group Ecdysozoa, which comprises animals that can shed their cuticle. Over 30,000 species of round worms are found in Nematoda [1] typically ranging in size from 0.2 mm to over 6 m. Nematode body structure is relatively simple and characterized as limbless, cylindrical, and elongated. Essentially the body plan is a "tube within a tube", the inner tube or alimentary canal, consists of a digestive tract and gonad which are surrounded by an outer tube; a body wall containing a series of dorsal and ventral longitudinal muscles attached to the hypodermis. These muscles are activated by the dorsal and ventral nerves and their contractions allow for locomotion in sinusoidal waves. In plant-parasitic nematodes, a primary infection structure called a stylet is located at the anterior end of the nematode which is followed by an esophageal region that connects the stylet to the intestines. A typical tylenchoid esophagus consists of an anterior procorpus, a median bulb and the posterior basal bulb. The median bulb functions in the transfer of enzymes involved in primary infection and facilitates the movement of plant nutrients into the intestine. Inside of the exterior body wall lies the pseudocoelom, a unlined, pressurized, fluid-filled cavity formed directly from the blastula surrounding the gut cavity. The pseudocoelom is filled with fluid which provides turgor pressure for the entire body containing the internal organs and aides in the transfer of nutrients, oxygen and metabolic products. The excretory system is composed of four distinctive cells, an excretory pore cell, a duct cell, one canal cell, and a fused pair of gland cells. Nematodes are enclosed within an exoskeleton called a cuticle which is secreted by inner hypodermal cells, and is primarily composed of collagens, insoluble proteins (cuticlins), glycoproteins and lipids. The cuticle plays an important role in movement, environmental protection and growth and development [2]. The typical male reproductive structures include a testis, a seminal vesicle and a vas deferens leading to a cloaca, while the female reproductive system is tubular containing one or two ovaries, seminal receptacles, an uterus, ovijector and a vulva.

EVOLUTION OF PLANT-PARASITIC NEMATODES

Why do some nematodes become plant parasites? The dynamic association of nematode and plant host has resulted in plant parasitism which has evolved three times culminating in substantial benefits for nematode survival and development [3, 4]. An existing evolutionary hypothesis places the origins of these ancient microscopic roundworms around 400 million years before the explosion of animal phyla (pre-"Cambrian explosion") [5]. Evidence suggests the initial presence of plant-parasitic nematodes to have occurred around 235 BC [6] while the first described plant parasitic nematodes were reported by Needham who observed symptoms of galling in wheat [7]. An agriculturally important species of plant-parasitic nematodes called root-knot nematodes, were initially identified by Berkeley who observed the presence of galls on cucumber roots [8].

The plant-nematode association has resulted in the development of specific feeding structures and secretory products that are involved in host infection and nutrient absorption. Plant parasitic nematodes are specialized by the stylet and subventral and dorsal esophageal glands which are considered the most significant evolutionary adaptations for plant parasitism [4, 9]. Plant-parasitic nematodes utilize a hollow, needle-like, protrusible stylet to probe plant tissue and release an assortment of proteinaceous secretions from the subventral and dorsal glands which comprises the integrity of the host cell and allow for nematode entry. These glandular secretions induce cellular remodifications that are essential for development of a metabolically active feeding cell [10]. Among the secretory molecules are a group of carbohydrate-active enzymes. Since cellulose is the primary component of plant cell walls, cellulases (β-1,4-endoglucanases) are secreted to degrade the cell wall which allows nematode entry into host tissue. Genomic analyses of root-knot nematodes have revealed the presence of a suite of enzymes called CAZymes (cellulases, xylanases and other glycosyl hydrolase family members (GHFs)) [11]. Beta-1,4-endoglucanase genes have been isolated from plant-parasitic cyst nematodes with catalytic domains belonging to family 5 of the glycosyl hydrolases [12, 13].

Glycosyl hydrolase families G5 and G45 have been identified in plant-parasitic nematodes. Plant-parasitic nematode GH5 cellulases show closes homologies with bacterial G5s, which suggests an initial horizontal gene transfer of bacterial G5 cellulases into nematode genomes during the evolution of the plant-parasitic order Rhabditida (suborder Tylenchina) [14, 15]. G45 cellulases have been found in plant-parasitic nematode *Bursaphelenchus xylophilus* of the Aphelenchida order [16]. Phylogenetic analyses have shown similarities in gene structure between G45 sequences found in these nematodes and ascomycetous fungi which supports the hypothesis of a horizontal gene transfer event from fungi to nematodes [17].

Plant-parasitic nematodes differ in lifestyles. Some nematodes will invade the plant cells while others simply obtain nutrition externally. Ectoparasitic nematodes remain outside the host cells and feed on plant roots while endoparasitic nematodes establish residence within plant tissue. An example of ectoparasitic nematode is Xiphinema (California dagger nematode) which transmits the Grapevine fanleaf virus. The resulting viral infection causes tremendous economic losses in grapes worldwide [18]. Endoparasitic nematodes are further divided into migratory and sedentary groups. Migratory endoparasitic nematodes move within the root and remove cytoplasm killing the host cell while sedentary nematodes become immobile after the development of a feeding site within the host tissue [19]. Migratory endoparasitic nematodes of economic significance include *Pratylenchus* spp. (lesion nematode), *Radopholus* spp. (burrowing nematodes) and *Hirschmanniella* (rice root nematode).

THE IMPACT OF PLANT-PARASITIC NEMATODES ON CROPS

Plant-parasitic nematodes are a costly burden in agricultural crop production. Over 4100 species of plant-parasitic nematodes have been identified [20]. Collectively, they cause an estimated \$80–\$118 billion dollars per year in damage to crops [21, 22]. Encompassing 15% of all identified nematode species, the most economically important species directly target plant roots of major production crops and prevent water and nutrient uptake resulting in reduced agronomic performance, overall quality and yields. Nematodes in the order Tylenchida are pathogens of plants, invertebrates, and fungi and are considered the most important agricultural pests [22].

Of all the important plant-parasitic nematodes, the most successful species are the sedentary groups which establish a permanent feeding site within the plant host and obtain nutrients while completing their lifecycles. Sedentary nematodes have a natural advantage over their migratory relatives due to a fascinating and complex method of host cell transformation resulting in the development a sustainable feeding structure. Interestingly, with over 4000 described plant-parasitic nematodes, only a small amount produce significant economic losses in crops. In a survey conducted on a variety of crops in the U.S, the major genera of phytoparasitic nematodes reported to cause crop losses were *Heterodera*, *Hoplolaimus*, *Meloidogyne*, *Pratylenchus*, *Rotylenchulus*, and *Xiphinema* [23].

Wheat

Wheat (*Triticum aestivum*) is the most important cereal crop in the world. A staple food source for 40% of the world's population, approximately 758 million tons are produced globally [24]. Wheat yields are significantly decreased by the presence of cereal cyst nematodes (*Heterodera* spp.) in the *Heterodera avenae* group (*H. avenae*, *Heterodera filipjevi*, and *Heterodera latipons*) which also damage other important cereals including barley (*Hordeum vulgare*) and oat (*Avena sativa*).

An estimated 3.4 million in profits are lost each year in U.S. wheat cultivating states Idaho, Oregon, and Washington [25]. In some wheat fields, the losses caused by *H. avenae* can range from 30 to 100% [26, 27]. In addition to cereal cyst nematodes, further losses of wheat are caused by root-lesion nematodes *Pratylenchus neglectus* and *Pratylenchus thornei*, and the seed gall or ear-cockle nematode, *Anguina tritici*. An inverse relationship between *H. avenae* and *P. neglectus* was shown on *P. neglectus* resistant and susceptible wheat cultivars infested with *H. avenae* [28] where a reduction in *P. neglectus* population densities was observed on both wheat genotypes. *Anguina tritici* is often a vector for *Rathayibacter tritici*, a Gram-positive soil bacterium which associates with *Clavibacter tritici* causing seed gall [29].

Rice

Rice (*Oryza sativa* L.) is a staple food crop for most of the world›s population with an estimated 480 million tons currently produced [30]. Plant-parasitic nematodes rank as one of the most important soil borne pests of rice and may account for annual yield losses of 10–25% worldwide. Over 100 species of nematodes affect rice production. *Meloidogyne* spp. is distributed worldwide and are significant pathogens of rice and other crops cultivated in temperate and tropical areas [31]. One of the most important species of *Meloidogyne*, is *M. graminicola*, may reduce rice yields up to 80% [32].

Symptoms of infection manifests as hook shaped galls, stunting, decreased tiller numbers and poor growth and reproduction [33]. The rice root-nematode *Hirschmanniella oryzae*, i.e., rice root nematode (RRN), is commonly found in irrigated rice production systems [34]. Widely distributed, *H. oryzae* has been reported in Asian countries such as India, Pakistan, Bangladesh, Sri Lanka, Nepal, Thailand, Vietnam, Indonesia, the Philippines, China, Korea and Japan [35] and in the U.S states, Louisiana and Texas.

Maize

Maize (*Zea mays*) is grown largely throughout the world with three largest production in North America Asia and Europe [21]. Over 50 species that are known to parasitize corn in the globally however, the most devastating genera include the root knot nematodes, *Meloidogyne* spp., the root lesion nematodes, *Pratylenchus* spp. and the cyst nematodes, *Heterodera* spp. [21]. In the U.S., the most economically important species are the lesion nematodes (*Pratylenchus* spp.) and the corn cyst nematode (*Heterodera zeae*). In most cases, symptoms of infection caused by these nematodes include poor development and leaf chlorosis with minor galling [36]. The needle nematode *Longidorus breviannulatus* is associated with stunting in corn and may cause economic losses in yields up to 60% [37].

Potato

The potato (*Solanum tuberosum*) is a member of the Solanaceae family, and is considered the third most important crop in the world with total world potato production estimated at over 376 million tonnes in 2013 [38]. Cyst nematodes are prolific pathogens of potato causing dramatic losses in yields. *Globodera rostochiensis* and *Globodera pallida* originate from S. America and are known pests of other members of the Solanaceae family including tomatoes and woody nightshade [39]. These nematodes are classified as quarantine pests in a number of countries including the U.S. and an estimated £ 50m year in profits are lost each year in the U.K. [40]. Other major plant-parasitic nematodes of potato include root-knot nematodes (*Meloidogyne* spp.), and the stem nematode *Ditylenchus destructor*. Among the four species of root-knot nematodes that affect potato production in the U.S., the Columbian root-knot nematode (*Meloidogyne chitwoodii*) is considered the most important species [41]. In addition to potato, sweetpotato (Ipomoea *batatas* L. Lam) is a major host for *D. destructor*, up to 100% yield losses have occurred in major production regions including the top producer China [42, 43]

Sweetpotato

The sweetpotato [*Ipomoea. batatas* (L) LAM] has been regarded as a plant of great significance throughout human history. Its cultivation dates to the prehistoric era, and it has been grown continuously as a staple food source. Global productions of sweetpotato is estimated at 105 million metric tons [44]. Currently, the sixth most important food crop, sweetpotato production has improved the economic status for communities throughout the world particularly in developing nations where it ranks as the fifth most important crop [44]. Approximately 10.2% of sweetpotato yields are lost each year due to the presence of plant-parasitic nematodes [20].

Root-knot nematodes (RKNs) are significant pests of sweetpotato causing symptoms of infection which include: stunted plant growth, yellowing of leaves, abnormal flower production, and gall production on roots leading to decreased nutrient and water absorption and necrosis and cracking on fleshy storage roots. Due to the economic importance of the storage root, root cracking is a primary concern for producers. Successful sweetpotato root-knot nematode resistant breeding programs involve the determination of resistance genes. Nematode resistance is governed by genotype [45] and is primarily quantitative [46]; therefore, the identification of genetic markers associated with root-knot nematode resistance requires broad scale molecular studies.

Root-knot Nematodes

In a recent survey, the top 10 most important genera of parasitic nematodes in molecular plant pathology were ranked based on scientific and economic importance [47]. Ranked at the top of the list are root-knot nematodes (*Meloidogyne* spp.). The root-knot nematode (*Meloidogyne* spp.) comprises over 100 species, with *Meloidogyne javanica*, *Meloidogyne arenaria*, *Meloidogyne hapla*, and *Meloidogyne incognita* representing the most devastating threat to agricultural crop production [48]. The *Meloidogyne* spp. are globally distributed, have enormous host range and develop dynamic disease complexes with fungal species and bacteria which may exacerbate disease incidences in cultivated plants. The lifecycle of *Meloidogyne* spp. involves four developmental stages including larval stage 1 (within the egg), larval stage 2 (migratory), larval stage juvenile 3 (sedentary), larval stage 4 (sedentary) and adult stage (sedentary). Under favorable environmental conditions, first stage moulting to J1 larval stage within the egg occurs resulting in hatching, with or without the presence of a chemical stimulus. Infective second-stage juveniles (J2s) are often attracted to root exudates and migrate to root tips where they infiltrate behind the root cap at the elongation zone. Root knot nematodes attenuate plant cells by stylet thrusting and secrete cell wall degrading enzymes to separate the middle lamella during intercellular migration through root cortex cells as they target the undifferentiated procambium cells of the vascular cylinder. During later stages in primary infection, dorsal gland activity increases to promote shuttling of secretory granules to the stylet where proteinaceous secretions are released in the development of the primary feeding site—the giant cell [49]. The multi-nucleated giant cell is a result of nematode-induced endoreduplication within the host cell in the absence of cytokinesis. Cellular ingrowths arise to sequester solutes from the xylem [50] further enhancing nutrient availability. J2 larvae moult into larval stage 3 (J3) during the initial intake of plant nutrients from giant cells. Additional moulting occurs resulting into the J4 and final adult stage. Further reproductive development in females results in the characteristic "apple" shape associated with the Greek nomenclature *Meloidogyne*. The lifecycle completes when eggs are released into the soil from the gelatinous egg matrix formed on epidermal root tissue. Root-knot nematode infection is typically characterized by stunted growth, wilting, root galling and abnormalities in root formation.

Cyst Nematodes

Cyst forming nematodes, or cyst nematodes, (*Heterodera* and *Globodera* spp.) rank second to root-knot nematode in agricultural and economic importance. The biology of cyst nematodes is similar to that of root-knot nematodes where J2 larvae infect the host and develop to adult stages within host tissue. In contrast, to root-knot nematode reproduction where eggs are deposited into a gelatinous matrix on root systems, eggs produced by cyst nematodes are preserved within the body of the female and are protected after her death until hatching under favorable conditions. Cyst nematodes enter root tips and induce specialized feeding structures in the infected plant roots called syncytia via esophageal gland secretions released by the stylet [51]. These secretions promote cell wall degradation and protoplast fusion of numerous adjacent cells to form the syncytium [52]. In agriculture, the most significant cyst nematode species are the potato cyst nematodes *Globodera rostochiensis* and *G. pallida*, the soybean cyst nematode (*Heterodera glycines*) and cereal cyst nematodes (CCNs) (including *Heterodera avenae* and *H. filipjevi*. In the U.S., losses due to *H. glycines* is estimated at 1.286 billion [53]. *Globodera pallida* originated in South America and is now widely distributed in 55 countries. Yield losses of potato due to *G. pallida* range from 50 to 80% in heavily infested soils [54]. Although the beet cyst nematode, *Heterodera schachtii*, is a primary pathogen of sugar beets, it can parasitize plant species in 23 different plant families with losses of 30% in the families of *Chenopodiaceae* [55, 56].

Lesion Nematodes

Ranked third among the most damaging nematodes in agriculture [57], approximately 70 species of root-lesion nematodes (*Pratylenchus* spp.) are distributed worldwide with a host range of nearly 400 plant species [57]. Among *Pratylenchus* spp., *P. thornei* is associated with yield reductions in wheat by as much as 85% in Australia, 70% in Israel, 50% in Oregon and 37% in Mexico [58]. Lesion nematodes are migratory, feeding mainly in the root cortex and may enter vascular tissues obtaining nutrients. Infection typically results in lesion formation and necrosis on roots with aboveground symptoms of chlorosis as well as reductions in leaf number and size [58, 59]. Host tissue injury resulting from infection may represent areas for secondary infection from other pathogens. Recently two new species of root-lesion nematodes (*Pratylenchus. kumamotoensis*, *Pratylenchus. pseudocoffeae*) were identified in Korea by morphometric and molecular analyses of internal transcribed spacer (ITS) and ribosomal DNA [60].

Burrowing Nematode

The burrowing nematode, *Radopholus similis* [(Cobb, 1893) Thorne, 1949] is a migratory plant parasitic nematode, listed as a quarantine plant pest worldwide [61]. Over 250 plant species serve as hosts for *R. similis* where it causes severe economic losses in yields. *R. similis* damages banana, citrus, pepper, coffee and other agronomic and horticultural crops and is considered the most important phytopathogenic nematode in banana-growing areas [62]. Effective control of *R. similis* remains problematic worldwide, and effective approaches must be identified and implemented. *Radopholus* Calreticulin (CRT) is a Ca^{2+}-binding protein that plays key roles in parasitism and represents a candidate target for controlling *R. similis. R. similis* CRT (*Rs-CST*) is expressed in the esophageal, reproductive and gastrointestinal regions as well as the eggs. Using plant-mediated RNA interference, *Rs-CRT* expression was significantly inhibited in the nematodes, and enhanced resistance was demonstrated in transgenic tomato plants [63]. In a bioassay-based study, phenylphenalenones extracted from Musa spp. showed anti-nematode effects on *R. similis* which was demonstrated by nematode motility inhibition [64].

NEMATODE PARASITISM GENES

Nematode parasitism is conferred by the actions of a variety of genes that are upregulated during host infection. In an earlier review, a comprehensive discussion highlighted the structure, origin and functions of nematode parasitism genes and further supported the acquisition of parasitism genes through horizontal transfer from bacteria [49]. Since parasitism genes are usually required for infection, they represent important targets for the development of control measures. Parasitism genes often encode for effectors which are proteins or chemicals that elicit an immune response and/or trigger changes in the host cell architecture [51]. Recently two effector genes (*MhTTL2* and *Mh265*) were identified in the root-knot nematode *M. hapla* and were shown to be upregulated during primary infection [65]. *MhTTL2* encodes for a secreted protein bearing a transthyretin-like protein domain and is expressed in the amphids, with a potential role in the nervous system while *Mh265* is expressed in subventral glands. Nematode effectors including expansin, β-1,4-endoglucanase and polygalacturonase are released during primary infection and feeding site development. In plants, expansin proteins are secreted during growth processes to allow for cell enlargement [66]. Nematodes are believed to cause differential expressions of plant genes encoding cell wall modifying proteins including expansins [67] quite possibly to mimic endogenous expansin production during feeding site development. HaEXPB2, a predicted expansin-like protein found in cereal cyst nematode *Heterodera avenae* was associated with cell death in tobacco plants [68]. During primary infection of tobacco, *HaEXPB2* gene expression was localized in subventral glands of J2 nematodes and was later found in the cell wall. Silencing of *HaEXPB2* by RNA interference was associated with reduced nematode infectivity. Transcriptome sequencing analyses of early stage *H. avenae* juveniles has revealed a variety of potential effectors including plant cell wall-modifying proteins and homologues of secreted proteins involved in the detoxification of reactive oxygen species (ROS) including: peroxiredoxin, glutathione peroxidase, glutathione-S-transferase [69]. ROS release is associated with onset of plant defense signaling. New evidence suggests that root-knot nematodes may utilize plant peroxidase to reduce ROS levels and parasitize plants bearing the *Mi-1* root-knot nematode resistance gene [70]. In plants, pathogens may trigger a hypersensitive response which involves programmed cell death (a form of apoptosis) in the site of infection to prevent pathogen colonization. Apoptosis regulator BAX (BCL-2 protein 4) is a member of the Bcl-2 family of proteins found in plants and animals [71]. Two secretory effector candidate genes (No. 5, No. 100) identified by transcriptome profiling in *Meloidogyne enterolobii* suppressed BAX-induced programmed cell death suggesting their roles as plant immune modulators for nematode infection [72]. The SPRY (SPla and the RYanodine Receptor) protein domain is most likely a scaffold for mediating protein-protein interactions [73]. SPRY effectors from *Globedera* spp. was shown to suppress the plant defense responses [74].

MOLECULAR BASIS OF NEMATODE RESISTANCE

The development of a resistance response may encompass a variety of physiological outcomes including: minor or complete absence of galling, differences in the degree of necrosis, the inability of the nematode to establish a permanent feeding site, and a decrease in female fecundity or egg output. To date, the majority of plant-parasitic nematode resistance genes bear the characteristic NBS-LRR (Nucleotide binding site—Leucine Rich Repeat) domains. These include the *Mi-1* gene from *Solanum peruvianum* (formerly *Lycopersicon peruvianum*) [75], *Hs1*$^{pro\text{-}1}$ from sugar beet [76] and *Gpa2* and *Gro1-4* from potato [77, 78].

Resistance to *Meloidogyne* in commercial resistant tomato cultivars (*Lycopersicon esculentum*) was originally identified in its wild relative *L. peruvianum* Mill. [79] followed by introgression of resistance into commercial breeding lines through backcrossing [80]. Several root-knot resistance gene homologues have been identified in tomato. *Mi-1.2* (referred to as *Mi-1*) confers resistance to multiple species of root-knot nematodes, [75] the potato aphid, *Macrosiphum euphoribiae* [81] and the whitefly, *Bemisia tabaci* [82]. *Rme1* is considered a potential component of the *Mi-1*-mediated signaling pathway as studies have indicated tomato *Rme1* mutants lack resistance to nematodes and whiteflies [66]. Molecular changes in *Rme1* protein conformation due to the presence of pathogens, may be recognized by *Mi-1.1* which signals the hypersensitive response in the "guard hypothesis" [83]. In carrots, inherited dominance of two root-knot nematode resistance genes *Mj1* [84] and *Mj2* [85] conferred resistance to *M. javanica*. The *RMIa* gene located in a subtelomeric position 300 kb physical distance between AMPP117 and AMPP116 markers and is associated with *M. incognita* resistance in peach (*Prunus* spp.) [86]. The Myrobalam plum (*Prunus cerasifera*) harbors dominant alleles (*Ma1*, *Ma2*, and *Ma3*) of a single gene *Ma*, a TIR-NBS-LRR class resistance gene, which confers broad spectrum resistance to multiple *Meloidogyne* spp. [87]. Using polymorphic sequencing analyses and genetic linkage mapping (RFLP, SSR) the *Ma* loci was precisely identified in the Myrobalan plum linkage group 7, while in a Japanese plum variety, a *Rjap* gene was localized at the same position in co-segregation with SSR markers previously associated with root-knot nematode resistance [88]. In sweetpotato, 275 candidate resistance gene analogs have been identified by degenerate PCR and molecular mining [89]. Plant-parasitic nematodes have been shown to manipulate host gene expression, therefore the identification of differential expression patterns of transcript levels for defense-related genes is a critical component in the determination of molecular factors of root-knot nematode resistance. Traditional identification of root-knot nematode resistance has involved the use of bulk segregant analysis [90] to map out qualitative traits between pooled plant genomes. Bulk segregant analysis has been used in tandem with random amplified polymorphic DNA assays to identify molecular markers at specific loci associated with root knot resistance in sweetpotato where genotypes are often isogenic [91]. Polymorphic events in resistance genes that confer effector recognition has been demonstrated in *Arabidopsis* resulting in a bifurcation that distinguishes resistant and susceptible allele clades [92].

Genome-wide expression profiling analyses using next-generation sequencing technologies are often employed in the analysis of host-nematode interactions. The resultant data from global transcriptome assays are used to target genetic traits associated with plant immune responses in response to various pathogens and to distinguish plant genotypes for resistance or susceptibility to certain diseases. Our general understanding of discreet molecular events involved in compatible (susceptible) and incompatible (resistant) plant-nematode interactions is limited in comparison to other significant host-pathogen associations. Recently, RNA-Sequencing has been frequently used in plant pathological studies to profile gene expression patterns in host plants and pathogens [93, 94]. Differential genetic expression profiles of many specific genes involved in plant immune responses has been shown in resistant and susceptible plants challenged by root-knot nematodes [48, 95]. The identification of novel defense-related transcripts and the elucidation of pathways involved in plant immune responses to nematodes have been recorded for important economic crops including cotton [96], rice [97], and soybean [98]. Transcriptome profiling of resistant and susceptible tobacco varieties infected with root-knot nematodes has shown differential expression patterns among genes involved in cell wall modification, auxin production and oxidative stress [99].

Plant Immune Responses

Due to their immobile lifestyle, plants have developed sophisticated molecular strategies to prevent pathogen invasion [100]. Plant defense has been characterized as a two- prong approach. In incompatible (resistant) plant-pathogen interactions, the presence of microbial/pathogen/-associated molecular patterns (M/PAMPs) including: toxins, glycoproteins, carbohydrates, fatty acids and proteins can trigger the upregulation of a network of host genes and corresponding proteins involved in an innate response termed pathogen-triggered immunity (PTI). Plant pathogens have evolved specialized effector molecules to suppress this first line of defense leading to effector-trigged susceptibility (ETS). In turn, plants have developed resistance genes which recognize specific effectors triggering a more robust defense response characterized as effector-triggered immunity (ETI). A hallmark of ETI is a hypersensitive cell death response (HR) at the infection site which prevents pathogen colonization [101].

Reactive Oxygen Species and Antioxidant Production

During plant metabolic processes, the accumulation of reactive oxygen species (ROS) by-products including superoxide anion (O_2^-), hydrogen peroxide (H_2O_2), singlet oxygen ($^1O_2$) and hydroxyl radicals (^-OH) is often continuous, as these highly reactive molecules are localized to various cellular compartments. ROS are primarily generated by NADPH oxidases and superoxide dismutases and production is associated with numerous abiotic and biotic stress responses. Activation of ROS was shown to be critical during the defense response to root-knot nematode invasion [102]. ROS accumulation is toxic to nematodes and can often lead to induced oxidative destruction of infected cells during the hypersensitive response, to prohibit pathogen colonization.

Increased ROS production is often correlated with the activation of antioxidant gene expression. These oxidative/reduction reactions must be tightly regulated to eliminate inadvertent plant tissue damage. Antioxidant enzymes including peroxidases are primarily responsible for the maintenance of a steady-state ROS level however, certain classes of peroxidases act as producers of ROS depending on the cyclic (catalytic or the hydroxylic) nature of the enzyme. ROS- producing Class III peroxidase genes were upregulated during an incompatible reaction in *H. avenae*-resistant wheat cultivars [103]. Peroxidase reduces H_2O_2 levels via H_2O_2-dependent polymerization of hydroxycinnamyl alcohols which promotes defense responses including lignin synthesis and cell-wall reinforcement by the cross-linkage of cell wall proteins [104]. Higher induction of peroxidase groups was observed in resistant plant species during *H. avenae* and *M. incognita* infection [105].

Pathogenesis-related Proteins

Presently, 17 families of pathogenesis-related (PR) proteins have been identified based primarily on their enzyme function, activity and amino acid sequence homologies [106]. The PR family are characterized as plant allergens inclusive of an assortment of proteins such as: b-1,3 glucanases, chitinases, proteinase inhibitors, defensins, ribonucleases and thionins. PR gene expression is often induced by ethylene, salicylic acid, jasmonic acid, xylanase, and systemin signaling pathways. The molecular functions of PR proteins are often species specific with great diversity in the mode of action and structure between protein groups. Most PRs possess antifungal, antiviral, antibacterial and insecticidal activity and are primarily involved in plant developmental processes and environmental stress responses. PR proteins were initially reported in tobacco leaves during a hypersensitive response to the tobacco mosaic virus (TMV) [107, 108] and have been induced in response a wide variety of pathogens including nematodes. During nematode infections, PR transcripts may accumulate in high concentrations and are associated with the long distance immune response termed systemic acquired resistance (SAR) [109]. Increased expression of *PR-1*(P4) transcripts was observed at 3 days' post-infection in the *G. rostochiensis*-infected resistant plants compared with the uninoculated controls [110].

Callose Deposition

Cell wall modifications often occur during plant-pathogen interactions which are demonstrated by the deposition of cell wall appositions leading to the development of papillae. Structural components associated with papillae formation are: callose, phenolics including lignin, phenolic conjugates such as phenolic–polyamines, reactive oxygen species, peroxidases, cell wall structural proteins (arabinogalactan proteins and hydroxyproline-rich glycoproteins) and cell wall polymers (pectin and xyloglucans). Callose (beta-1-3-glucan) deposition, lignification and suberization are plant developmental processes further associated with the restriction of systemic pathogen movement during PTI. Defense-associated cell wall strengthening through lignin and callose synthesis is signaled by cell wall degradation in a feedback mechanism which occurs in response to pathogens [111]. In addition to promoting declines in localized microbial populations, callose deposition also prevents the translocation of PTI-suppressive effectors. Interestingly, the cuticular chitin derivatives of plant-parasitic nematodes may activate the innate immune response. Although the cuticle is generally believed to be devoid of chitin, it is possible that chitin derivatives or chitin previously deposited in the stylet are recognized by the host which activates callose deposition at the site of penetration. The overexpression of the ethylene response transcription factor RAP2.6 in *Arabidopsis* enhanced plant basal resistance to *H. schachtii* [112]. Increased expression of jasmonic acid-related genes and callose deposition were observed at nematode infection sites.

WRKY Transcription Factors

WRKY transcription factors are transcriptional regulators of many developmental processes in plants and are associated with abiotic and biotic stress responses. The WRKY domain is almost exclusive to plants characterized by a highly-conserved core WRKYGQK motif and a zinc finger region. The critical role of WRKY transcription factors (WRKY TFs) in plant defense responses has been well documented [113, 114]. Their ability to bind to pathogen responsive cis acting W-box promoter elements in *PR1* genes is indicative of their role in plant immunity [113]. *Arabidopsis WRKY72* was reported to have a significant contribution to *Mi-1*-mediated defense against RKNs, potato aphids [114] and oomycete pathogen *Hyaloperonospora arabidopsidis* the causal agent of downy mildew [115]. *WRKY* gene expression is altered during plant-parasitic nematode interactions. The development of cyst nematode *H. schachtii* feeding site (syncytia) involves the up-regulation of WRKY23 [116]. Conversely, endogenous *WRKY33* gene expression levels were strongly downregulated in syncytia formed in *Arabidopsis* roots, while plants overexpressing *WRKY33* showed a 20–30% reduction in the presence of female nematodes [117] a possible indication of its role in plant defense.

Calreticulin Proteins

In animals, endoplasmic reticulum (ER) localized calreticulin proteins are integral components in calcium homeostasis as well as protein folding and are involved in other significant cellular functions [118]. Ubiquitously expressed in plants, calreticulin performs similar functions to its animal counterpart despite 50% differences in amino acid sequence homology. Plant calreticulin is described as a molecular calcium-binding chaperone that promotes protein folding, calcium signaling and homeostasis, and oligomeric assembly in a calreticulin/calnexin cycle. Calreticulin may interact with a majority of monoglucosylated glycoproteins synthesized in the ER, while certain isoforms have been associated with the expression and quality control of the elongation factor Tu receptor-like protein kinase (EFR) [119] an important event in M/PAMP-triggered immune responses. The significance of calreticulin isoform-3 (*AtCRT-3*) function through gene deletion was identified in *Arabidopsis* plants [120]. Plant transformants with repressed *AtCRT*-3 gene activity were impaired in perception of M/PAMP-associated efl-18 and deficient in EFR protein expression and anthocyanin content. Furthermore, they concluded that AtCRT-3 may be involved in the unfolding and activation of EFR based on its primary molecular function and recognition of EFR N-glycosyl binding sites. Recently, studies have shown that root-knot nematodes secrete calreticulin, which plays an important role in infection [121].

Plant Proteinase Inhibitors

Plants utilize an arsenal of defensive mechanisms to evade infection from nematodes. One important strategy involves limiting nematode feeding capabilities. Plant proteinase inhibitors are involved in many physiological processes including protein turnover and proteolysis during metabolism however; other evidence has supported an alternative role in defense against plant pathogens [122]. Plant proteinase inhibitors degrade nematode proteases preventing the breakdown of food material which reduces nutrient absorption in the nematode. As early as 1947, the idea of proteinaceous protease inhibitors was formulated as Mickel and Standish observed differences in larval development on soybean cultivars [123]. The applicability of proteinase-inhibitors in nematode resistance was initially demonstrated in transgenic potato expressing a serine proteinase-inhibitor cowpea trypsin inhibitor (CpTI) [124]. CpTI expression directly influenced the sexual fate of *G. pallida* toward a higher ratio of smaller males with reduced damage observed on roots. Out of the four major classes of plant proteinases inhibitors (cysteine, serine, aspartic, metallo-proteinases) cysteine and serine proteinase inhibitors have gained considerable interest as effective defense molecules nematodes due to their specificity in the degradation of the major digestive enzymes (proteases) in plant-parasitic nematodes [125].The effectiveness of proteinase inhibitors can be attributed to its small size, which benefits its inclusion with nutrient molecules absorbed by some plant-parasitic nematodes. In tomato, overexpression of phytocystatin gene, *CeCPI* isolated from taro (*Colocasia esculenta*) showed enhanced resistance to root-knot nematodes demonstrated by reduced galling and an influence on sex determination [126]. In sweetpotato, sporamin which is classified as a Kunitz-type trypsin inhibitor, accounts for 60–80% of total soluble protein. Sporamin is constitutively expressed in the tuberous root in comparison to in the stem or leaves and is expressed systemically in response to wounding and other abiotic stresses [127]. In previous studies, three forms of sweetpotato sporamin showed strong trypsin inhibitory activity *invitro* [128]. Additional research has resulted in the identification of sporamin-mediated resistance to cyst nematodes [129]. Decreased nematode development correlated with trypsin inhibitor activity of sporamin which was the critical factor for inhibition of growth and development of cyst nematodes on sugar beet roots. Plant genotypes that produce high sporamin levels may have a selective advantage in defense to plant-parasitic nematodes.

Plant Hormones

The roles of plant developmental hormones, ethylene, jasmonic acid and salicylic acid have been well established during plant immunity [130, 131]. Jasmonic acid (JA) and ethylene (ET) signaling pathways work synergistically while the salicylic acid (SA) pathway is antagonistic to JA/ET pathways [132]. In a prior study, exogenous ethyhlene (ethephon) and jasmonic acid (methyl jasmonate) application triggered the induction of PR proteins and the activation of systemic defense against root-knot nematodes on rice [133] These findings suggest a critical role of an active intact jasmonic acid pathway during the activation of systemically induced resistance. The combination of exogenous jasmonic acid and biogenic elicitor arachidonic acid, decreased galling on tomato roots two-fold in comparison to controls [134]. The role of salicylic acid has been well documented in the efficacy of host resistance to root-knot nematodes. Pathogenesis-related protein expression was associated with salicylic acid-dependent systemic required resistance in tomatoes pretreated with salicylic acid under root-knot nematode challenge [109]. Expression of a *NahG* which encodes for an enzyme that degrades salicylic acid to catechol, reduced *Mi-1* gene- mediated root-knot nematode resistance in transgenic tomatoes [135].

DISEASE MANAGEMENT OF PLANT-PARASITIC NEMATODES

Cultural Control

For many years, crop rotation and cover cropping are often utilized in integrated pest management protocols to reduce plant-parasitic nematode incidence and replenish soil nutrient levels. Soil nematode levels have been effectively decreased by rotational cultivation of non-host cultivars however, the wide host range of *Meloidogyne spp.* often diminishes the effectiveness of crop rotation [136]. Planting corn as a rotational crop has been shown to reduce northern root-knot nematode (*M. hapla*) incidence however; population densities of other *Meloidogyne spp.* may increase with persistent cultivation. Plant species with resistance to mixed *Meloidogyne* populations have been identified. Leguminous cover crops *Mucuna pruriens* L., and *Crotalaria spectabilis* showed multiple resistance to three species of root-knot nematodes (*Meloidogyne arenaria, M. incognita, M. javanica*) [137]. In certain cases, the very nature of crop production may suppress the magnitude of infection. Rice is cultivated under flooding conditions which does not favor the nematode lifestyle. In Taiwan, crop rotations with rice or taro combined with cultural control methods including flooding and bare fallowing was shown to decrease nematode soil populations and increase strawberry yields [138].

Plant Extracts

Plant extracts often contain a myriad of compounds which demonstrate nematode suppressive properties. Ethanolic extracts of *Azadirachta indica* (neem), *Withania somnifera* (ashwagandha), *Tagetes erecta* (marigold) and *Eucalyptus citriodora* (eucalyptus) were reported to show nematicidial activity against *Meloidogyne incognita*, *Helicotylenchus multicinctus* and *Hoplolaimus* which was comparable to chemical nematicide controls [139]. In other reports, increased plant growth and development were shown in plants propagated with the addition of a variety of extracts. Root-knot nematode egg hatch and larval development was dramatically reduced by leaf extracts from *Hunteria umbellata* and *Mallotus oppositifolius* which coincided with increased growth of cashew seedlings [140]. Plant height, fruit production and weights of *M. incognita*-infected tomato were significantly increased by the addition of ethanol extracts from *Azadirachta indica* leaves, *Capsicum annuum* fruits, *Zingiber officinale* rhizomes and *Parkia biglobosa* seeds in comparison to non-treated controls [141].

Biological Control

With increasing demands in organic agriculture and concerns for environmental welfare, the use of chemical pesticides has decreased. Alternative means of pest management such as the use of biological controls are of great interest for crop producers. The efficacy of nematophagous bacteria and fungi in the control some nematode pests, including cyst and root-knot nematodes has been well-documented [142, 143]. Parasitic bacteria of *Pasteuria spp.* have been reported to infect 323 nematode species including both plant-parasitic nematodes and free-living nematodes [144]. Three methods of application for *P. penetrans* were evaluated for nematode control including seed, transplant, and post-plant treatments [145]. In greenhouse studies involving cucumber, all three *Pasteuria* treatments were shown to reduce galling caused by *M. incognita* as well as soil nematode numbers and nematode reproduction. In other reports, *M. incognita* suppression was observed in field soil treated with *P. penetrans* in comparison to untreated soil [146]. Other genera of bacteria including *Bacillus* spp. have shown great promise in nematode management. *B. cereus* strain S2 treatment resulted in a mortality of 90.96% to *M. incognita* [147]. *B. firmus* YBf-10 exhibited nematicidal activity against *M. incognita*, which was clearly demonstrated by an inhibition of egg hatch and motility [148]. Nematophagous fungi *Pochonia chlamydosporia* has potential as a biological control agent for *M. incognita* in vegetable crops. Along with crop rotational methods, *P. chlamydosporia* was shown to reduce nematode levels in soil previously used for root-knot nematode susceptible tomato [149]. Nematophagous fungal products including chitinases show great potential for the development of biopesticides. Certain root-knot nematode species have transparent protective chitin-containing shells. Purified chitinase LPCHI1 from *Lecanicillium psalliotae* was shown to degrade *M. incognita* eggs [150].

Host Resistance

Chemical nematicides are often used in the management of root-knot nematodes however; EPA restrictions in some soil fumigants due to increased environmental toxicity coupled with the expensive costs associated new nematicide development limit their availability. The very nature of these mammalian pesticides poses a significant risk to humans. Plant-parasitic nematodes often reside in plant tissue which makes soil delivery applications of the chemical challenging. The incorporation of plant varieties that harbor multiple resistance to an array of plant pathogens is an attractive and practical approach for plant breeders. However, the conserved use of specific genotypes of disease resistant cultivars may contribute to increased pathogen aggressiveness resulting in epiphytotic conditions; therefore the identification of additional resistant varieties becomes increasingly necessary for long term control. For many years crops have been artificially selected for their inherent disease-resistant properties through phenotypic screenings and genetic analyses. Nematode-resistant genes found in gene pools of a variety of plant species have been introgressed into the genomes of economically important crops with natural susceptibility through transgenic technologies such as agrobacterium-mediated transformation [151, 152].

Plants synthesize and release an array of volatile organic compounds in response to damage. Plant terpenes/terpenoids are secondary metabolites produced by terpene synthases in plants and are involved plant survival and biotic and abiotic stress responses. Functional characterization of one member of the soybean TPS gene family, designated GmAFS suggested an anti-nematode role [153]. Transgenic hairy roots overexpressing GmAFS were generated in an *H. avenae*-susceptible soybean line. Plants showed significantly higher resistance to *H. avenae* burden than controls.

RNA interference (RNAi) is a method of gene silencing observed in a wide range of organisms. This method of gene silencing has become a useful tool for biologists to study biological processes and has been developed into a novel control strategy for engineering plants with nematode resistance. First identified in plants [154] the mechanism of action was elucidated in the nematode model organism *C. elegans* [155]. RNAi involves the suppression of specific transcripts to minimum expression levels as a method of post-transcriptional gene silencing during developmental processes and is believed to be a response to double-stranded viral entry. RNAi is premised on the cell's ability to recognize and degrade double-stranded RNA (dsRNA). The dsRNA is processed into small interfering RNA (siRNA) by the enzyme Dicer, a ribosome III-like enzyme. Double-stranded siRNA is unwound into two single-stranded RNAs and one strand serves as a guide which associates with the RNA-induced silencing complex (RISC). This complex associate with the specific complementary mRNA expressed in the cell where the RNAse H enzyme Argonaute degrades the mRNA resulting in gene silencing. Since the discovery of RNA-interference, researchers have developed transgenic constructs that specifically target genes for functional characterizations. More recently, plants have been engineered to expresses double-stranded RNA that silence important genes in plant-parasitic nematodes [156, 157]. As nematodes feed on the plant cytoplasm, the uptake of the siRNA triggers the endogenous RNAi mechanism within the nematode, silencing the target gene involved in infection [158]. The RNAi approach was applied, using sequence fragments from *M. incognita* genes that encode for two heat-shock protein 90 (HSP90) and isocitrate lyase (ICL). Heterologous expression of RNAi constructs in tobacco plants correlated to a significant level of resistance against *M. incognita.* Delayed galling and decreased egg production was observed in plants expressing HSP90 dsRNA. The *16D10* effector gene encodes for a secretory peptide synthesized in the subventral esophageal glands of root-knot nematodes which plays an important role in giant cell formation cells [156]. *In planta* expression of 16D10 dsRNA in Arabidopsis conferred in resistance effective against the four major root-knot nematode species [156]. In transgenic lines of potato expressing a 16D10 RNAi construct (Mc16D10L), the number of *M. chitwoodi* egg masses and eggs was significantly decreased in comparison to empty vector controls [159]. *Mc16D10L* expression was reduced in eggs and juveniles developed on transgenic potato which suggest a stable heritability of the construct. Decreased egg production was also observed in transgenic grape lines expressing *16D10L* [160].

The use of site-specific DNA endonucleases including Zinc finger nucleases (ZFNs), [161] transcription activator-like effector nucleases (TALENs) [162] and now clustered regularly interspaced short palindromic repeats (CRISPR)/Cas9 [163] have equipped researchers with the ability to specifically inactivate genes and target genetic regions for homologous recombination of input DNA. In general, double-stranded breaks introduced by nucleases activates DNA repair mechanisms which generate mutations in the target sequence conferring a loss of expression i.e., gene editing. Homologous recombination of exogenously supplied sequences can result in genetic modifications (knock-ins). CRISPR technology has important advantages over TALENS and ZFNs including; ease of use [164] target site selection [165] and overall efficiency, although off-target effects remains an important issue of concern [166]. CRISPR/Cas9 system may be used to alter the expression of resistance genes for constitutive expression against plant-parasitic nematodes. For example, point mutations in the *snc1* (suppressor of npr1-1, constitutive 1) locus in *Arabidopsis* plants resulted in constitutive expression of pathogenesis-related proteins and enhanced disease resistance against two plant pathogens [167]. The mutation was mapped to a single nucleotide change in 120-kb region on chromosome 4 which contains a cluster of resistance genes. In a recent sweetpotato study, putative disease resistance gene *DRL23* showed elevated expression in resistant sweetpotato genotypes when compared to susceptible plants at days 14 and 46 post-inoculation with *Meloidogyne incognita* inoculum [168]. To identify any polymorphisms in amino sequences between *DRL23* from resistant and susceptible cultivars, protein alignments using the NCBI BLAST (Basic Local Alignment Search Tool) was performed. Interestingly, variations in amino acid sequences occurred between resistant (positions 187–231) and susceptible (positions 57–102) which corresponded to the NBS domain. Mutations in the NB-ARC domain often abolish R-protein function, indicative of the functional relevance of this domain [169]. Precise targeting by CRISPR may be useful in restoring gene function by sequence replacement in defense-related genes thereby enhancing resistance to nematode infection.

ACKNOWLEDGMENTS

The authors would like to acknowledge the IBREED program under USDA-NIFA Grant #2014-38821-22448 and the Tuskegee University George Washington Carver Agricultural Experiment Station.

REFERENCES

1. Hugot J, Baujard P, Morand S. Biodiversity in helminths and nematodes as a field of study: An overview. Nematology. 2001;3:199-208. DOI: 10. 1163/156854101750413270
2. Page A, Stepek G, Winter A, Pertab D. Enzymology of the nematode cuticle: A potential drug target? International Journal for Parasitology: Drugs and Drug Resistance. 2014;4:133-141. DOI: 10. 1016/j. ijpddr. 2014. 05. 003
3. Kiontke K, Fitch D. Nematodes. Current Biology. 2013;23:862-864. DOI: http://dx. doi. org/10. 1016/j. cub. 2013. 08. 009
4. Maier T, Hewezi T, Peng J, Baum TJ. Isolation of whole esophageal gland cells from plant-parasitic nematodes for transcriptome analyses and effector identification. Molecular Plant-Microbe Interactions. 2013;26:31-35. DOI: 10. 1094/MPMI-05-12-0121-FI
5. Poinar GO. 1983. The Natural History of Nematodes. Prentice Hall, Englewood Cliffs, NJ
6. Noel GR. History, distribution, and economics. In: Riggs R, Wrather JA, editors. Biology and Management of the Soybean Cyst Nematode. American Phytopathological Society;1992. pp. 1-13
7. Needham T. A Letter from Mr. Turbevil Needham, to the President; Concerning Certain Chalky Tubulous Concretions, Called Malm: With Some Microscopical Observations on the Farina of the Red Lily, and of Worms Discovered in Smutty Corn. Philosophical Transactions of the Royal Society of London. 1742;42:462-471 DOI:10. 1098/rstl. 1742. 0101
8. Berkeley M. Vibrio forming cysts on the roots of cucumbers. Gardeners' Chronicle. 1855; 7:220
9. Quentin M, Abad P, Favery B. Plant parasitic nematode effectors target host defense and nuclear functions to establish feeding cells. Frontiers in Plant Science. 2013;4:1-7. DOI: 10. 3389/fpls. 2013. 00053

10. Davis EL, Hussey RS, Mitchum MG and Baum TJ. Parasitism proteins in nematode-plant interactions. Current Opinion in Plant Biology. 2008;11:360-366. DOI: 10. 1016/j. pbi. 2008. 04. 003

11. Abad P, Gouzy J, Aury J, Castagnone-Sereno P, Danchi EGJ, Deleury E, Perfus-Barbeoch L, Anthouard V, Artiguenave F, Blok VC, Caillaud MC, Coutinho PM, Dasilva C, De Luca F, Deau F, Esquibet M, Flutre T, Goldstone JV, Hamamouch N, Hewezi T, Jaillon O, Jubin C, Leonetti P, Magliano M, Maier TR, Markov GV, McVeigh P, Pesole G, Poulain J, Robinson-Rechavi M, Sallet E, Segurens B, Steinbach D, Tytgat T, Ugarte E, van Ghelder C, Veronico P, Baum TJ, Blaxter M, Bleve-Zacheo T, Davis EL, Ewbank JJ, Favery B, Grenier E, Henrissat B, Jones JT, Laudet V, Maule AG, Quesneville H, Rosso MN, Schiex T, Smant G, Weissenbach J, Wincker P. Genome sequence of the metazoan plant-parasitic nematode Meloidogyne incognita. Nature Biotechnology. 2008;26:909-915. DOI: 10. 1038/nbt. 1482

12. Smant G, Stokkermans J, Yan Y, de Boer JM, Baum TJ, Wang X, Hussey R, Gommers F, Henrissat B, Davis E, Helder J, Schots A, Bakker J. Endogenous cellulases in animals: Isolation of β-1,4-endoglucanase genes from two species of plant-parasitic cyst nematodes. PNAS. 1998;95:4906-4911

13. Yan Y, Smant G, Stokkermans J, Qin L, Helder J, Baum T, Schots A, Davis E. Genomic organization of four beta-1,4-endoglucanase genes in plant-parasitic cyst nematodes and its evolutionary implications. Gene. 1998;220:61-70

14. Jones J, Furlanetto C, Kikuchi T. Horizontal gene transfer from bacteria and fungi as a driving force in the evolution of plant parasitism in nematodes. Nematology. 2005;7:642-646. DOI: 10. 1163/156854105775142919

15. Rybarczyk-Mydłowska K, Maboreke H, van Megen H, van den Elsen S, Mooyman P, Smant G, Bakker J, Helder J. Rather than by direct acquisition via lateral gene transfer, GHF5 cellulases were passed on from early Pratylenchidae to root-knot and cyst nematodes. BMC Evolutionary Biology. 2012;12:221. DOI: 10. 1186/1471-2148-12-221

16. Kikuchi T, Jones J, Aikawa T, Kosaka H, Ogura N. A family of glycosyl hydrolase family 45 cellulases from the pine wood nematode Bursaphelenchus xylophilus. FEBS Letters. 2004;572:201-205. DOI: 10. 1016/j. febslet. 2004. 07. 039

17. Palomares-Rius J, Hirooka Y, Tsa I, Masuya H, Hino A, Kanzaki N, Jones J, Kikuchi T. Distribution and evolution of glycoside hydrolase family 45 cellulases in nematodes and fungi. BMC Evolutionary Biology. 2014;14: 69. DOI: 10. 1186/1471-2148-14-69

18. Villate L, Fievet V, Hanse B, Delemarre F, Plantard O, Esmenjaud D, van Helden M. Spatial distribution of the dagger nematode Xiphinema index and its associated Grapevine fanleaf virus in French vineyard. Phytopathology. 2008;98:942-948. DOI: 10. 1094/PHYTO-98-8-0942

19. Williamson V, Hussey R. Nematode pathogenesis and resistance in plants. The Plant Cell. 1996;8:1735-1745. DOI: 10. 1105/tpc. 8. 10. 1735

20. Decraemer W, Hunt D. Structure and classification. In: Perry R, Moens M, editors. Plant Nematology. Oxfordshire: CAB International;2006. pp. 3-32. DOI: 10. 1079/9781845930561. 0000

21. Nicol J, Turner D, Coyne L, den Nijs L, Hockland S, Maafi Z. Current nematode threats to world agriculture. In: Jones J, Gheysen G, Fenoll C, editors. Genomics and Molecular Genetics of Plant-Nematode Interactions. Berlin:Springer Science Business Media; 2011. pp. 21-43. DOI 10. 1007/978-94-007-0434-3_2

22. Sasser J, Freckman D. A world perspective on nematology: The role of the society. In: Veech J, Dickson D, editors. Vistas on Nematology; Society of Nematologists, Inc. : Hyattsville, MD . pp. 7-14

23. Koenning S, Overstreet C, Noling J, Donald P, Becker J, Fortnum B. Survey of crop losses in response to phytoparasitic nematodes in the United States for 1994. Journal of Nematology. 1999;31(4S): 587-618

24. FAO. Cereal Supply and Demand Brief [Internet]. 2017. Available from: http://www. fao. org/ worldfoodsituation/csdb/en/ [Accessed: 10-03-2017]

25. Smiley R, Guiping Y. Cereal cyst nematodes. Biology and management in Pacific Northwest wheat, barley, and oat crops. A Pacific Northwest Extension Publication Oregon State University [Internet] 2010. Available from: http://ir. library. oregonstate. edu/xmlui/bitstream/ handle/1957/18917/pnw620. pdf [Accessed: 15-03-2017]

26. Bonfil D, Dolgin B, Mufradi I, Asido S. Bioassay to forecast cereal cyst nematode damage to wheat in fields. Precision Agriculture. 2004;5: 329-344. DOI: 10. 1023/B:PRAG. 0000040804. 97462. 02

27. Nicol J, Elekçioğlu H, Bolat N, Rivoal R. The global importance of the cereal cyst nematode (Heterodera spp.) on wheat and international approaches to its control. Communications in Agricultural and Applied Biological Sciences. 2004;72: 677-686

28. Lasserre, F, Rivoal, R, Cook, R. Interactions between Heterodera avenae and Pratylenchus neglectus on wheat. Journal of Nematology. 1994;26:336-344

29. Riley T, Reardon T. Isolation and characterization of Clavibacter tritici associated with Anguina tritici in wheat from Western Australia. Plant Pathology. 1995;44: 805-810. DOI: 10. 1111/j. 1365-3059. 1995. tb02739. x

30. Childs, Nathan. 2017. U. S. 2016/17 Export Forecast Lowered 2. 0 Million Cwt to 110. 0 Million cwt. USDA-ERS Situation and Outlook. RCS-17B https://www. ers. usda. gov/ webdocs/publications/rcs17b/rcs-17b. pdf?v=42787

31. Trudgill D, Blok V. Apomictic, polyphagous root-knot nematodes: exceptionally successful and damaging biotrophic root pathogens. Annual Review of Phytopathology. 2001;39:53-77. doi: 10. 1146/annurev. phyto. 39. 1. 53

32. Soriano I, Prot J, Matias D. Expression of tolerance for Meloidogyne graminicola in rice cultivars as affected by soil type and flooding. Journal of Nematology. 2000;32:309-317

33. Pokharel R, Abawi G, Zhang N, Duxbury J, Smart, C. Characterization of isolates of Meloidogyne from rice-wheat production fields in Nepal. Journal of Nematology. 2007;39: 221-230

34. Kyndt T, Fernandez D, Gheysen G. Plant-parasitic nematode infections in rice: Molecular and cellular insights. Annual Review of Phytopathology. 2014;52:135-153. DOI: 10. 1146/ annurev-phyto-102313-050111

35. Bridge J Plowright R, Peng D. Nematode parasites of rice. In: Luc M, Sikora R, Bridge J, editors. Plant Parasitic Nematodes in Subtropical and Tropical Agriculture. 2nd ed. Egham:CABI Bioscience; 2005. pp. 87-130. DOI: 10. 1079/9780851997278. 0000

36. Norton D. Maize nematode problems. Plant Disease. 1983;67:253-256

37. Norton D, Hoffmann J. Longidorus breviannulatus n. sp. (Nematoda: Longidoridae) associated with stunted corn in Iowa. Journal of Nematology. 1975;7:168-171

38. FAOSTAT. World production of potato. [Internet]. 2015. Available from http://www. nationalpotatocouncil. org/files/1114/4223/8719/Pg. _78_World_Potato_Production. pdf [Accessed: 20-03-2017]

39. Turner S, Evans K. The origins, global distribution and biology of potato cyst nematodes (Globodera rostochiensis (Woll.) and G. pallida Stone). In: Marks R, Brodie B. editors. Potato Cyst Nematodes: Biology, Distribution, and Control. Cambridge: University Press; 1998. pp. 7-26

40. Jones L, Koehler A, Trnka M, Balek J, Challinor A, Atkinson H, Urwin P. Climate change is predicted to alter the current pest status of Globodera pallida and G. rostochiensis in the UK. Global Change Biology. DOI: 10. 1111/gcb. 13676

41. Santo G, O'Bannon J, Finley A, Golden A. Occurrence and host range of a new root-knot nematode (Meloidogyne chitwoodi) in the Pacific Northwest. Plant Disease. 1980;64:951-952. DOI: 10. 1094/PD-64-951

42. Xu Z, Zhao Y, Yang D, Sun H, Zhang C, Xie Y. Attractant and repellent effects of sweet potato root exudates on the potato rot nematode, Ditylenchus destructor. Nematology. 2015;17:117-124. DOI: 10. 1163/15685411-00002856

43. Zhang S, Zhang S, Wang H, Chen Y. Characteristics of sweetpotato stem nematode in China. Acta Phytopathologica Sinica. 2006;36:22-27

44. CIP International Potato Center. Sweetpotato Facts and Figures. 2014. Available from: http:// cipotato. org/sweetpotato/facts-2/. [Accessed: 20-03-2017]

45. Bonsi C, Phills B. Reaction of twelve sweetpotato cultivars and breeding lines to root-knot species with three experimental methods. HortScience. 1979;14:539-541

46. Cervantes-Flores J, Yencho G, Davis E. Detection of quantitative trait loci and inheritance of root-knot nematode resistance in sweetpotato. HortScience. 2008;133:841-851

47. Jones J, Haegeman A, Danchin E, Gaur H, Helder J, Jones M, Kikuchi T, Manzanilla-Lopez R, Palomares-Rius J, Wesemael W, Perry R. Top 10 plant-parasitic nematodes in molecular plant pathology. Molecular Plant Pathology. . 2013;14:946-961. DOI: 10. 1111/mpp. 12057

48. Postnikova O, Hult M, Shao J, Skantar A, Nemchinov L. Transcriptome analysis of resistant and susceptible alfalfa cultivars infected with root-knot nematode Meloidogyne incognita. PloS One. 2015;10:e0118269. DOI: 10. 1371/journal. pone. 0118269

49. Davis E, Hussey R, Baum T, Bakker J, Schots A, Rosso M, Abad P. Nematode parasitism genes. Annual Review of Phytopathology. 2000;38:365-396. DOI: 10. 1146/annurev. phyto. 38. 1. 365

50. Caillaud M, Dubreuil G, Quentin M, Perfus-Barbeoch L, Lecomte P, de Almeida Engler J, Abad P, Rosso M, Favery B. Root-knot nematodes manipulate plant cell functions during a compatible interaction. Journal of Plant Physiology. 2008;165:104-113. DOI: 10. 1016/j. jplph. 2007. 05. 007

51. Hewezi T, Baum T. Manipulation of plant cells by cyst and root-knot nematode effectors. Molecular Plant-Microbe Interactions. 2013;26:9-16. DOI: 10. 1094/MPMI-05-12-0106-FI

52. Gheysen G, Fenoll C. Gene expression in nematode feeding sites. Annual Review of Phytopathology. 2002;40:191-219. Epub 2002 Feb 20 DOI:10. 1146/ annurev. phyto. 40. 121201. 093719

53. Wrather A, Mitchum M. Soybean cyst nematodes: Diagnosis and Management. [Internet] 2010. Available from: http://extension. missouri. edu/p/g4450 [Accessed: 23-03-2017]

54. PM 7/40 (3) Globodera rostochiensis and Globodera pallida. Bulletin OEPP/EPPO Bulletin. 2013:43. DOI: 10. 1111/epp. 12025

55. Abawi G, Mai W. Effects of initial population densities of Heterodera schachtii on yield of cabbage and table beets in New York State. Phytopathology. 1980;70(6):481-485

56. Muller J. The economic importance of Heterodera schachtii in Europe. Helminthologia. 1999;36(3):205-213

57. Davis E, MacGuidwin A. Lesion nematode disease. The Plant Health Instructor. [Internet]. 2000. Available from: http://www. apsnet. org/edcenter/intropp/lessons/Nematodes/Pages/ LesionNematode. aspx [Accessed: 23-03-2017]. DOI: 10. 1094/PHI-I-2000-1030-02

58. Smiley R. Root-lesion nematodes: Biology and management in Pacific Northwest wheat cropping systems. [Internet]. 2015. Available from: https://catalog. extension. oregonstate. edu/sites/catalog/files/project/pdf/pnw617_1. pdf. [Accessed: 23-03-2017]

59. Jones M, Fosu-Nyarko J. Molecular biology of root lesion nematodes (Pratylenchus spp.) and their interaction with host plants. Annals of Applied Biology. 2014;164:163-181. DOI: 10. 1111/aab. 12105

60. Kim D, Chun J, Lee KY. Pratylenchus kumamotoensis and P. pseudocoffeae (Nematoda, Pratylenchidae) newly recorded in Korea. Zookeys. 2016;600:1-5. DOI: 10. 3897/zookeys. 600. 8508

61. Smith I, Charles L, editors. Distribution Maps of Quarantine Pests for Europe. Wallingford: CABI International; 1998. pp. 1-78

62. Sarah J, Gowen S, De Waele D, Tessera M, Quimio A. Nematode pathogens. In: Jones D, editors. Diseases of Banana, Abacá and Ensete. Wallingford: CABI Publishing; 1999. pp. 295-303

63. Li Y, Wang K, Xie H, Wang Y, Wang D, Xu C, Huang X, Wang D. Nematode calreticulin, RsCRT is a key effector in reproduction and pathogenicity of Radopholus similis. PloS One. 2015;10:1-20. DOI: 10. 1371/journal. pone. 0129351.

64. Hölscher D, Dhakshinamoorthy S, Alexandrov T, Becker M, Bretschneider T, Buerkert A, … Swennen R. Phenalenone-type phytoalexins mediate resistance of banana plants (Musa spp.) to the burrowing nematode Radopholus similis. PNAS. 2014;11:105-110. DOI: 10. 1073/pnas. 1314168110

65. Gleason C, Polzin F, Habash S, Zhang L, Utermark J, Grundler F, Elashry A. Identification of two Meloidogyne hapla genes and an investigation of their roles in plant-nematode interaction. MPMI. 2017;30:101-112. DOI: http://dx. doi. org/10. 1094/MPMI-06-16-0107-R

66. Bashline L, Lei L, Li S, Gu Y. Cell wall, cytoskeleton, and cell expansion in higher plants. Molecular Plant. 2014;7:586-600. DOI: 10. 1093/mp/ssu018

67. Fudali S, Sobczak M, Janakowski S, Griesser M, Grundler FM, Golinowski W. Expansins are among plant cell wall modifying agents specifically expressed during development of nematode-induced syncytia. Plant Signaling & Behavior. 2008;3:969-971. DOI: 10. 4161/psb. 6169

68. Liu J, Peng H, Cui J, Huang W, Kong L, Clark J, Jian H, Wang G, Peng D. Molecular characterization of a novel effector expansin-like protein from Heterodera avenae that induces cell death in Nicotiana benthamiana. Scientific Reports. 2016;6:35677. DOI: 10. 1038/ srep35677

69. Zheng M, Long H, Zhao Y, Lin L, Xu D, Zhang H, Liu F, Deng G, Pan Z, Yu M. RNA-Seq based identification of candidate parasitism genes of cereal cyst nematode (Heterodera avenae) during incompatible infection to Aegilops variabilis. PloS One. 2015;10:e0141095. DOI: http://doi. org/10. 1371/journal. pone. 0141095

70. Guan T, Shen J, Fa Y, Su Y, Wang X, Li H. Resistance-breaking population of Meloidogyne incognita utilizes plant peroxidase to scavenge reactive oxygen species, thereby promoting parasitism on tomato carrying Mi-1 gene. Biochemical and Biophysical Research Communications 2017;482:1-7. DOI: 10. 1016/j. bbrc. 2016. 11. 040

71. Lacomme C, Santa Cruz S. Bax-induced cell death in tobacco is similar to the hypersensitive response. PNAS. 1999;96:7956-7961. DOI: 10. 1073/pnas. 96. 14. 7956

72. Li X, Yang D, Niu J, Zhao J, Jian H. De novo analysis of the transcriptome of Meloidogyne enterolobii to uncover potential target genes for biological control. International Journal of Molecular Sciences. 2016;17:1442. DOI: 10. 3390/ijms17091442

73. Postma W, Slootweg E, Rehman S, Finkers-Tomczak A, Tytgat T, Van Gelderen K, Lozano-

Torress J, Roosien J, Pomp R, van Schaik C, Bakker J, Goverse A, Smant G. The effector SPRYSEC-19 of Globodera rostochiensis suppresses CC-NB-LRR-mediated disease resistance in plants. Plant Physiology. 2012;160:944-954. DOI: 10. 1104/pp. 112. 200188

74. Ali S, Magne M, Chen S, Obradovic N, Jamshaid L, Wang X, Belair G, Moffett P. Analysis of Globodera rostochiensis effectors reveals conserved functions of SPRYSEC proteins in suppressing and eliciting plant immune responses. Frontiers in Plant Science. 2015;6:623. DOI: 10. 3389/fpls. 2015. 00623

75. Milligan S, Bodeau J, Yaghoobi J, Kaloshian I, Zabel P, Williamson V. The root-knot nematode resistance gene Mi from tomato is a member of the leucne zipper, nucleotide binding, leucine-rich repeat family of plant genes. Plant Cell. 1998;10:1307-1319

76. Cai D, Kleine M, Kifle S, Harloff H, Sandal N, Marcker K, Klein-Lankhorst R, Salentijn E, Lange W, Stiekema W, Wyss U, Grundler F, Jung C. Positional cloning of a gene for nematode resistance in sugar beet. Science. 1997;275:832-834

77. Van der Vossen E, van der Voort J, Kanyuka K, Bendahmane A, Sandbrink H, Baulcombe D, Bakker J, Stiekema W, Klein-Lankhorst R. Homologues of a single resistance-gene cluster in potato confer resistance to distinct pathogens: A virus and a nematode. The Plant Journal. 2000;23:567-576. DOI: 10. 1046/j. 1365-313x. 2000. 00814. x

78. Paal J, Henselewski H, Muth J, Meksem K, Menendez C, Salamini F, Ballvora A, Gebhardt C. Molecular cloning of the potato Gro1-4 gene conferring resistance to pathotype Ro1 of the root cyst nematode Globodera rostochiensis, based on a candidate gene approach. The Plant Journal. 2004;38:285-287. DOI: 10. 1111/j. 1365-313X. 2004. 02047. x

79. Smith P. Embryo culture of a tomato species hybrid. Proceedings of the American Society for Horticultural Sciences. 1944;44: 413-416

80. Frazier W, Dennett R. Isolation of Lycopersicon esculentum type tomato lines essentially homozygous resistant to root-knot. Proceedings of the American Society for Horticultural Science. 1949;54:225-236

81. Rossi M, Goggin F, Milligan S, Kaloshian I, Ullman D, Williamson V. The nematode resistance gene Mi of tomato confers resistance against the potato aphid. Proceedings of the National Academy of Sciences of the United States of America. 1998;95: 9750-9754

82. Nombela G, Williamson V, Muniz M. The root-knot nematode resistance gene Mi-1. 2 of tomato is responsible for resistance against the whitefly Bemisia tabaci. Molecular Plant-Microbe Interactions. 2003;16:645-649. DOI: 10. 1094/MPMI. 2003. 16. 7. 645

83. Martinez de Illarduya O, Nombela G, Hwang C, Williamson V, Muniz M, Kaloshian I. Rme1 is necessary for Mi-1 resistance and acts early in the resistance pathway. Molecular Plant-Microbe Interactions. 2004;17:55-61. DOI: 10. 1094/MPMI. 2004. 17. 1. 55

84. Ali A, Matthews W, Cavagnaro P, Iorizzo M, Roberts P, Simon P. Inheritance and mapping of Mj-2, a new source of root-knot nematode (Meloidogyne javanica) resistance in carrot. Journal of Heredity. 2014;105:288-291. DOI: 10. 1093/jhered/est090

85. Simon P, Matthews W, Roberts P. Evidence for simply inherited dominant resistance to Meloidogyne javanica in carrot. Theoretical and Applied Genetics. 2000;100:735-742. DOI:10. 1007/s001220051346

86. Duval H, Hoerter M, Polidori J, Confolent C, Masse M, Moretti A, Van Ghelder C, Esmenjaud D. High-resolution mapping of the RMia gene for resistance to root-knot nematodes in peach. Tree Genetics and Genomes. 2014;10:297-306. DOI: 10. 1007/s11295-013-0683-z

87. Claverie M, Dirlewanger E, Bosselut N, Van Ghelder C, Voisin R, Kleinhentz M, Lafargue B, Abad P, Rosso M, Chalhoub B, Esmenjaud D. The Ma gene for complete-spectrum resistance to Meloidogyne species in Prunus is a TNL with a huge repeated C-terminal post-LRR region. Plant Physiology. 2011;156:779-792. DOI: 10. 1104/pp. 111. 176230

88. Claveric M, Bosselut N, Lecouis A, Voisin R, Lafargue B, Poizat C, Kleinhentz M, Laigret F, Dirlewanger E, Esmenjaud D. Location of independent root-knot nematode resistance genes in plum and peach. Theoretical and Applied Genetics. 2004;108:765-773. DOI: 10. 1007/s00122-003-1463-1

89. Yang Y, Rosen B, Scoffield J, He G. Isolation and analysis of resistance gene homologues in sweetpotato. Plant Breeding. 2010;129:519-525 DOI: 10. 1111/j. 1439-0523. 2009. 01711. x

90. Michelmore R, Paran I, Kesseli R. Identification of markers linked to disease-resistance genes by bulked segregant analysis: A rapid method to detect markers in specific genomic regions by using segregating populations. PNAS. 1991;88:9828-9832. DOI: 10. 1073/pnas. 88. 21. 9828

91. Ukoskit K, Thompson P, Watson C. Identifying a randomly amplified polymorphic DNA (RAPD) marker linked to a gene for root-knot nematode resistance in sweetpotato. Journal of the American Society of Horticultural Science. 1997;122:818-821

92. Mauricio R, Stahl E, Korves T, Tian D, Kreitman M, Bergelson J. Natural selection for polymorphism in the disease resistance gene Rps2 of Arabidopsis thaliana. Genetics. 2003;163:735-746

93. Kawahara Y, Oono Y, Kanamori H, Matsumoto T, Itoh T, Minami E. Simultaneous RNA-Seq analysis of a mixed transcriptome of rice and blast fungus interaction. PLoS One. 2012;7:e49423

94. Yang F, Li W, Jorgensen H. Transcriptional reprogramming of wheat and the hemibiotrophic pathogen Septoria tritici during two phases of the compatible interaction. PLoS One. 2013;8:e81606. DOI: 10. 1371/journal. pone. 0081606

95. Oliveira J, Andrade N, Martins-Miranda A, Soares A, Gondim D, Araujo-Filho J, Freire-Filho F, Vasconcelos I. Differential expression of antioxidant enzymes and PR-proteins in compatible and incompatible interactions of cowpea (Vigna unguiculate) and the root-knot nematode Meloidogyne incognita. Plant Physiology and Biochemistry. 2012;51:145-152. DOI: 10. 1016/j. plaphy. 2011. 10. 008

96. Li R, Rashotte A, Singh N, Lawrence K, Weaver D, Locy R. Transcriptome analysis of cotton (Gossypium hirsutum L.) genotypes that are susceptible, resistant and hypersensitive to reniform nematode (Rotylenchulus reniformis). PloS One. 2015;10:1-27. DOI: 10. 1371/journal. pone. 014326

97. Petitot A, Dereeper A, Agbessi M, Da Silva C, Guy J, Ardisson M, Fernandez D. Dual RNA-seq reveals Meloidogyne graminicola transcriptome and candidate effectors during the interaction with rice plants. Molecular Plant Pathology. 2016;17:860-874. DOI: 10. 1111/mpp. 12334

98. Wan J, Vuong T, Jiao Y, Joshi T, Zhang H, Xu D, Nguyen H. Whole-genome gene expression profiling revealed genes and pathways potentially involved in regulating interactions of soybean with cyst nematode (Heterodera glycines Ichinohe). BMC Genomics. 2015;16:1-14. DOI: 10. 1186. s12864-015-1316-8

99. Xing X, Li X, Zhang M, Wang Y, Liu B, Xi Q, Zhao D, Wu Y, and Yang T. Transcriptome analysis of resistant and susceptible tobacco (Nicotiana tabacum) in response to root-knot nematode Meloidogyne incognita infection. Biochemical and Biophysical Research Communications. 2017: 482:1114-1121. DOI: 10. 1016/j. bbrc. 2016. 11. 167

100. Dangl J, Jones J. Plant pathogens and integrated defence responses to infection. Nature. 2001;411:826-833. DOI: 10. 1038/35081161

101. Melillo M, Leonetti P, Bongiovanni M, Castagnone-Sereno P, Bleve-Zacheo T. Modulation of reactive oxygen species activities and H_2O_2 accumulation during compatible and incompatible tomato-root-knot nematode interactions. New Phytologist. 2006;170:501-512. DOI: 10. 1111/j. 1469-8137. 2006. 01724

102. Kawano T. Roles of the reactive oxygen species-generating peroxidase reactions in plant defense and growth induction. Plant Cell Reports. 2003;21:829-837. DOI:10. 1007/s00299-003-0591-z

103. Simonetti E, Veronico P, Melillo M, Delibes A, Andres M, López-Braña I. Analysis of class III peroxidase genes expressed in roots of resistant and susceptible wheat lines infected by Heterodera avenae. MPMI. 2009;22:1081-1092. DOI:10. 1094/MPMI -22-9-1081

104. Graham M, Graham T. Rapid accumulation of anionic peroxidases and phenolic polymers in soybean cotyledon tissues following treatment with Phytophtora megasperma f. sp. Glycinea wall glucan. Plant Physiology. 1991;94:1445-1455. DOI:0032-0889/91/97/1445/11

105. Zacheo G, Orlando C, Bleve-Zacheo T. Characterization of anionic peroxidases in tomato isolines infected by Meloidogyne incognita. Journal of Nematology. 1993;25:249-256

106. van Loon L, van Strien E. The families of pathogenesis-related proteins, their activities, and comparative analysis of PR-1 type proteins. Physiological and Molecular Plant Pathology. 1999;55:85-97. http://dx. doi. org/10. 1006/pmpp. 1999. 0213

107. Van Loon L, Van Kammen A. Polyacrylamide disc electrophoresis of the soluble leaf proteins from Nicotiana tabaum var. 'Samsun' and 'Samsun NN'. II, Changes in protein constitution after in infection with TMV. Virology. 1970;40:199-201

108. Gianinazzi S, Martin C, Vallee J. Hypersensibilite aux virus, temperature et proteins solubles chez le Nicotiana xanthi n. c. Apparition de nouvelles macromolecules lors de la repression de la synthese virale. Comptes Rendus de l'Académie des Sciences. 1970;270:2383-2386

109. Molinari S, Fanelli E, Leonetti P. Expression of tomato salicylic acid (SA)-responsive pathogenesis-related genes in Mi-1-mediated and SA-induced resistance to root-knot nematodes. Molecular Plant Pathology. 2014;152:55-64. DOI: 10. 1111/mpp. 12085

110. Uehara T, Sugiyama S, Matsuura H, Arie T, Masuta C. Resistant and susceptible responses in tomato to cyst nematode are differentially regulated by salicylic acid. Plant & Cell Physiology. 2010;51:1524-1536. DOI: 10. 1093/pcp/pcq109

111. Hi J, Kyndt T, He W, Vanholme B, Gheysen G. B-aminobutyric acid-induced resistance against root-knot nematodes in rice is based on increased basal defense. MPMI. 2015;28:519-533. DOI: 10. 1094/MPMI-09-14-0260-R

112. Amjad Ali M, Abbas A, Kreil D, Bohlmann H. Overexpression of the transcription factor RAP2. 6 leads to enhanced callose deposition in syncytia and enhanced resistance against the beet cyst nematode Heterodera schachtii in Arabidopsis roots. BMC Plant Biology. 2013;13:1-17. DOI: 10. 1186/1471-2229-13-47

113. Rushton P, Torres J, Parniske M, Wernert P, Halhlbrock K, Somssich I. Interaction of elicitor-induced DNA-binding proteins with elicitor response elements in the promoters of parsley PR1 genes. EMBO Journal. 1996;15:5690-5700

114. Atamian H, Eulgem T, Kaloshian I. SIWRKY70 is required for Mi-1 mediated resistance to aphids and nematodes in tomato. Planta 2012;235:299-309. DOI: 10. 1007/s00425-011-1509-6

115. Bhattarai K, Atamian H, Kaloshian I, Eulgem T. WRKY72-type transcription factors contribute to basal immunity in tomato and Arabidopsis as well as gene-for-gene resistance mediated by the tomato R gene Mi-1. The Plant Journal. 2010;63:229-240. DOI: 10. 1111/j. 1365-313X. 2010. 04232

116. Grunewald W, Karimi M, Wieczorek K, Van de Cappelle E, Wischnitzki E, Grundler F, Inze D, Beeckman T, Gheysen G. A role for AtWRKY23 in feeding site establishment of plant-parasitic nematodes. Plant Physiology. 2008;146:358-368. DOI: 10. 1104/pp. 108. 119131

117. Amjad Ali M, Wieczorek K, Kreil D, Bohlmann H. The beet cyst nematode Heterodera schachtii modulates the expression of WRKY transcription factors in syncytia to favour its

development in Arabidopsis roots. PLoS One. 2014;9:e102360. DOI: 10. 1371/journal. pone. 0102360

118. Michalak M, Corbett E, Mesaeli N, Nakamura K, Opas M. Calreticulin: one protein, one gene, many functions. Biochemical Journal. 1999;344:281-291

119. Saijo Y, Tintor N, Lu X, Rauf P, Pajerowska-Mukhtar K, Haweker H, Dong X, Robatzek S, Schulze-Lefert P. Receptor quality control in the endoplasmic reticulum for plant innate immunity. EMBO Journal. 2009;28:3439-3449. DOI: 10. 1038/emboj. 2009. 263

120. Christensen A, Svensson K, Thelin L, Zhang W, Tintor N, Prins D, Funke N, Michalak M, Schulze-Lefert P, Saijo Y, Sommarin M, Widell S, Persson S. Higher plant calreticulins have acquired specialized functions in Arabidopsis. PLoS One. 2010;5:e11342. DOI: 10. 1371/ journal. pone. 0011342

121. Jaouannet M, Magliano M, Arguel M, Gourgues M, Evangelisti E, Abad P, Rosso M. The root-knot nematode calreticulin Mi-CRT is a key effector in plant defense suppression. Molecular Plant-Microbe Interactions. 2013;26:97-105. DOI: 10. 1094/MPMI-05-12-0130-R

122. Laskowski M, Kato I. Protein inhibitors of proteinases. Annual Review of Biochemistry. 1980;49:593-626. DOI: 10. 1146/annurev. bi. 49. 070180. 003113

123. Mickel C, Standish J. Susceptibility of processed soy flour and soy grits in storage to attack by Tribolium castaneum. University of Minnesota Agricultural Experimental Station Technical Bulletin. 1947, 178: 1-20

124. Hepher, A. , Atkinson HJ. 1992. Nematode control with proteinase inhibitors. European Patent Application Number 92301890. 7, Publication Number 0 502 730 A1

125. Urwin P, McPherson M, Atkinson H. Enhanced transgenic plant resistance to nematodes by dual proteinase inhibitor constructs. Planta. 1998;204:472-479. DOI: 10. 1007/s004250050281

126. Chan Y, Yang A, Chen J, Yeh K, Chan M. Heterologous expression of taro cystatin protects transgenic tomato against Meloidogyne incognita infection by means of interfering sex determination and supressing gall formation. Plant Cell Reports. 2010;29:231-238. DOI: 10. 1007/s00299-009-0815-y

127. Senthilkumar R, Yeh K. Multiple biological functions of sporamin related to stress tolerance in sweetpotato (Ipomoea batatas Lam). Biotechnology Advances. 2012;30:1309-1317. DOI: 10. 1016/j. biotechadv. 2012. 01. 022

128. Yeh K, Chen J, Lin M, Chen Y, Lin C. Functional activity of sporamin from sweetpotato (Ipomoea batatas Lam.): A tuber storage protein with trypsin inhibitory activity. Plant Molecular Biology. 1997;33:565-570

129. Cai D, Thurau T, Tian Y, Lange T, Yeh K, Jung C. Sporamin-mediated resistance to beet cyst nematodes (Heterodera schachtii Schm.) is dependent on trypsin inhibitory activity in sugar beet (Beta vulgaris L.) hairy roots. Plant Molecular Biology. 2003;51:839-849. DOI: 10. 1023/A:1023089017906

130. Loake G, Grant M. Salicylic acid in plant defence-the players and protagonists. Current Opinion in Plant Biology. 2007;10:466-472. DOI: 10. 1016/j. pbi. 2007. 08. 008

131. Liao Y, Tiam M, Zhang H, Li X, Wang Y, Xia X, Zhou J, Zhou Y, Yu J, Shi K, Klessig D. Salicylic acid binding of mitochondrial alpha-ketoglutarate dehydrogenase E2 affects mitochondrial oxidative phosphorylation and electron transport chain components and plays a role in basal defense against tobacco mosaic virus in tomato. New Phytologist. 2015;205:1296-1307. DOI: 10. 1111/nph. 13137

132. Glazebrook J. Contrasting mechanisms of defense against biotrophic and necrotrophic pathogens. Annual Review of Phytopathology. 2005;43:205-227. DOI: 10. 1146/annurev. phyto. 43. 040204. 135923

133. Nahar K, Kyndt T, De Vleesscchauwer D, Hofte M, Gheysen G. The jasmonate pathway is a key player in systemically induced defense against root-knot nematodes in rice. Plant Physiology. 2011;157:305-316. DOI: 10. 1104/pp. 111. 177576

134. Vasyukova N, Zinovieva S, Udalova Z, Gerasimova N, Ozeretskovskaya O, Sonin M. Jasmonic acid and tomato resistance to the root-knot nematode Meloidogyne incognita. Doklady Biological Sciences. 2009;428:448-450. DOI: 10. 1134/S0012496609050160

135. Branch C, Hwang C, Navarre D, Williamson V. Salicylic acid is part of the Mi-1-mediated defense response to root-knot nematode in tomato. Molecular Plant-Microbe Interactions. 2004;7:351-356

136. Sikora R, Fernandez E. Nematode parasites of vegetables. In: Luc M, Sikora R, Bridge J, editors. Plant parasitic nematodes in subtropical and tropical. Wallingford: CABI; 2005. pp. 319-392. DOI: dx. doi. org/10. 1079/9780851997278. 0000

137. Osei K, Gowen S, Pembroke B, Brandenburg R, Jordan D. Potential of leguminous cover crops in management of a mixed population of root-knot nematodes (Meloidogyne spp.). Journal of Nematology. 2010;42:173-178

138. Chen P, Tsay T. Effect of crop rotation on Meloidogyne spp. and Pratylenchus spp. populations in strawberry fields in Taiwan. Journal of Nematology. 2006;38:339-344

139. Khan A, Sayed M,. Shaukat S, Handoo Z. Efficacy of four plant extracts on nematodes associated with papaya in Sindh, Pakistan. Nematologia Mediterranea 2008;36:93-98

140. Okeniyi M, Afolami S, Fademi O, Oduwaye O. Effect of botanical extracts on root-knot nematode (Meloidogyne incognita) infection and growth of cashew (Anacardium occidentale) seedlings. Academia Journal of Biotechnology. 2013;1:81-86

141. Bawa J, Mohammed I, Liadi S. Nematicidal effect of some plants extracts on root-knot nematodes (Meloidogyne incognita) of tomato (Lycopersicon esculentum). World Journal of Life Science and Medical Research. 2014;3:81-87

142. Stirling G. Biological Control of Plant-parasitic Nematodes. Wallingford: CAB International; 1991. 282 p

143. Meyer S. United States Department of Agriculture – Agricultural Research Service research programs on microbes for management of plant-parasitic nematodes. Pest Management Science. 2003;59:665-670

144. Chen Z, Dickson D. Review of Pasteuria penetrans: Biology, ecology, and biological control potential. Journal of Nematology. 1998;30:313-340

145. Kokalis-Burelle N. Pasteuria penetrans for control of Meloidogyne incognita on tomato and cucumber and M. arenaria on snapdragon. Journal of Nematology. 2015;47:207-213

146. Weibelzahl-Fulton E, Dickson D, Whitty E. Suppression of Meloidogyne incognita and M. javanica by Pasteuria penetrans in field soil. Journal of Nematology. 1996;28:43-49

147. Gao H, Qi G, Yin R, Zhang H, Li C, Zhao X. Bacillus cereus strain S2 shows high nematicidal activity against Meloidogyne incognita by producing sphingosine. Scientific Reports. 2016;6:28756. DOI: 10. 1038/srep28756

148. Xiong J, Zhou Q, Luo H, Xia L, Li L, Sun M, Yu Z. Systemic nematicidal activity and biocontrol efficacy of Bacillus firmus against the root-knot nematode Meloidogyne incognita. World Journal of Microbiology and Biotechnology. 2015;31:661-667. DOI: 10. 1007/s11274-015-1820-7

149. Atkins S, Hidalgo-Diaz L, Kalisz H, Mauchline T, Hirsch P, Kerry B. Development of a new management strategy for the control of root-knot nematodes (Meloidogyne spp) in organic vegetable production. Pest Management Science. 2003;59:183-189. DOI:10. 1002/ps. 603

150. Gan Z, Yang J, Tao N, Liang L, Mi Q, Li J, Zhang K. Cloning of the gene Lecanicillium psalliotae chitinase Lpchi1 and identification of its potential role in the biocontrol of root-knot nematode Meloidogyne incognita. Applied Microbiology and Biotechnology. 2007;76:1309-1317. DOI:10. 1007/s00253-007-1111-9

151. Vishnudasan D, Tripathi M, Rao U, Khurana P. Assessment of nematode resistance in wheat transgenic plants expressing potato proteinase inhibitor (PIN2) gene. Transgenic Research. 2005;14:665-675. DOI:10. 1007/s11248-005-5696-4

152. Matthews B, Beard H, Brewer E, Kabir S, MacDonald M, Youssef R. Arabidopsis genes, AtNPR1, AtTGA2 and AtPR-5, confer partial resistance to soybean cyst nematode (Heterodera glycines) when overexpressed in transgenic soybean roots. BMC Plant Biology. 2014;14:1-19. DOI: 10. 1186/1471-2229-14-96

153. Lin J, Wang D, Chen X, Kollner T, Mazarei M, Guo H, Pantalone V, Arellii P, Stewart C, Chen F. An (E,E)-@-farnesene synthase gene of soybean has a role in defence against nematodes and is involved in synthesizing insect-induced volatiles. Plant Biotechnology Journal. 2017;15:510-519. DOI: 10. 1111/pbi. 12649

154. Ecker J, Davis R. Inhibition of gene expression in plant cells by expression of antisense RNA. PNAS. 1986;83:5372-5376. DOI:10. 1073/pnas. 83. 15. 5372

155. Fire A, SiQun X, Montgomery M, Kostas S, Driver S, Mello C. Potent and specific genetic inferference by double-stranded RNA in Caenorhabditis elegans. Nature. 1998;391:806-811. DOI: 10. 1038/35888

156. Huang G, Allen R, Davis E, Baum T, Hussey R. Engineering broad root-knot resistance in transgenic plants by RNAi silencing of a conserved and essential root-knot nematode parasitism gene. PNAS. 2006;103:14302-14306. DOI:10. 1073/pnas. 0604698103

157. Yadav B, Veluthambi K, Subramaniam K. Host-generated double stranded RNA induces RNAi in plant-parasitic nematodes and protects the host from infection. Molecular & Biochemical Parasitology. 2006;148:219-222. DOI:10. 1016/j. molbiopara. 2006. 03. 013

158. Lilley C, Davis L, Urwin P. RNA interference in plant parasitic nematodes: a summary of the current status. Parasitology. 2012;139:630-640. DOI: 10. 1017/S0031182011002071

159. Dinh P, Brown C, Elling A. RNA interference of effector gene Mc16D10L confers resistance against Meloidogyne chitwoodi in Arabidopsis and potato. Phytopathology. 2014;104:1098-1106. DOI: http://dx. doi. org/10. 1094/PHYTO-03-14-0063-R

160. Yang Y, Jittayasothorn Y, Chronis D, Wang X, Cousins P, Zhong G. Molecular characteristics and efficacy of 16D10 siRNAs in inhibiting root-knot nematode infection in transgenic grape hairy roots. PLoS One. 2013;8:e69463. DOI: 10. 1371/journal. pone. 0069463

161. Bibikova M, Beumer K, Trautman JK, Carroll D. Enhancing gene targeting with designed zinc finger nucleases. Science. 2003;300:764. DOI:10. 1126/science. 1079512

162. Forsyth A, Weeks T, Richael C, Duan H. Transcription activator-like effector nucleases (TALEN)-mediated targeted DNA insertion in potato plants. Frontiers in Plant Science. 2016;7:1572. DOI: 10. 3389/fpls. 2016. 01572

163. Redman M, King A, Watson C, King D. What is CRISPR/Cas9?. Archives of Disease in Childhood. Education and Practice Edition. 2016;101:213-215. DOI: 10. 1136/archdischild-2016-310459

164. Gupta R, Musunuru K. Expanding the genetic editing tool kit: ZFNs, TALENs, and CRISPR-Cas9. Journal of Clinical Investigation. 2014;124:4154-4161. DOI: 10. 1172/JCI72992

165. Mali P, Yang L, Esvelt K, Aach J, Guell M, DiCarlo J, Norville J, Church G. RNA-guided human genome engineering via Cas9. Science. 2013;339:823-826. DOI: 10. 1126/science. 1232033

166. Fu Y, Foden J, Khayter C, Maeder M, Reyon D, Joung J, Sander J. High-frequency off-target mutagenesis induced by CRISPR-Cas nucleases in human cells. Nature Biotechnology. 2013;31:822-826. DOI: 10. 1038/nbt. 2623

167. Zhang Y, Goritschnig S, Dong X, Li X. A Gain-of-Function Mutation in a Plant Disease Resistance Gene Leads to Constitutive Activation of Downstream Signal Transduction Pathways in suppressor of npr1-1, constitutive 1. The Plant Cell. 2003;15:2636-2646. DOI: http://doi. org/10. 1105/tpc. 015842

168. Bernard G, Egnin M, Bonsi C, Mortley D, Witola W, Samuels S, Land C, Lawrence K. Efficient evaluation of physical and molecular plant immune responses to root-knot nematode infection in selected sweetpotato cultivars. In Vitro Cellular & Developmental Biology. 2016;52:437. DOI:10. 1007/s11627-016-9771-8

169. Dinesh-Kumar S, Tham W, Baker B. Structure-function analysis of the tobacco mosaic virus resistance gene N. PNAS. 2000;97:14789-14794. DOI: 10. 1073/pnas. 97. 26. 14789

11

The Need for Assessment of Risks Arising from Interactions between NGT Organisms from an EU Perspective

Franziska Koller[1] , Meike Schulz[1] , Matthias Juhas[2] , Andreas BauerPanskus[2] and Christoph Then[2]

[1] Fachstelle Gentechnik und Umwelt (FGU), Munich, Germany
[2] Testbiotech, Munich, Germany

ABSTRACT

Background

New genomic techniques (NGTs) allow new genotypes and traits to be developed in different ways and with different outcomes compared to previous genetic engineering methods or conventional breeding (including non-targeted mutagenesis). EU GMO regulation requires an assessment of their direct and indirect effects that may be immediate, delayed or cumulative. Such effects may also result from the interactions of NGT organisms simultaneously present in a shared receiving environment or emerge from a combination of their traits. This review elaborates such potential interactions based on a literature review and reasoned scenarios to identify possible pathways to harm.

Main Findings

NGT organisms might be introduced into the environment and food chains on a large-scale, involving many traits, across a broad range of species and within short periods of time. Unavoidably, this would increase the likelihood that direct or indirect effects will occur through interactions between NGT organisms that are, for example simultaneously present within a shared environment. It has to be assumed that the cumulative effects of these NGT organisms may exceed the sum of risks identified in the distinct 'events'. Consequently, risk assessors and risk managers not only need to consider the risks associated with individual NGT organisms ('events'), but should also take account of risks resulting from their potential interactions and combinatorial effects. In addition, a prospective technology assessment could help the risk manager in defining criteria to minimize potential unintended interactions between NGT organisms through limiting the scale of releases.

Conclusions

If genetically engineered (GE) organisms derived from NGTs are released into the environment, their potentially negative impacts need to be minimized. As with all GE organisms, it is, therefore, crucial to not only assess the risks of the individual events, but also their potential interactions which can trigger direct and indirect effects with adverse impacts. It is necessary to develop hypotheses and specific scenarios to explore interactions between NGT organisms and possible pathways to harm from the perspective of the precautionary principle. In addition, the introduction prospective technology assessment could provide an instrument for the risk manager to control the scale of releases of NGT organisms.

Keywords: *New genomic techniques, Genetically engineered organisms, Genome editing, GMO regulation, Risk assessment, Direct and indirect effects, Interactions, Cumulative long-term effects, Accumulated risks, Prospective technology assessment*

BACKGROUND

According to EU GMO legislation [1], inter alia, genetically engineered (GE) organisms (or 'genetically modified organisms', GMOs) derived from "*recombinant nucleic acid techniques*" [Annex 1A, Part 1 of 1] fall within the scope of the regulation. As clarified by the EU Court of Justice (Case C-528/16), this also applies to organisms derived from new genomic techniques (NGT).

As a general principle, the EU requires each individual genetically engineered organism ('event') to undergo risk assessment on a case-by-case basis before it is released into the environment or placed onto the market. The detailed risk assessment requirements are set out in Annex II of Directive 2001/18/EC [1] which was amended by Commission Directive (EU) 2018/350 [2]. It foresees the risk assessment of each event, taking into account its intended and unintended effects since "*intended and unintended changes can have either direct or indirect, and either immediate or delayed effects on human health and on the environment.*" [Annex (C1) of 2]. Therefore, as introduced in Annex (C1) by Commission Directive (EU) 2018/350 [2], the risk assessment "*shall identify the intended and unintended changes resulting from the genetic modification and shall evaluate their potential to cause adverse effects on human health and on the environment.*"

In the context of Commission Directive (EU) 2018/350, risk assessment cannot be confined to the individual event only, it also needs to take interactions involving other GE organisms into account. This is further underlined in Recital 19 of the Directive 2001/18/EC [1]: "*A case-by-case environmental risk assessment should always be carried out prior to a release. It should also take due account of potential cumulative long-term effects associated with the interaction with other GMOs and the environment.*" Furthermore, as defined in the amended Annex (C3) of Commission Directive (EU) 2018/350 [2], "*adverse effects may occur directly or indirectly through exposure pathways or other mechanisms which may include: (...) interactions with other organisms (...)*". In conclusion, risk assessment must also include potential interactions between GE organisms which are released into a shared receiving environment and potential combinations of their traits.

EU GMO regulation contains further specific provisions relating to interactions between GE organisms or a combination of their traits in risk assessment. For example, Annex II of Directive 2001/18/EC [1] in its "*Principles for the environmental risk assessment*" gives weight to cumulative long-term effects: "*A general principle for environmental risk assessment is also that an analysis of the cumulative long-term effects relevant to the release and the placing on the market is to be carried out. 'Cumulative long-term effects' refers to the accumulated effects of consents on human health and the environment (...).*" Furthermore, similarly to Commission Directive (EU) 2018/350 [2], Commission Implementing Regulation (EU) No 503/2013 [3] also requires the assessment of stacked events in regard to their "*potential additive, synergistic or antagonistic effects resulting from the combination of the transformation events.*"

The European Food Safety Authority (EFSA) in its "*guidance on the environmental risk assessment of genetically modified plants*" [4] considers effects resulting from interactions between genetically engineered plants, such as those causing indirect effects on management and production systems. The risks of long-term cumulative effects and stacked events are also taken into account. However, one example not specifically mentioned concerns interactions between GE organisms within a shared receiving environment that are released within a short period of time and may, therefore, not be considered to be long-term cumulative.

For the purpose of this review, there are several categories which have to be distinguished by using specific terminology: (1) EU GMO regulation refers to GMOs which have to undergo mandatory approval processes and other GMOs which are exempt from these approval processes, e.g., plants derived from physical and chemical mutagenesis. The wording 'genetic engineering' (GE) is used throughout the publication as a synonym for those GMOs which have to undergo mandatory approval processes. (2) The wording 'established genomic techniques' (EGTs) is used to distinguish older transgenic plants (derived from non-targeted insertions of transgenes) from those more recently generated using NGTs [see also 5]. It is important to understand that both these categories (EGT and NGT) refer to GMOs which have to undergo mandatory approval processes (GE).

A soaring number of NGT applications across many traits and species may soon be released into the environment within a short period of time [see, for example, 6]. Against this backdrop, and in light of existing evidence regarding the impact of large-scale cultivation on the environment, the purpose of this review is to highlight the need for assessment of environmental risks arising from interactions between NGT organisms. We started from horizon scanning of studies on the environmental risk assessment of transgenic plants reporting unintended effects from cultivation, including interactions between different events and their traits. Further research was conducted on examples to explore the potential interactions of NGT organisms that may be released into a shared environment. Databases that provide a comprehensive overview of NGT applications [such as 6, 7] were used to select examples for relevant organisms. Problem formulation is a crucial step in risk assessment. Therefore, we developed plausible risk scenarios to examine such potential interactions. Since the issue of potential interactions between NGT organisms is not yet well reflected in scientific literature, most of our analysis had to be done 'from scratch'. Therefore, systematic and continuous horizon scanning was the most crucial aspect in terms of our methodology, followed by targeted analyses of potentially relevant publications.

Our review provides a first, albeit non-comprehensive overview of findings in regard to interactions between GE organisms, in particular between NGT organisms that may cause direct or indirect effects. In this context, we consider interactions such as enabled by simultaneous presence of several NGT events belonging to the same species or to different species within a shared receiving environment. These interactions maybe additive, synergistic, antagonistic or cumulative.

As shown in the review, there are good reasons why interactions between NGT organisms deserve the particular attention of the risk assessor and the risk manager: plants developed with NGTs may include many more different traits and species compared to transgenic plants approved for the market so far. In addition, NGT applications may be relevant to all domains of life, including non-domesticated species [see, for example, 8]. If these assumptions are correct, NGT organisms might be introduced into the environment on a large-scale in terms of numbers and traits, across a broad range of species and within short periods of time. Unavoidably, this would also increase the likelihood that direct or indirect effects will, for example, occur through interactions between those organisms. Therefore, their intended and unintended interactions and potentially emerging hazards may need more attention and consideration compared to EGT organisms.

SPECIFIC TECHNICAL CHARACTERISTICS OF NGTS

NGTs, also known as genome editing or new genetic engineering, allow new genotypes and traits to be generated in different ways and with different outcomes compared to previously used genetic engineering methods or conventional breeding (including non-targeted mutagenesis) [9,10,11].

So-called site directed nucleases (SDN), such as CRISPR/Cas (clustered regularly interspaced short palindromic repeats/CRISPR associated) [12], are highly relevant in this context: they can be designed to target specific DNA sequences in the genome to knock out gene functions (i.e., SDN-1), to induce repair mechanisms for specific alterations of particular nucleotides (i.e., SDN-2) or whole genes (i.e., SDN-3). Depending on whether a repair template is used or not, these methods can induce either non-specific changes (SDN-1) via non-homologous end joining (NHEJ) repair mechanisms or induce specific changes to nucleotide sequences (SDN-2 or SDN-3) via homologous recombination mediated by homology directed repair (HDR). The induced changes at or around the target site can be substitutions, deletions or insertions of one or more base pairs. Depending on the specific SDN-1 or SDN-2 application, more extensive overall changes are possible. For example, multiplexing can target several genes simultaneously in a single application [13,14,15]. Repeated applications of SDN-1 or SDN-2 can also be combined [16]. Changes involving the insertion of whole (cis- or trans-) genes (including gene-stacking) are also possible (SDN-3) and are mediated by the use of specific donor DNA [9, 17]. For this review, we mostly focused on applications using CRISPR/Cas which is currently the most important tool for developing NGT organisms [8]. Other nucleases, such as TALENs (transcription activator-like effector nucleases) or variations of CRISPR nucleases [see, for example, 8], are also relevant, but so far of less importance for NGT applications in plants and animals.

The following section describes some specific characteristics relevant to NGT applications using CRISPR/Cas and also illustrates their technical potential and associated risks by giving special weight to the perspective of the precautionary principle:

Greater Precision

In comparison to EGTs, the NGTs can be used to introduce genetic changes with much greater precision. Typically, SDNs can be used to directly target sites [12, 18, 19], whereas previous transformation processes introduce additional DNA sequences at random sites [see, for example, 20–22]. However, NGTs are based on processes involving several technical steps that, in the case of plants, very often include transformation processes, e.g., biolistic methods or the use of *Agrobacterium tumefaciens*, which are also used in EGTs. These non-targeted methods are used to introduce the nucleases into the cells [16] and may lead to unintended effects in off-target regions [for example 23, 24] As pointed out in several publications, there are additional reasons why higher precision still appears to be challenging and should be improved [for overview, see 9, 16, 25–27].

In comparison to conventional breeding in plants which also uses non-targeted mutagenesis, the overall number of mutations is typically lower in NGT plants [25]. However, these comparisons need to be put into context: conventional breeding methods depend on high genetic diversity that can be used for crossing and selection. Thus, the higher number of mutations caused by non-targeted mutagenesis is generally desired while, at the same time, some of the mutations are considered to be disadvantageous [28].

Furthermore, the specific sites of the mutations and the (intended or unintended) resulting gene combinations from the NGTs may, in many cases, be unlikely to occur with conventional methods (see below). These genetic changes may thus cause unintended direct or indirect effects within the complex networks of genes, proteins and other biologically active molecules not so far observed (see also below). Some of these unintended metabolic and physiological effects can also be considered to be 'trade-offs' which can still emerge in cases where the genetic intervention is targeted and precise (see below).

Overcoming the Limitations of Natural Genome Organization

NGTs can be used to achieve genomic changes extending beyond what is known from conventional breeding, even without the insertion of additional genes. If compared to methods of conventional breeding (including non-targeted mutagenesis), NGTs can overcome the boundaries of natural genome organization. Relevant factors include repair mechanisms, gene duplications, genetic linkages and further epigenetic mechanisms [see, for example, 29–37]. By overcoming these boundaries, NGTs can make the genome much more extensively available for genetic changes [10, 16]. The resulting genotypes (the patterns of genetic changes) can be vastly different compared to those derived from conventional breeding, both in regard to intended and unintended changes [38, 39] even though there may still be some limitations to the effectiveness of the nucleases [40]. This means that it is possible to generate genotypes which are highly unlikely to result from natural processes or traditional breeding techniques. As a result, more 'extreme' biological characteristics can be achieved with NGTs in comparison to conventional breeding methods. These can, however, also be associated with more significant 'trade-offs' in comparison to conventional breeding [41,42,43,44,45].

Changes in the Allelic Diversity of Populations within Short Periods of Time

For example, Barbour et al. [46] showed that a higher allelic diversity in plants has an impact on different species within an experimental food web. This may also play a crucial role in the stability of ecosystems and food webs. CRISPR/Cas applications can, in particular, be used to make gene variants within a population more uniform, i.e., the frequency of the abundance of different allelic variants can be reduced, the alleles can be changed or the respective gene (-family) can be blocked in its functions. In general, in regard to allelic uniformity, CRISPR/Cas applications are very much more efficient than conventional breeding methods, including the knocking out of many or all copies of a gene family in parallel using SDN-1 processes [47]. Therefore, if there are large-scale releases of NGT organisms into the environment in short periods of time, their impact on genetic diversity and associated ecosystems can extend far beyond what might be expected compared to natural processes and conventional breeding techniques.

Pervasive Changes even without the Insertion of Additional Genes

Even without the insertion of additional genes, changes in genotypes and phenotypes can be pervasive and involve major changes in gene expression, metabolism in the cells and characteristics of the organisms [see, for example, 47]. Changes can be brought about by, for example, knocking out most or all copies of a gene family, changing several different genes in parallel (multiplexing), or altering elements responsible for gene regulation [13,14,15,16]. Such technical interventions can, lead to major and unprecedented changes in plant composition, resulting in traits without a 'history of safe use' also be associated with unintended effects [38, 39, 41, 47,48,49]. As the case of de novo domesticated tomatoes [47] examined by EFSA [48] shows, the NGT process results in a combination of known gene variants with a genomic background of *S. pimpinellifolium,* thus resulting in 'new' tomatoes without known comparators.

Wide Range of Species and Applications

The range of species accessible to NGTs extends far beyond applications of previously used genetic engineering techniques (EGTs). While their effectiveness may differ from case to case (especially in regard to SDN-2 and SDN-3 processes), these applications include a wide range of food plant species and livestock, and also non-domesticated species including trees and other plants, insects, vertebrates and microorganisms, thus extending across all domains of life [overview in: 5, 38, 39]. Several specific NGT applications are designed for use in wild populations, including gene drives (SDN-3) [52, 53] and the intended release of genetically engineered viruses, also including so-called Horizontal Environmental Genetic Alteration Agents (HEGAA) [54, 55]. Many of the species targeted by NGT applications also have the potential to persist and spread over longer periods of time without effective control. This may give rise to next-generation effects which were not observed in the laboratory [56].

Complex Interactions—Also Triggered by Simultaneous Presence in the Environment

Large numbers of GE organisms derived from NGTs, including various species with a wide range of different characteristics (intended or unintended), could be released into the same receiving environment within a short period of time [see, for example, 8]. Depending on the scale of the releases, their duration and the characteristics of the organisms, these NGT organisms may also intentionally or unintentionally interact with each other. A number of applications are already designed for complex interactions after release into the receiving environment, e.g., changes in the microbiome of the soil [57,58,59], in plants [60,61,62,63], in insects [64,65,66,67,68,69,70,71,72] or in corals [73]. Moreover, some of the applications use a technique known as 'paratransgenesis' which aims to change the biological characteristics of the host by genetically engineering its microbiome [74].

In summary, sections (a–f) listed above, all illustrate the novelty of NGTs that allows the development of new genotypes and traits in different ways and with different outcomes than could have been expected with earlier GE methods or conventional breeding (including non-targeted mutagenesis).

SCENARIOS FOR INTERACTIONS BETWEEN NGT ORGANISMS THAT ARE RELEVANT TO RISK ASSESSMENT

Given the specific characteristics listed above, both direct and indirect effects resulting from interactions between NGT organisms may have an extensive impact on ecosystems. This is especially relevant to large-scale releases of NGT organisms which may comprise a broad range of species and traits. Such large-scale releases may be driven by expectations of hypothetical benefits from NGT organisms [75], and at the same time, lead to high- and long-term environmental exposure to NGT organisms. Large-scale releases undoubtedly increase the likelihood of direct or indirect effects from interactions between the NGT organisms. Therefore, the need to risk assess the interactions between NGT organisms may be much more crucial in comparison to previous applications of genetic engineering [see also 76]. In this context, the development of risk scenarios can help to generate plausible hypotheses (problem formulation) and guide the steps in risk assessment [see 4]. The following section contains examples of possible relevant scenarios:

Scenario 1: Interactions Resulting from Releases of NGT Events involving Different Traits and Several Species

The first hypothesis, we suggest should be tested, is: 'Releases of different NGT events into a shared receiving environment may lead to a scaling up of adverse impacts due to interactions between the NGT organisms. There may be a tipping point for such releases which could trigger irreversible damage caused by exposure to effects unlikely to result from natural processes [77]. This hypothesis is based on the following specific characteristics of NGTs as described above: (i) the differences between the genotypes and phenotypes of NGT organisms compared to those which can be expected to evolve naturally or are derived from conventional breeding (see characteristics b, c and d); (ii) the broad range of species across all domains of life, with a possibly significant number of the NGT organisms having the potential to persist and spread without effective control (see characteristics e); (iii) the technical potential of NGTs allowing the development of various GE organisms with a wide range of different characteristics (intended or unintended) within a short period of time, all off which may be released into a shared receiving environment (characteristics a and f). The potential interactions between NGT organisms may be additive, synergistic, antagonistic or cumulative, and may cause direct or indirect effects with immediate or delayed adverse environmental impacts.

Camelina sativa with changes in oil content [78] could be the starting point for testing this hypothesis. It is an example which can be used to exemplify several of the technical characteristics of NGT plants as mentioned [38]: both, its genotype and phenotype go beyond what was achieved using conventional breeding, thus causing 'extreme' variants of its biological characteristics (for more details see below, Scenario 2). Furthermore, this species has the potential to persist, propagate and spread uncontrollably in the environment. The biological characteristics resulting from the genetic intervention may cause a change in interactions with many species within the receiving environment: as shown by Kawall, 2021 [38], this may affect pollinators, pest insects and other wild life species feeding on the plants. However, we are not (yet) aware of enough data from other NGT organisms belonging to other species that may share the same environment to establish a specific scenario as outlined in the first hypothesis. We, therefore, refrained from presenting a specific example for Scenario 1 and instead introduced it as an example in Scenario 2.

A summarized reasoning of our first hypothesis may read as follows: the intended and/or unintended effects resulting from NGT applications mean that the release of the NGT organisms may not be 'neutral' to the ecosystems. Disruptive, i.e., adverse effects, are more likely or less likely depending on their biological characteristics (intended or unintended), environmental exposure (as caused by the number of organisms, traits and events released, their distribution and persistence) and their potential interactions. Even if distinct individual events are considered to be 'safe', uncertainties or even unknowns will emerge from their interactions with other NGT organisms released into the same environment. Therefore, environmental risk assessment of NGT organisms should take their interactions into account, as these may cause adverse environmental effects. Potential adverse effects that should be included in Scenario 1 comprise damage to biodiversity, breakdown in food production or disruption of ecosystem services.

This first hypothesis is mostly set out in general terms and describes numerous impact factors and potential interactions between GE organisms. The development of a more specific hypothesis would be needed in order to draw conclusions for regulatory decision-making. We have, therefore, developed a more specific second scenario focusing on different NGT traits, generated within the same species.

Scenario 2: Interactions Emerging from Releases of Several NGT Events from one Species but with Different Traits

The second hypothesis that we suggest should be tested, is: 'The unintended effects of different traits introduced into the genome of one species if accumulated by simultaneous cultivation and/or by further stacking and/or spontaneous crossings of the events, may lead to a scaling up of hazards due to unintended interactions.' In this scenario, we have chosen NGT applications in plants of the same species to discuss interactions between their traits (and the respective events) that may trigger direct or indirect effects that are associated with hazards. In this context, the overall impact may also depend on the susceptibility of the species to a range of common pathogens and their potential for gene flow, crossings and the degree of intended stackings. We, therefore, selected two species used in several NGT applications (SDN-1): *Camelina sativa* and *Triticum aestivum*. One of the reasons for choosing *Camelina sativa* are the biological characteristics of this species, which is able to persist and spread in the environment. It can also spontaneously cross with other varieties of the same species and other wild relative species [38]. *Triticum aestivum* was chosen because of the many NGT applications that offer a wide range of different traits [79].

Example 1: In *Camelina sativa,* NGT applications are primarily used to change the quantity and quality of oil [80]. The aim in most of the plants being developed is to lower the percentage of polyunsaturated fatty acids (PUFA). These fatty acids (PUFA) are generally considered to be desirable and beneficial for healthy food. However, for use as agrofuel, the aim is to increase the oxidative stability of the oil by reducing the content of PUFA. At the same time, the intention is also to increase the quantity of oil. Several metabolic pathways can be used to impact the oil content of the plants by changing the genotype at different sites [80]. *Camelina sativa* is an allohexaploid species, which means that many alleles are present in several copies. As explained above, NGTs have the novel potential to overcome this constraint by changing all copies of a gene at the same time (technical characteristics b & d). Recent attempts at CRISPR/Cas9-induced gene mutagenesis in camelina have been successful [78, 81, 82], but have also resulted in negative effects, e.g., smaller growth and a reduced number of seeds, due to the pervasive changes in the metabolism of fatty acids [45].

In regard to scenario 2, it is crucial that NGT camelina can persist, propagate and spontaneously cross. This means that new combinations of NGT traits may occur and persist unnoticed. In some cases, the resulting plants may suffer from low fitness [45] and therefore are not likely to persist in the environment for longer periods of time. However, the biological characteristics associated with a reduced content of PUFA in the plants suggest a more complex landscape: as shown by Kawall [38] in *Camelina sativa* with changed oil composition [78], the genetic intervention may trigger direct and indirect effects and impact various other functions, e.g., plant defense mechanisms, interactions with pollinators or associated food webs. In worst case scenarios, some of these characteristics may be associated with enhanced spread and a severe impact on ecosystems: for example, spontaneous crossings of NGT camelina may, unnoticed and with no intention, result in plant compositions that negatively impact the health of wild species feeding on the plants. In these circumstances, some of these wild species may suffer from a population decrease, whereas the plants might gain an advantage due to reduced losses from herbivores. This may lower the chances of controlling the spread of the plants in the environment, and thus severely impact both natural plant populations of species able to cross with the NGT plants and populations of animal species feeding on the plants.

Example 2: the combination of traits may also play a role in other species being developed for various NGT applications, e.g., *Triticum aestivum*. We are currently aware of more than 20 NGT projects focusing on bread wheat (*Triticum aestivum*) [79]. To exemplify our scenarios, we selected three traits under development (see below). The traits were introduced by using NGTs (SDN-1) and other multistep processes (involving previously used genetic engineering methods such as biolistic methods). *Triticum aestivum* has a huge genome, comprising six sets of chromosomes [83] which is a severe constraint in conventional wheat breeding since, in many cases, a high number of gene duplications are involved in a specific trait. As explained above, NGTs have the novel potential to overcome this constraint by changing all copies of a gene at the same time (technical characteristics b & d). As far as the selected NGT traits (see below) are concerned, there are reasons to assume that the intended (on-target) genetic alterations and resulting more 'extreme' traits are linked to 'trade-offs' as well as unintended biological characteristics.

***Trait 1, reduction in gluten*:** Gluten proteins in wheat are thought to trigger several gluten-related disorders, including celiac disease [84]. It is known that alpha-gliadin peptides contribute to the overall concentration of gluten in bakery products [79]. Their genes occur within a large family of genes that are present in multiple copies at different locations in the genome. With the help of the CRISPR/Cas nuclease, scientists succeeded in 2018 in switching many of them off: 35 out of the 45 genes necessary to produce alpha-gliadins were knocked out [49]. This resulted in a new wheat genotype that is highly complex in regard to risk assessment [11]. As EFSA, in 2021 [11] states: "*(...) the large number of mutations required to achieve gluten-free wheat is far beyond any plant previously assessed. This is likely to require SynBio approaches to correctly identify all gliadins and glutenins in the hexaploid genome of bread wheat and to identify an engineering strategy that introduced mutations of the correct nature and positions in each gene to prevent the accumulation of any peptide fragments associated with initiation of the inflammatory cascade*". Regardless, the application of CRISPR/Cas resulted in biological characteristics that go beyond what can be achieved with conventional breeding. This 'extreme' trait may be associated with specific 'trade-offs': gliadins are, for example, known to play an important role in the response of the plants to stress conditions, including drought and heat [85,86,87]. Therefore, large reductions in the content of alpha-gliadins may also unintentionally impact the heat and/or drought tolerance of this new genotype.

***Trait 2, reduction in acrylamide*:** CRISPR/Cas9 was used to reduce the content of the free amino acid, asparagine, in wheat [42]. Free asparagine is present in higher concentrations in wheat grain. It is a precursor for acrylamide, which forms during the baking, toasting and high-temperature processing of foods made from wheat. Acrylamide has been shown to be carcinogenic. The gene (asn2) targeted in this case, occurs a total of six times in the wheat genome. In some of the NGT wheat plants developed by Raffan et al. [42], the asparagine content in wheat grain was reduced by 90% compared to the wild type, something which has not previously been achieved using other methods. This 'extreme' trait is associated with 'trade-offs': while the gene function involved in production of the amino acid asparagine was successfully blocked, this also creates other problems since asparagine is involved in seed germination, plant growth, stress response and defense mechanisms. It was found that some lines of this CRISPR-wheat almost lost their capacity to germinate [42]. There is as yet no published data on the resistance of these NGT plants to biotic and abiotic stressors.

***Trait 3, reduction in susceptibility to powdery mildew*:** the mildew resistance locus (mlo) gene in barley is of interest in several projects. There are three different mlo genes involved in resistance to powdery mildew found in natural populations. In one study, the mlo gene was targeted in hexaploid wheat by TALENs [88]. The nuclease introduced alterations in all three homoeoalleles of mlo in wheat, enabling their parallel knock-out. This has never previously been achieved using non-targeted mutagenesis or other breeding methods [see 38]. The simultaneous knock-out of the three homoeoalleles conferred a broad-spectrum resistance to powdery mildew in the new wheat lines. However, some unintended effects were described in these lines (i.e., leaf chlorosis under growth conditions), which were not observed to the same degree in randomly mutated plants [89]. Growth aberration, accelerated senescence, induced necrosis, increased susceptibility to other fungal pathogens are unintended effects described in the context of this trait. To a certain extent these 'trade-offs' are also known from conventional breeding and may be overcome only by further research [43].

Some of the interactions and combinatorial effects, such as reduced fitness of crop plants or lowered germination rate in seeds, might easily be detected by the breeders. Others, such as impacts on ecosystems and food web might be overlooked and remain undetected for a longer period of time. Effects that may occur from spontaneous crossings are a particular challenge in risk assessment and risk management. As mentioned, spontaneous crossings would be expected in species like camelina, but not necessarily in wheat. However, research is underway to develop new varieties by using specific lines of wheat which show a much higher potential for spontaneous crossings [90]. The idea behind this research is to ease crossings from wild relative species with desirable characteristics by enhancing the likelihood of crossover between related (homoeologous) chromosomes. If such varieties are grown in the fields in future, they may also increase the rate of spontaneous crossing with NGT lines.

To sum up the examples of Scenario 2, we would like to highlight preliminary observations regarding (i) the susceptibility of the overall plant population to stressors if varieties with different traits are cultivated together; (ii) genomic effects that may occur from further crossings and (iii) accumulation of unintended genetic changes due to the technical processes of NGTs.

(i) As mentioned, the susceptibility of the overall plant population to biotic and abiotic stressors may be affected if NGT plant varieties with different traits are cultivated together. One reason for this assumption is a common range of pathogens which may affect plant health. Increased susceptibility to plant diseases of a variety with one trait may also cause enhanced pest pressure and damage in varieties with other traits. For example, if varieties with traits of (unintended) higher susceptibility to biotic stressors are grown together with varieties with traits of (unintended) reduced tolerance to abiotic stressors, this may cause the collapse of plant populations which would otherwise have been successfully cultivated.

(ii) Furthermore, different traits can be stacked by technical means or conventional breeding or spontaneous crossings, and thus result in offspring with biological characteristics which were absent in the parental events. This may, for example, lead to plant compositions which negatively impact the ecosystems, the food webs, the health of wild species and consumers. In general, if traits do not have a history of conventional breeding, the effects resulting from their interactions and combinations may be hard to predict [see 56]. Even if each of the events themselves are considered to be 'safe' in risk assessment, their offspring may show next-generation effects associated with unexpected risks caused by genomic interactions. Such genomic interactions may, for example, be caused by epistasis: current research on NGT applications in tomatoes shows that the effects of cryptic gene variants may depend on their genetic background [see, for example, 70,71,72]. Cryptic variations are considered to be mutations that, regardless of whether they occur naturally or are introduced by technical processes, have little or no phenotypic consequences unless exposed to additional genetic or environmental interactions. These cryptic variations may then lead to unpredictable and sometimes detrimental outcomes due to epistatic interactions with other genetic variations [91, 92, 94]. These findings are also relevant to other plant species, such as wheat [95,96,97]. Therefore, the genomic interactions emerging from gene flow, from conventional crossings and technical stacking are relevant to the assessment of intended and unintended genetic changes caused by the processes of NGT.

(iii) Finally, further crossings may also lead to accumulations of unintended off-target genetic alterations, caused by the multistep processes of NGT (see technical characteristics) involving for example *Agrobacterium tumefaciens* or biolistic methods to generate the above-described NGTs traits [42, 49, 78, 88]. They are known for causing specific unintended effects in EGTs [20,21,22,23] and NGTs [24, 26, see also 98]. However, so far, in many cases of NGT applications as well as in the context of the examples used in Scenario 2, no comprehensive data on potential off-target effects have been published. In future, specific attention should be paid to the assessment of unintended genetic effects caused by the multistep processes inherent to NGTs, since they are also of relevance to the assessment of potential interactions both between and combinations of NGT organisms.

A summarized reasoning of our second hypothesis may read as follows: If NGTs are used to generate different traits in one species, the resulting intended and/or unintended genetic changes may lead to interactions between the NGT organisms, and thus result in effects that are relevant to risk assessment. Simultaneous cultivation, further crossings and technical stacking of the various events need to be taken into account. The resulting effects may be dependent on specific combinations of intended or unintended genetic variants, the intended traits and/or the exposure to stress conditions in the receiving environment. Even if all individual events were considered to be 'safe', uncertainties or unknowns will still remain due to interactions of the intended and unintended genetic changes and associated effects in each event. Therefore, the environmental risk assessment of individual events is not sufficient to predict and assess all these interactions. Potential adverse effects may impact plant health and their response to biotic and abiotic stressors, causing a breakdown in food production or disruption in agro-ecological systems. Additional direct or indirect effects (not discussed in here) may emerge in the context of food safety if the harvest of the different traits is mixed into diets.

SOME EXPERIENCE FROM TRANSGENIC PLANTS

So far only a few traits (mainly herbicide tolerance and insecticidal toxicity) have been established in transgenic plants. Nevertheless, several unintended interactions between those plants have already been observed and discussed, and are associated with environmental risks. For example, potential disruptive effects on ecosystems have been described by Vázquez-Barrios et al. [99] in regard to glyphosate-resistant transgenic cotton that produces insecticidal Bt toxins. These transgenic cotton plants have successfully invaded and outcrossed into natural cotton populations in Mexico, which is one of the centers of diversity for wild cotton *Gossypium hirsutum* [100]. The authors reported that the expression of both transgenic traits in wild cotton under natural conditions changed extra-floral nectar production, and thus changed its association with different ant species. Vázquez-Barrios et al. [99] discuss to which extent the genomic and metabolic interactions of the combined traits promote the spread of the transgenic cotton. Further research is needed to identify the underlying causes, for example, by comparing in more detail the single traits with the combined traits occurring in spontaneous crossings.

In Brazil, populations of white flies (*Bemisia tabaci*) are increasing in fields where insecticidal transgenic soybeans are grown. Originally, the rise in the number of white flies was explained by a reduction in insecticide sprayings. However, laboratory experiments revealed other findings [101]: the white flies suck fluid from the plants and appear to benefit from specific biological characteristics of the transgenic soybeans. This finding seems to be especially true for transgenic soybeans which are glyphosate-resistant and produce Bt toxins. Insects feeding on these plants were more fertile and had significantly more offspring, but both effects were absent if the transgenic soybeans were only resistant to glyphosate. Increasing numbers of white flies also promote plant diseases: the white flies transmit plant viruses when they feed on the plants and their excretions facilitate the occurrence of fungal diseases. Almeida et al. [101] state that the exact causes for the strongly increased number of white flies are unknown. One possibility: the Bt insecticides, which are not toxic for the white flies, might have stimulating effects. Unexpected genomic interactions in the soybean varieties are also being considered. There have been previous reports of an increase in the spread of pest insects in Brazilian transgenic soybean: experts warned in 2014 that another pest insect, the southern armyworm (*Spodoptera eridania*), was increasingly spreading in fields with glyphosate-resistant transgenic soybeans which produce Bt toxins [102]. This effect was apparently not observed in fields with transgenic plants only inheriting one of the traits.

Interactions between the transgenic traits were also described in another case in Brazil [103]: according to their findings, the spread of Amaranthus weeds (*Amaranthus palmeri*) in soybean fields is facilitated by the cultivation of the transgenic herbicide-resistant plants. It was found that if black armyworm larvae *(Spodoptera cosmioides)* fed on *A. palmeri,* this had positive effects on its biological and reproductive parameters. In addition, and unexpectedly, the larvae of *S. cosmioides* also show increased fitness if they feed on transgenic soybeans producing Bt toxins (Cry1Ac). Thus, the spread of the larvae benefited from both traits, the herbicide resistance (and its indirect effects) and the Bt trait (and its unintended direct effects). Consequently, the black armyworm, in particular, can become a plant pest in fields where transgenic soybeans with a combination of traits are grown.

There are also some countries in where transgenic organisms from different domains of life were (intentionally or unintentionally) released into an environment where they might interact with each other. For example, in Brazil, genetically engineered crops [104], fish [105], mosquitoes [106] and pest insects [107] might share the same environment and have some potential to persist and propagate. However, no findings on interactions between those populations have been published.

There are also some findings from transgenic plants which do not include interactions between GE organisms but are, nevertheless, of relevance to the scenarios described above: transgenic wheat with intended resistance to fungal diseases was successfully grown in the greenhouse but showed lower yield and susceptibility to a toxic fungal disease (ergot disease) in field trials [108]. This example shows that the unintended effects of GE organisms may indeed exceed those which can be expected in conventionally bred varieties with the same genetic background. It also shows that environmental conditions may be decisive for the occurrence of unintended effects, which may then also influence interactions between different GE traits within the same species.

It seems that some of this already existing experience may also be relevant in the elaboration of our suggested scenarios. However, due to the specific characteristics of the NGTs summarized above, these scenarios will need further consideration and elaboration before conclusions can be drawn.

DISCUSSION: THE NEED FOR RISK ASSESSMENT OF INTERACTIONS BETWEEN NGT ORGANISMS AND THE ROLE OF TECHNOLOGY ASSESSMENT

As shown above, the effects resulting from the processes used to generate NGT organisms cannot be generally equated with those derived from conventional breeding, even if no additional genes are inserted. While physical and chemical mutagens (which to some degree also exist in nature) are not likely to cause other mutations compared to those occurring spontaneously, SDN-1 applications of targeted biotechnological mutagens, such as CRISPR/Cas, can produce results (genotypes and phenotypes) that are unlikely to occur with other methods and processes.

If NGT organisms are introduced into the environment on a large-scale, in terms of numbers, traits and events, then such large-scale releases would unavoidably increase the likelihood of direct or indirect effects occurring through interactions between those organisms. Therefore, their intended and unintended interactions and potentially resulting hazards will need specific attention. A lack of awareness of the overall impact of such large-scale releases may have serious consequences for future generations. In the past, technologies meant to solve problems in certain areas (energy, food production, transport) frequently created new problems, e.g., climate change, nuclear waste, chemical pollution and extinction of species [109]. Given the high technical potential of the above-described NGTs, comprehensive risk assessment may become vital for averting another man-made technology crisis and safeguarding planetary health [110].

NGT organisms which have not adapted through evolutionary processes, may disturb or disrupt ecological networks in many ways. In general, intended or unintended, direct and indirect effects resulting from NGT applications and the subsequent release of the derived organisms, cannot not be seen as 'neutral' to the functioning and services of the ecosystems. From our findings, we identified several factors which are relevant in this context: (1) The differences (in regard to intended and unintended effects) of the NGT organisms compared to plants derived from conventional breeding or found in nature; (2) their combination (caused by simultaneous presence in a shared receiving environment and/or further crossings and/or or technical stacking); and (3) the scale of their release into the environment, which determines exposure and the statistical likelihood of (undesirable) interactions with each other and the environment. Whatever the case, even if the individual events are considered to be safe, the overall scale of releases (number of organisms, different traits and involved species) still needs to be taken into account.

Decision-making on potential releases of NGT organisms in the EU is guided by the precautionary principle in order to prevent eco- and food systems from being confronted with too many risks, uncertainties and unknowns. To this end, the development of hypotheses to explore potential interactions in regard to risk assessment is a crucial step. There are several potential environmental risks that involve interactions between the NGT organisms and the environment, such as (i) disturbance or disruption of ecological interactions of the plants with their associated microbiomes and/or pollinators; (ii) the weakening of resistance (resilience) to biotic or abiotic stressors; (iii) evolutionary mismatch effects that complicate future evolutionary processes; and (iv) endangering biodiversity by the uncontrolled (invasive) spread of NGT organisms and their offspring. Some of these effects have already been shown to be relevant factors in the risk assessment of individual NGT organisms, e.g., *Camelina sativa* with changed oil composition [38]. At the same time, the NGT camelina has the potential to persist in the environment and spread uncontrollably. If these plants are, for example, grown together with other NGT camelina, interactions may occur due to gene flow, crossings and spontaneous offspring between the events. In summary, the hypothesis that the overall impact of several NGT organisms may exceed the sum of effects observed in individual events if they are released into a shared receiving environment is plausible, especially if this involves large numbers of organisms as well as several traits and/or many species. There may also be potential tipping points linked to parallel or successive large-scale releases of NGT organisms into a shared receiving environment that could trigger irreversible damage.

Interactions between the NGT organisms and other GE organisms may play a decisive role in their overall environmental impact. In this context, it is not only the long-term accumulated effects that should be taken into account, as large numbers and a great variety of NGT organisms may be released into the ecosystems within short periods of time, and thus also trigger unintended combinatorial effects in a short time. These hazards may, however, escape the attention of risk assessors as EFSA [4] guidance does not consider such hazards in detail. Risk assessors may, therefore, see the need to further develop guidelines to ensure that problem formulation and all subsequent steps in risk assessment include all relevant hazards and also leave sufficient space to develop and assess the hypotheses. As Eckerstorfer et al. [111] state, trait related as well as process related effects have to be taken into account in this context: "*To this end, we suggest that two sets of considerations are considered: (1) trait related-considerations to assess the effects associated with the newly developed trait(s); and (2) method-related considerations to assess unintended changes associated with the intended trait(s) or with other modifications in the GE plant (...) Based on these considerations, further guidance should be developed to ensure the high safety standards provided by the current regulatory framework for GMOs in the EU for GE plants in an adequate and efficient way, taking into account the existing knowledge and experience in a case-specific manner. This guidance should thus strengthen the case-specific approach that is recommended by numerous EU and Member States institutions.*" Adequate methods to generate the necessary data for risk assessment are, for example, whole genome sequencing, the application of 'omics' [16] and comparative analysis of plant composition and phenotypical characteristics [4]. In addition, potential interactions may be tested in controlled environments [46] and NGT plants can be exposed to defined stress conditions and subjected to experimental crossings [56].

However, even if adequate methodology is applied, it is self-evident that uncertainties will still play a crucial role in this context. As EFSA in its guidance for environmental risk assessment (ERA) correctly states [4, point 2.3.3.8]: "*It is recognised that an ERA is only as good as our state of scientific knowledge at the time it was conducted. Thus, under current EU legislation, ERAs are required to identify areas of uncertainty or risk which relate to areas outside current knowledge and the limited scope of the ERA. (...) It is recognised that an environmental risk assessment is limited by the nature, scale and location of experimental releases, which biospheres have been studied and the length of time the studies were conducted.*" EFSA [4] proposes several strategies to deal with the different levels of uncertainties and knowledge gaps. However, given the complex nature of effects emerging from interactions between GE organisms, the uncertainties and knowledge gaps might, in many cases, make it impossible to draw sufficiently reliable conclusions. Therefore, cut-off criteria [56, 112] may be necessary to avoid the release of GE organisms (including NGT organisms) if safety is not demonstrated.

In addition, risk assessors and risk managers should consider more general aspects: as argued above, the release of NGT organisms may not be generally considered to be 'neutral' to the ecosystems from the perspective of environmental protection. Their (undesirable) impacts may be escalated depending on the number of organisms and traits being released into a shared ecosystem. Similarly to environmental pollution with plastics and chemicals, it is not always an individual product which creates the real problems, but rather the sum of diverse effects. Environmental problems created by the release of NGT organisms may last as long as or longer than those caused by plastics and pesticides, especially if they can persist and propagate in the environment and thus impact many future generations. For this reason, there may be a case for generally restricting the introduction of GE organisms into the environment. Consequently, reliable criteria and robust mechanisms may be needed to justify any releases of these organisms. For example, the EU Commission [75] does discuss the potential benefits of NGT organisms, including mitigating the impacts of climate change or promoting sustainability in agriculture and food production. Therefore, instruments and criteria may be needed to distinguish traits with 'real benefits' from those which are simply 'empty promises'.

On this basis, the elaboration of future scenarios within a prospective technology assessment (TA), in addition to risk assessment, may help to develop regulatory instruments and define criteria to minimize potential adverse effects, and also identify applications with a sound expectation of real benefits. Crucial TA principles are, for example, summarized in the GAO "Technology Assessment Design Handbook" published in 2021: "*New technologies can have a range of effects, potentially both positive and disruptive, that TAs can explore. GAO has broadly defined TA as the thorough and balanced analysis of significant primary, secondary, indirect, and delayed interactions of a technological innovation with society, the environment, and the economy and the present and foreseen consequences and effects of those interactions.*" [113].

In general, case-specific risk assessment as foreseen in EU GMO regulation can be seen as an 'end-of-pipe' safety control mechanism for individual organisms ('events') just before they enter the market. In contrast, TA can deal more generally with (groups of) products derived from specific (new) technologies (ideally) before the final products reach the market. In the EU, it could become a tool for making risk management decisions, for example, to control the overall scale of releases of NGT organisms. However, so far, there is no established decision-making process to derive such conclusions. At the same time, the development of suitable methods and criteria is urgently needed: if, in the near future, NGT organisms are released and marketed to the extent proposed by several stakeholders, then interactions between NGT organisms are likely to become unavoidable in many regions of the world, including the EU.

While TA cannot replace the risk assessment of individual organisms ('events'), it can nevertheless help in political decision-making to seek a balance between the potential benefits and reducing the overall risks of adverse effects on biodiversity and planetary health. If NGT organisms are, for example, applied in agriculture, their potential negative impacts may be minimized by only approving organisms which are considered to be safe and come with a reasonable expectation of providing substantial benefits. Limiting the number and scale of releases of NGT organisms also seems to be a necessary precondition for a reliable assessment of their interactions and associated risks.

CONCLUSIONS

New genomic techniques (NGTs) allow new genotypes and traits to be developed in different ways, and with different outcomes compared to previous genetic engineering methods or conventional breeding (including non-targeted mutagenesis).

Plants developed with NGTs may comprise many more different traits and species compared to transgenic plants approved for the market so far. In addition, NGT applications may be relevant to all domains of life, including non-domesticated species.

Due to the intended or unintended effects resulting from the application of NGTs, the release of the NGT organisms may not be 'neutral' to the ecosystems. The occurrence of disadvantageous interactions and disruptive effects will be more likely or less likely, depending on how their biological characteristics (intended or unintended) differ from those of conventionally bred or naturally occurring plants, also including the degree of environmental exposure, their combinations and conditions in the receiving environment. Large-scale releases of NGT organisms across a broad range of species will increase the likelihood of direct and indirect risks associated with interactions between GE organisms, especially in terms of numbers and traits. Whatever the case, it has to be assumed that the overall impact of numerous NGT organisms being released into a shared receiving environment may exceed the sum of effects observed in distinct events. These observations could be a particular cause for concern if NGT-GMOs are released without sufficient regulation and control.

Environmental risk assessment of the individual events is not sufficient to predict or assess these interactions. Consequently, risk assessors and risk managers should not only consider the risks associated with individual NGT organisms, but should also take into account risks emerging from interactions between GE organisms and their potential pathways to harm. Risk scenarios involving several events with different traits, belonging to either the same species or to several species, can be used to develop plausible hypotheses, define hazards and guide the risk assessment in accordance with the precautionary principle. In this context, the sufficiency of the current guidelines for risk assessment should be reviewed in detail and amended as necessary.

Combinatorial effects typically increase the level of complexity and decrease the level of predictability. Therefore, if the complexity of direct and indirect effects caused by interactions in between NGT organisms and with their environment does not allow final conclusions to be drawn on their environmental safety, we propose the introduction of cut-off criteria which allow decisions to be taken in the face of uncertainties [56, 112].

In addition, the risk manager should also consider broader aspects: similarly to the need to reduce the use of plastics and toxic substances, such as pesticides, there may also be a need to restrict the introduction of genetically engineered organisms into the environment. Therefore, reliable instruments and criteria may also be needed to assess the anticipated benefits ensuing from the release of NGT organisms, e.g., mitigating the impact of climate change or promoting sustainability in agriculture and food production. A general limit to the scale of releases of NGT organisms is also likely to be a necessary precondition for a reliable assessment of their interactions. Therefore, additional instruments and criteria established within prospective technology assessment will be needed to distinguish traits with 'real benefits' from those which are simply 'empty' promises.

ACKNOWLEDGEMENTS

We like to thank Nina Valenzuela (Testbiotech) for her editing and the experts of the Bundesamt für Naturschutz (BfN) for giving their feedback.

REFERENCES

1. European Parliament, Council of the European Union (2001) Directive 2001/18/EC of the European Parliament and of the Council of 12 March 2001 on the deliberate release into the environment of genetically modified organisms and repealing Council Directive 90/220/EEC—Commission Declaration
2. European Commission (2018) Commission Directive (EU) 2018/350 of 8 March 2018 amending Directive 2001/18/EC of the European Parliament and of the Council as regards the environmental risk assessment of genetically modified organisms
3. European Commission (2013) Commission Implementing Regulation (EU) No 503/2013 of 3 April 2013 on applications for authorisation of genetically modified food and feed in accordance with Regulation (EC) No 1829/2003 of the European Parliament and of the Council and amending Commission Regulations (EC) No 641/2004 and (EC) No 1981/2006 Text with EEA relevance
4. EFSA Panel on Genetically Modified Organisms (GMO) (2010) Guidance on the environmental risk assessment of genetically modified plants. EFSA J 8:1879. https://doi.org/10.2903/j.efsa.2010.1879

5. EFSA Panel on Genetically Modified Organisms (GMO), Mullins E, Bresson J-L et al (2022) Criteria for risk assessment of plants produced by targeted mutagenesis, cisgenesis and intragenesis. EFSA J 20:e07618. https://doi.org/10.2903/j.efsa.2022.7618
6. Joint Research Centre (2021) New Genomic Techniques market dashboard. In: Data-Modelling platform of resource economics. https://datam.jrc.ec.europa.eu/datam/mashup/NEW_GENOMIC_TECHNIQUES/index.html. Accessed 8 Mar 2023
7. BVL - the Federal Office of Consumer Protection and Food Safety (Berlin, DE), WFSR - Wageningen Food Safety Research (formerly RIKILT) of Wageningen UR (Wageningen, NL) (2023) The European GMO database. In: European GMO Initiative for a Unified Database System (EUginius). https://euginius.eu/euginius/pages/home.jsf. Accessed 9 Mar 2023
8. Joint Research Centre (European Commission) (2021) Current and future market applications of new genomic techniques. Publications Office of the European Union, Luxembourg
9. Eckerstorfer MF, Dolezel M, Heissenberger A et al (2019) An EU perspective on biosafety considerations for plants developed by genome editing and other New Genetic Modification Techniques (nGMs). Front Bioeng Biotechnol 7:1–13. https://doi.org/10.3389/fbioe.2019.00031
10. Kawall K (2019) New possibilities on the horizon: genome editing makes the whole genome accessible for changes. Front Plant Sci 10:525. https://doi.org/10.3389/fpls.2019.00525
11. EFSA Panel on Genetically Modified Organisms (GMO) (2021) Evaluation of existing guidelines for their adequacy for the molecular characterisation and environmental risk assessment of genetically modified plants obtained through synthetic biology. EFSA J 19:e06301. https://doi.org/10.2903/j.efsa.2021.6301
12. Jinek M, Chylinski K, Fonfara I et al (2012) A programmable dual-RNA-guided DNA endonuclease in adaptive bacterial immunity. Science 337:816–821. https://doi.org/10.1126/science.1225829
13. Raitskin O, Patron NJ (2016) Multi-gene engineering in plants with RNA-guided Cas9 nuclease. Curr Opin Biotechnol 37:69–75. https://doi.org/10.1016/j.copbio.2015.11.008
14. Wang H, La Russa M, Qi LS (2016) CRISPR/Cas9 in genome editing and beyond. Annu Rev Biochem 85:227–264. https://doi.org/10.1146/annurev-biochem-060815-014607
15. Zetsche B, Heidenreich M, Mohanraju P et al (2017) Multiplex gene editing by CRISPR-Cpf1 using a single crRNA array. Nat Biotechnol 35:31–34. https://doi.org/10.1038/nbt.3737
16. Kawall K, Cotter J, Then C (2020) Broadening the GMO risk assessment in the EU for genome editing technologies in agriculture. Environ Sci Eur 32:106. https://doi.org/10.1186/s12302-020-00361-2
17. Sander JD, Joung JK (2014) CRISPR-Cas systems for editing, regulating and targeting genomes. Nat Biotechnol 32:347–355. https://doi.org/10.1038/nbt.2842
18. Doudna JA, Charpentier E (2014) Genome editing. The new frontier of genome engineering with CRISPR-Cas9. Science 346:1258096. https://doi.org/10.1126/science.1258096
19. EFSA Panel on Genetically Modified Organisms (GMO) (2020) Applicability of the EFSA Opinion on site-directed nucleases type 3 for the safety assessment of plants developed using site-directed nucleases type 1 and 2 and oligonucleotide-directed mutagenesis. EFSA J 18:e06299. https://doi.org/10.2903/j.efsa.2020.6299
20. Forsbach A, Schubert D, Lechtenberg B et al (2003) A comprehensive characterization of single-copy T-DNA insertions in the *Arabidopsis thaliana* genome. Plant Mol Biol 52:161–176. https://doi.org/10.1023/a:1023929630687
21. Makarevitch I, Svitashev SK, Somers DA (2003) Complete sequence analysis of transgene loci from plants transformed via microprojectile bombardment. Plant Mol Biol 52:421–432. https://doi.org/10.1023/a:1023968920830

22. Gelvin SB (2017) Integration of agrobacterium T-DNA into the plant genome. Annu Rev Genet 51:195–217. https://doi.org/10.1146/annurev-genet-120215-035320
23. Yue J, VanBuren R, Liu J et al (2022) SunUp and Sunset genomes revealed impact of particle bombardment mediated transformation and domestication history in papaya. Nat Genet 54:715–724. https://doi.org/10.1038/s41588-022-01068-1
24. Braatz J, Harloff H-J, Mascher M et al (2017) CRISPR-Cas9 targeted mutagenesis leads to simultaneous modification of different homoeologous gene copies in polyploid oilseed rape (*Brassica napus*). Plant Physiol 174:935–942. https://doi.org/10.1104/pp.17.00426
25. Modrzejewski D, Hartung F, Lehnert H et al (2020) Which factors affect the occurrence of off-target effects caused by the use of CRISPR/Cas: a systematic review in plants. Front Plant Sci 11:574959. https://doi.org/10.3389/fpls.2020.574959
26. Biswas S, Tian J, Li R et al (2020) Investigation of CRISPR/Cas9-induced SD1 rice mutants highlights the importance of molecular characterization in plant molecular breeding. J Genetics Genomics 47:273–280. https://doi.org/10.1016/j.jgg.2020.04.004
27. Höijer I, Emmanouilidou A, Östlund R et al (2022) CRISPR-Cas9 induces large structural variants at on-target and off-target sites in vivo that segregate across generations. Nat Commun 13:627. https://doi.org/10.1038/s41467-022-28244-5
28. Ahloowalia BS, Maluszynski M (2001) Induced mutations—a new paradigm in plant breeding. Euphytica 118:167–173. https://doi.org/10.1023/A:1004162323428
29. Wendel JF, Jackson SA, Meyers BC, Wing RA (2016) Evolution of plant genome architecture. Genome Biol 17:37. https://doi.org/10.1186/s13059-016-0908-1
30. Lin T, Zhu G, Zhang J et al (2014) Genomic analyses provide insights into the history of tomato breeding. Nat Genet 46:1220–1226. https://doi.org/10.1038/ng.3117
31. Jones DM, Wells R, Pullen N et al (2018) Spatio-temporal expression dynamics differ between homologues of flowering time genes in the allopolyploid *Brassica napus*. Plant J 96:103–118. https://doi.org/10.1111/tpj.14020
32. Belfield EJ, Ding ZJ, Jamieson FJC et al (2018) DNA mismatch repair preferentially protects genes from mutation. Genome Res 28:66–74. https://doi.org/10.1101/gr.219303.116
33. Huang Y, Li G-M (2018) DNA mismatch repair preferentially safeguards actively transcribed genes. DNA Repair 71:82–86. https://doi.org/10.1016/j.dnarep.2018.08.010
34. Filler Hayut S, Melamed Bessudo C, Levy AA (2017) Targeted recombination between homologous chromosomes for precise breeding in tomato. Nat Commun 8:15605. https://doi.org/10.1038/ncomms15605
35. Frigola J, Sabarinathan R, Mularoni L et al (2017) Reduced mutation rate in exons due to differential mismatch repair. Nat Genet 49:1684–1692. https://doi.org/10.1038/ng.3991
36. Halstead MM, Kern C, Saelao P et al (2020) A comparative analysis of chromatin accessibility in cattle, pig, and mouse tissues. BMC Genomics 21:698. https://doi.org/10.1186/s12864-020-07078-9
37. Monroe JG, Srikant T, Carbonell-Bejerano P et al (2022) Mutation bias reflects natural selection in *Arabidopsis thaliana*. Nature 602:101–105. https://doi.org/10.1038/s41586-021-04269-6
38. Kawall K (2021) Genome-edited *Camelina sativa* with a unique fatty acid content and its potential impact on ecosystems. Environ Sci Eur 33:38. https://doi.org/10.1186/s12302-021-00482-2
39. Kawall K (2021) The generic risks and the potential of SDN-1 applications in crop plants. Plants 10:2259. https://doi.org/10.3390/plants10112259

40. Weiss T, Crisp PA, Rai KM et al (2022) Epigenetic features drastically impact CRISPR–Cas9 efficacy in plants. Plant Physiol 190:1153–1164. https://doi.org/10.1093/plphys/kiac285

41. Nonaka S, Arai C, Takayama M et al (2017) Efficient increase of γ-aminobutyric acid (GABA) content in tomato fruits by targeted mutagenesis. Sci Rep 7:7057. https://doi.org/10.1038/s41598-017-06400-y

42. Raffan S, Sparks C, Huttly A et al (2021) Wheat with greatly reduced accumulation of free asparagine in the grain, produced by CRISPR/Cas9 editing of asparagine synthetase gene *TaASN2*. Plant Biotechnol J 19:1602–1613. https://doi.org/10.1111/pbi.13573

43. Spanu PD (2022) Slicing the cost of bread. Nat Plants 8:200–201. https://doi.org/10.1038/s41477-022-01115-z

44. Kishimoto K, Washio Y, Yoshiura Y et al (2018) Production of a breed of red sea bream Pagrus major with an increase of skeletal muscle mass and reduced body length by genome editing with CRISPR/Cas9. Aquaculture 495:415–427. https://doi.org/10.1016/j.aquaculture.2018.05.055

45. Lee K-R, Jeon I, Yu H et al (2021) Increasing monounsaturated fatty acid contents in hexaploid *Camelina sativa* seed oil by FAD2 gene knockout using CRISPR-Cas9. Front Plant Sci 12:702930. https://doi.org/10.3389/fpls.2021.702930

46. Barbour MA, Kliebenstein DJ, Bascompte J (2022) A keystone gene underlies the persistence of an experimental food web. Science 376:70–73. https://doi.org/10.1126/science.abf2232

47. Zsögön A, Čermák T, Naves ER et al (2018) *De novo* domestication of wild tomato using genome editing. Nat Biotechnol 36:1211–1216. https://doi.org/10.1038/nbt.4272

48. EFSA Panel on Genetically Modified Organisms (GMO) (2022) Evaluation of existing guidelines for their adequacy for the food and feed risk assessment of genetically modified plants obtained through synthetic biology. EFSA J 20:e07410. https://doi.org/10.2903/j.efsa.2022.7410

49. Sánchez-León S, Gil-Humanes J, Ozuna CV et al (2018) Low-gluten, nontransgenic wheat engineered with CRISPR/Cas9. Plant Biotechnol J 16:902–910. https://doi.org/10.1111/pbi.12837

50. Testbiotech (2021) Testbiotech comment on the IUCN report "Genetic frontiers for conservation, an assessment of synthetic biology and biodiversity conservation." In: testbiotech. https://www.testbiotech.org/content/testbiotech-comment-iucn-report-genetic-frontiers-conservation-assessment-synthetic-biology. Accessed 28 Sep 2022

51. Secretariat of the Convention on Biological Diversity (2022) CBD Technical Series 100: Synthetic Biology. The Biosafety Clearing-House (BCH) Synthetic Biology:196

52. Gantz VM, Bier E (2015) Genome editing. The mutagenic chain reaction: a method for converting heterozygous to homozygous mutations. Science 348:442–444. https://doi.org/10.1126/science.aaa5945

53. Frieß JL, von Gleich A, Giese B (2019) Gene drives as a new quality in GMO releases—a comparative technology characterization. PeerJ 7:e6793. https://doi.org/10.7717/peerj.6793

54. Lentzos F, Rybicki EP, Engelhard M et al (2022) Eroding norms over release of self-spreading viruses. Science 375:31–33. https://doi.org/10.1126/science.abj5593

55. Pfeifer K, Frieß JL, Giese B (2022) Insect allies—assessment of a viral approach to plant genome editing. Integr Environ Assess Manag. https://doi.org/10.1002/ieam.4577

56. Bauer-Panskus A, Miyazaki J, Kawall K, Then C (2020) Risk assessment of genetically engineered plants that can persist and propagate in the environment. Environ Sci Eur 32:32. https://doi.org/10.1186/s12302-020-00301-0

57. Temme K, Zhao D, Voigt CA (2012) Refactoring the nitrogen fixation gene cluster from *Klebsiella oxytoca*. Proc Natl Acad Sci USA 109:7085–7090. https://doi.org/10.1073/pnas.1120788109
58. Shelake RM, Pramanik D, Kim J-Y (2019) Exploration of plant-microbe interactions for sustainable agriculture in CRISPR era. Microorganisms 7:E269. https://doi.org/10.3390/microorganisms7080269
59. Shulse CN, Chovatia M, Agosto C et al (2019) Engineered root bacteria release plant-available phosphate from phytate. Appl Environ Microbiol 85:e01210-e1219. https://doi.org/10.1128/AEM.01210-19
60. Vorholt JA, Vogel C, Carlström CI, Müller DB (2017) Establishing causality: opportunities of synthetic communities for plant microbiome research. Cell Host Microbe 22:142–155. https://doi.org/10.1016/j.chom.2017.07.004
61. Checcucci A, diCenzo GC, Ghini V et al (2018) Creation and characterization of a genomically hybrid strain in the nitrogen-fixing symbiotic bacterium *Sinorhizobium meliloti*. ACS Synth Biol 7:2365–2378. https://doi.org/10.1021/acssynbio.8b00158
62. Hettiarachchige IK, Elkins AC, Reddy P et al (2019) Genetic modification of asexual Epichloë endophytes with the perA gene for peramine biosynthesis. Mol Genet Genomics 294:315–328. https://doi.org/10.1007/s00438-018-1510-x
63. Arif I, Batool M, Schenk PM (2020) Plant microbiome engineering: expected benefits for improved crop growth and resilience. Trends Biotechnol 38:1385–1396. https://doi.org/10.1016/j.tibtech.2020.04.015
64. Ren X, Hoiczyk E, Rasgon JL (2008) Viral paratransgenesis in the malaria vector *Anopheles gambiae*. PLoS Pathog 4:e1000135. https://doi.org/10.1371/journal.ppat.1000135
65. Fang W, Vega-Rodríguez J, Ghosh AK et al (2011) Development of transgenic fungi that kill human malaria parasites in mosquitoes. Science 331:1074–1077. https://doi.org/10.1126/science.1199115
66. Rangberg A, Diep DB, Rudi K, Amdam GV (2012) Paratransgenesis: an approach to improve colony health and molecular insight in honey bees (*Apis mellifera*)? Integr Comp Biol 52:89–99. https://doi.org/10.1093/icb/ics089
67. De Vooght L, Caljon G, De Ridder K, Van Den Abbeele J (2014) Delivery of a functional anti-trypanosome nanobody in different tsetse fly tissues via a bacterial symbiont, *Sodalis glossinidius*. Microb Cell Fact 13:156. https://doi.org/10.1186/s12934-014-0156-6
68. Gilbert JA, Medlock J, Townsend JP et al (2016) Determinants of human African trypanosomiasis elimination via paratransgenesis. PLoS Negl Trop Dis 10:e0004465. https://doi.org/10.1371/journal.pntd.0004465
69. Bilgo E, Lovett B, Fang W et al (2017) Improved efficacy of an arthropod toxin expressing fungus against insecticide-resistant malaria-vector mosquitoes. Sci Rep 7:3433. https://doi.org/10.1038/s41598-017-03399-0
70. Leonard SP, Perutka J, Powell JE et al (2018) Genetic engineering of bee gut microbiome bacteria with a toolkit for modular assembly of broad-host-range plasmids. ACS Synth Biol 7:1279–1290. https://doi.org/10.1021/acssynbio.7b00399
71. Lovett B, Bilgo E, Millogo SA et al (2019) Transgenic *Metarhizium* rapidly kills mosquitoes in a malaria-endemic region of Burkina Faso. Science 364:894–897. https://doi.org/10.1126/science.aaw8737
72. Leonard SP, Powell JE, Perutka J et al (2020) Engineered symbionts activate honey bee immunity and limit pathogens. Science 367:573–576. https://doi.org/10.1126/science.aax9039

73. Levin RA, Voolstra CR, Agrawal S et al (2017) Engineering strategies to decode and enhance the genomes of coral symbionts. Front Microbiol 8:1220. https://doi.org/10.3389/fmicb.2017.01220

74. Wilke ABB, Marrelli MT (2015) Paratransgenesis: a promising new strategy for mosquito vector control. Parasit Vectors 8:342. https://doi.org/10.1186/s13071-015-0959-2

75. European Commission (2021) Study on the status of new genomic techniques under Union law and in light of the Court of Justice ruling in Case C-528/16 - Commission Staff Working Document - SWD(2021) 92 final

76. Heinemann JA, Paull DJ, Walker S, Kurenbach B (2021) Differentiated impacts of human interventions on nature: scaling the conversation on regulation of gene technologies. Elementa 9:00086. https://doi.org/10.1525/elementa.2021.00086

77. Breckling B, von Gleich A (2020) Gene Drives Touching Tipping Points. In: von Gleich A, Schröder W (eds) Gene drives at tipping points: precautionary technology assessment and governance of new approaches to genetically modify animal and plant populations. Springer International Publishing, Cham, pp 29–56

78. Morineau C, Bellec Y, Tellier F et al (2017) Selective gene dosage by CRISPR-Cas9 genome editing in hexaploid *Camelina sativa*. Plant Biotechnol J 15:729–739. https://doi.org/10.1111/pbi.12671

79. Verma AK, Mandal S, Tiwari A et al (2021) Current status and perspectives on the application of CRISPR/Cas9 gene-editing system to develop a low-gluten, non-transgenic wheat variety. Foods 10:2351. https://doi.org/10.3390/foods10102351

80. Gomez-Cano F, Chu Y-H, Cruz-Gomez M et al (2022) Exploring *Camelina sativa* lipid metabolism regulation by combining gene co-expression and DNA affinity purification analyses. Plant J 110:589–606. https://doi.org/10.1111/tpj.15682

81. Aznar-Moreno JA, Durrett TP (2017) Simultaneous targeting of multiple gene homeologs to alter seed oil production in *Camelina sativa*. Plant Cell Physiol 58:1260–1267. https://doi.org/10.1093/pcp/pcx058

82. Jiang WZ, Henry IM, Lynagh PG et al (2017) Significant enhancement of fatty acid composition in seeds of the allohexaploid, *Camelina sativa*, using CRISPR/Cas9 gene editing. Plant Biotechnol J 15:648–657. https://doi.org/10.1111/pbi.12663

83. Guan J, Garcia DF, Zhou Y et al (2020) The battle to sequence the bread wheat genome: a tale of the three kingdoms. Genomics Proteomics Bioinformatics 18:221–229. https://doi.org/10.1016/j.gpb.2019.09.005

84. Gatti S, Lionetti E, Balanzoni L et al (2020) Increased prevalence of celiac disease in school-age children in Italy. Clin Gastroenterol Hepatol 18:596–603. https://doi.org/10.1016/j.cgh.2019.06.013

85. Blumenthal C, Bekes F, Gras PW et al (1995) Identification of wheat genotypes tolerant to the effects of heat stress on grain quality. Cereal Chem 72:539–544

86. Phakela K, van Biljon A, Wentzel B et al (2021) Gluten protein response to heat and drought stress in durum wheat as measured by reverse phase—high performance liquid chromatography. J Cereal Sci 100:103267. https://doi.org/10.1016/j.jcs.2021.103267

87. Marín-Sanz M, Iehisa JCM, Barro F (2022) New transcriptomic insights in two RNAi wheat lines with the gliadins strongly down-regulated by two endosperm specific promoters. Crop J 10:194–203. https://doi.org/10.1016/j.cj.2021.04.009

88. Wang Y, Cheng X, Shan Q et al (2014) Simultaneous editing of three homoeoalleles in hexaploid bread wheat confers heritable resistance to powdery mildew. Nat Biotechnol 32:947–951. https://doi.org/10.1038/nbt.2969

89. Acevedo-Garcia J, Spencer D, Thieron H et al (2017) *mlo*-based powdery mildew resistance in hexaploid bread wheat generated by a non-transgenic TILLING approach. Plant Biotechnol J 15:367–378. https://doi.org/10.1111/pbi.12631

90. Martín AC, Alabdullah AK, Moore G (2021) A separation-of-function ZIP4 wheat mutant allows crossover between related chromosomes and is meiotically stable. Sci Rep 11:21811. https://doi.org/10.1038/s41598-021-01379-z

91. Soyk S, Lemmon ZH, Sedlazeck FJ et al (2019) Duplication of a domestication locus neutralized a cryptic variant that caused a breeding barrier in tomato. Nat Plants 5:471–479. https://doi.org/10.1038/s41477-019-0422-z

92. Alonge M, Wang X, Benoit M et al (2020) Major impacts of widespread structural variation on gene expression and crop improvement in tomato. Cell 182:145-161.e23. https://doi.org/10.1016/j.cell.2020.05.021

93. Jobson E, Roberts R (2022) Genomic structural variation in tomato and its role in plant immunity. Mol Hortic 2:7. https://doi.org/10.1186/s43897-022-00029-w

94. Rodríguez-Leal D, Lemmon ZH, Man J et al (2017) Engineering quantitative trait variation for crop improvement by genome editing. Cell 171:470-480.e8. https://doi.org/10.1016/j.cell.2017.08.030

95. Ji L, Neumann DA, Schmitz RJ (2015) Crop epigenomics: identifying, unlocking, and harnessing cryptic variation in crop genomes. Mol Plant 8:860–870. https://doi.org/10.1016/j.molp.2015.01.021

96. Jiang Y, Schmidt RH, Zhao Y, Reif JC (2017) A quantitative genetic framework highlights the role of epistatic effects for grain-yield heterosis in bread wheat. Nat Genet 49:1741–1746. https://doi.org/10.1038/ng.3974

97. Pramanik D, Shelake RM, Kim MJ, Kim J-Y (2021) CRISPR-mediated engineering across the central dogma in plant biology for basic research and crop improvement. Mol Plant 14:127–150. https://doi.org/10.1016/j.molp.2020.11.002

98. Heinemann J, Clark K, Hiscox TC et al (2023) Are null segregants new combinations of heritable material and should they be regulated? Front Genome Ed 4:59. https://doi.org/10.3389/fgeed.2022.1064103

99. Vázquez-Barrios V, Boege K, Sosa-Fuentes TG et al (2021) Ongoing ecological and evolutionary consequences by the presence of transgenes in a wild cotton population. Sci Rep 11:1959. https://doi.org/10.1038/s41598-021-81567-z

100. Wegier A, Piñeyro-Nelson A, Alarcón J et al (2011) Recent long-distance transgene flow into wild populations conforms to historical patterns of gene flow in cotton (*Gossypium hirsutum*) at its centre of origin. Mol Ecol 20:4182–4194. https://doi.org/10.1111/j.1365-294X.2011.05258.x

101. Almeida MF, Tavares CS, Araújo EO et al (2021) Plant resistance in some modern soybean varieties may favor population growth and modify the stylet penetration of *Bemisia tabaci* (Hemiptera: Aleyrodidae). J Econ Entomol 114:970–978. https://doi.org/10.1093/jee/toab008

102. Bortolotto OC, Silva GV, de Freitas BA et al (2014) Development and reproduction of *Spodoptera eridania* (Lepidoptera: Noctuidae) and its egg parasitoid *Telenomus remus* (Hymenoptera: Platygastridae) on the genetically modified soybean (*Bt*) MON 87701×MON 89788. Bull Entomol Res 104:724–730. https://doi.org/10.1017/S0007485314000546

103. Páez Jerez PG, Hill JG, Pereira EJG et al (2022) The role of genetically engineered soybean and Amaranthus weeds on biological and reproductive parameters of *Spodoptera cosmioides* (Lepidoptera: Noctuidae). Pest Manag Sci 78:2502–2511. https://doi.org/10.1002/ps.6882

104. Fernandes GB, Silva ACdL, Maronhas MES et al (2022) Transgene flow: challenges to the on-farm conservation of maize landraces in the Brazilian semi-arid region. Plants 11:603. https://doi.org/10.3390/plants11050603

105. Magalhães ALB, Brito MFG, Silva LGM (2022) The fluorescent introduction has begun in the southern hemisphere: presence and life-history strategies of the transgenic zebrafish *Danio rerio* (Cypriniformes: Danionidae) in Brazil. Stud Neotrop Fauna Environ. https://doi.org/10.1080/01650521.2021.2024054

106. Evans BR, Kotsakiozi P, Costa-da-Silva AL et al (2019) Transgenic *Aedes aegypti* mosquitoes transfer genes into a natural population. Sci Rep 9:13047. https://doi.org/10.1038/s41598-019-49660-6

107. Francisco M (2021) Armyworm meets Friendly moth. Nat Biotechnol 39:532. https://doi.org/10.1038/s41587-021-00932-5

108. Zeller SL, Kalinina O, Brunner S et al (2010) Transgene × environment interactions in genetically modified wheat. PLoS ONE 5:e11405. https://doi.org/10.1371/journal.pone.0011405

109. European Environment Agency (EEA) (2001) Late lessons from early warnings: the Precautionary Principle 1896–2000. European Environment Agency, Copenhagen

110. Horton R, Lo S (2015) Planetary health: a new science for exceptional action. Lancet 386:1921–1922. https://doi.org/10.1016/S0140-6736(15)61038-8

111. Eckerstorfer MF, Grabowski M, Lener M et al (2021) Biosafety of genome editing applications in plant breeding: considerations for a focused case-specific risk assessment in the EU. Biotech 10:10. https://doi.org/10.3390/biotech10030010

112. Then C, Kawall K, Valenzuela N (2020) Spatiotemporal controllability and environmental risk assessment of genetically engineered gene drive organisms from the perspective of European Union genetically modified organism regulation. Integr Environ Assess Manag 16:555–568. https://doi.org/10.1002/ieam.4278

113. US Government Accountability Office (GAO) (2021) Technology assessment design handbook, Report no. GAO-21-347G. Science, Technology Assessment, and Analytics team (STAA), Washington DC

12

Parasitic Contamination of Water Sources in Akure, Ondo State, Nigeria

I. A. Simon-Oke , O. J. Afolabi and E. T. Obimakinde

Biology Department, Federal University of Technology, Akure, Nigeria

ABSTRACT

Background

Availability of good water source is essential to every community in other to allay the risk of water-borne infection and diseases. In this study, the isolation of parasites and rate of parasitic contamination from different water sources were evaluated in Akure, Nigeria. A total of 816 water samples were collected from wells, streams, boreholes, and rain in the study areas. The samples were examined using calcium carbonate floatation and stained microscopic methods. Also, parameters (temperature, pH, and turbidity) of the different water sources were measured.

Results

Of all the water sources, stream water samples recorded the highest prevalence (45%), followed by well water (24%), rain water (21%), and borehole water having the least prevalence of 10% with significant difference. Different developmental stages of both protozoan and helminthic parasites were isolated from all the sampled water sources. Protozoa parasites isolated were Cryptosporidium parvum, Gardia spp., and Entamoeba histolytica with prevalence of 33.2, 19.9, and 13.0% respectively. Dracunculus medinensis and Enterobius vermicularis with prevalence of 10.3% and 4.0% respectively were helminthes recovered. It was observed that the occurrence of the parasites in the water sources was affected by the water parameters (temperature, pH, and turbidity). All the water sources harbored at least one parasite except for the borehole water sources in Akure North in which no parasite was isolated.

Conclusion

High parasitic contamination of these water sources imply that water should be treated before consumption to reduce the risk of contracting water-borne disease. Also, government at the local level should provide borehole water system for the communities.

Keywords: *Water-borne, Parasites, Contamination, Protozoa, Helminths, Akure*

BACKGROUND

Water is of fundamental importance to human life, animals, and plants. It is of equal importance with the air we breathe in maintaining the vital processes of life, and it makes up 60% of body weight in human body (Bonjoch, Balleste, & Blanch, 2004).

Water-borne parasitic infections are considered a threat and of public health importance especially in developing countries (Oyedeji, Olutiola, & Mononuola, 2010). Water is inevitably the source of life on earth and without it, life sustenance becomes difficult. Water of good quality is of basic importance to human physiology, and man's continued existence depends very much on its availability (Okonko, Ogunnusi, Adejoye, & Shittu, 2008).

Drinking water could be gotten from sources such as borehole/tap water, well water, dams, rivers, streams, lakes, municipal water, and rain water. Every community of humans, animals, or plants has one or more of these as their source of drinking water. Pollution of groundwater with pathogenic microorganisms is generally believed to be a consequence of migration or introduction of faecal material either from humans or animals into the subsurface. Faecal pollution can reach groundwater from many concentrated pond sources such as cesspools, landfills, leaking sewer lines, and filled septic systems (Sadallah & Al-Najar, 2014).

Over 3 million deaths per year are attributed to water-borne diarrhoeal diseases especially among infants and young children in poor communities in Africa, Asia, and South America (Anon., 1997). Parasitic infections affect work and productivity as they are usually associated with a diminished capacity to carry out physical work (Chollom et al., 2013). Despite the promotion of public health and improvement of life style in the recent years, parasitic diseases have remained a public health problem in many parts of the world. Water is a major source for acquiring several pathogenic agents including bacteria, viruses, and parasites. These biological agents can be transmitted via non-sanitized water (Dura, Kambourova, & Simeonova, 2006; LV et al., 2013). According to World Health Organization reports, more than 80 infectious diseases can be transmitted by water (Ayaz et al., 2011). Water quality problems and massive contamination remain unsolved leading to transmission of various water-borne diseases.

Therefore, there is a need for continuous research on water quality and sanitation which brought about the isolation and determination of rate of parasitic contamination of different water sources in the study areas. Research of such will provide information on the status of water sources in an environment which will help to reduce the risk of water-borne infections and diseases.

MATERIALS AND METHODS

Study Area

The study was carried out in Akure (North and South), the capital city of Ondo State, South-Western Nigeria (Fig. 1). It lies between latitude 7° 15′ 0″ N and longitude 5° 11′ 42″ E. The town is situated in the tropical rainforest zone of Nigeria. The temperature ranges from 25.2 °C to 28.1 °C with an average annual rainfall of 2378 mm and a relative humidity of 80%. It has a population of 588,000 based on 2006 population census, and the populace is made up of mainly Yoruba ethnic group. The major source of water in Akure is subsurface water, and the commonest is well water (Igbekele, 2010).

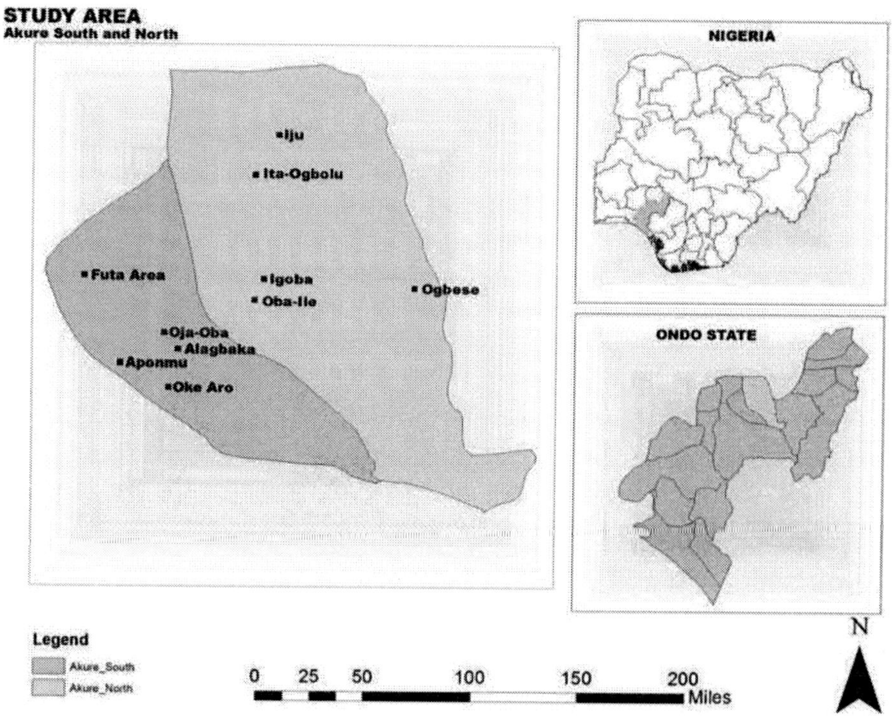

Figure 1. Map of the sampling sites.

Study Design

The study was conducted for parasitological evaluation of different water sources which randomly selected in different towns within the study areas. The major towns sampled in Akure North were Iju, Ita-Ogbolu, Igoba, Ogbese, and Oba-Ile while Futa area, Alagbaka, Oja-Oba, Oke Aro, and Aponmu were major areas sampled in Akure South. Sources of sampled water include well water, stored rain water, borehole, and streams. The sites were sampled twice in a month for three consecutive months each for dry season (December, 2017 to February, 2018) and wet seasons (May to July, 2018). The sampled water from the streams was collected from the upper and the lower course of the water body (Iyaji, Lawal, Omowaye, & Yaro, 2016).

Collection of Water Samples

Water samples were collected from wells, streams, boreholes, and rain water in clean bottles. The samples were labeled with dates of collection, nature or source of water, the site of collection, and transported to the laboratory of Department of Biology, Federal University of Technology, Akure, for further analysis.

Water parameters measured were temperature (measured with mercury-filled thermometer in °C), turbidity (measured with secchi disc), and pH (measured with SETRA pH 25, pH meter).

Capped sample bottles (100 ml) were washed and rinsed with clean warm water, well corked, and properly wrapped with foil paper. The bottles were placed in the autoclave and sterilized for an hour at 121 °C (Cheesebrough, 2006). After an hour, the bottles were carefully removed from the autoclave and placed in an air-tight and neat plastic bucket and taken to the sample sites for collection. At each sample site, the bottles were careful removed from the bucket one at a time, and water samples were collected into each of the bottles simultaneously.

For samples taken from boreholes, after turning the pump's nozzle on, water was allowed to flow out for 20 s before collecting the water directly into the bottles as it flows from the water outlet. This was to allow dirt, microbes, or other water contaminants which had previously settled at the base of the tank to flow out before the samples were taken.

For well samples, the water was collected using an already washed neat rubber water fetcher with the bottle bent at an angle of 90° during each collection to prevent contamination from the environment. After the collection of the water samples, parameters of water, temperature, turbidity, and pH of the water samples were measured.

Isolation and Identification of Parasites

One hundred milliliters of water sample was treated with 1 g calcium carbonate and left for 2 h for water particles to settle at the bottom of the bottle. The supernatant was carefully decanted while the sediment was dissolved by adding 1 ml of hydrogen sulphate (iv) acid and allowed to stand for another 2 h. The dissolved sediments were centrifuged at 3000 rpm for 15 min. The supernatant was discarded while the sediments were smeared on grease-free slides (Cheesebrough, 2006).

With the use of pipette, the filtrate was obtained and used to prepare two slides for each sample: one was stained with Lugol's iodine and viewed directly under the microscope (Bakir et al., 2003) while the other was stained with acid fast stain using Ziehl-Neelsons carbol fuchsin stain (FERN; certified suitable for staining acid fast organisms in smears and tissue section) using the cold carbol fuchsin technique. A smear of the sediment was made on grease-free glass slides and was allowed to air-dry for a few minutes, and the smeared slide was fixed with methanol for 3 min to preserve the parasite on the slide after which the carbol fuchsin was used to stain the slides for 15 min and rinsed under tap water. One percent of acid alcohol was used to decolorize the slide for 15 s, and the slides were again rinsed in tap water to remove excess acid alcohol. The slides were counter stained with 0.4% methylene blue for 60 s and rinsed under tap water, air dried, and examined under × 10 and × 40 objective lenses of binocular light microscope (Cheesebrough, 2006). Images of all parasites viewed under the microscope were taken using a digital camera of high resolution power and saved accordingly after which were properly identified using taxonomic keys according to Cheesebrough (2006).

Statistical Analysis

Data were analysed using simple descriptive statistics (chi-square and t test) using the SPSS version 21.0 software. P values less than 0.05 were considered to be statistically significant. All charts were created using Microsoft Excel.

RESULTS

A total of 816 water samples were collected in the study areas. Four hundred and eight water samples were from both Akure North and South (102 samples from each water sources).

Table 1 shows the prevalence of parasitic contamination in different water sources in the two study areas. It was observed that in Akure North and South, water from the streams had the highest prevalence of 53.9% and 30.4% respectively. Water samples from boreholes in the South recorded the lowest prevalence of 18.6% while in Akure North, there was no parasitic contamination (0%). Statistical analysis revealed no significant difference in parasitic contamination of water sources ($p > 0.05$).

Table 1. Prevalence of parasitic contamination in water sources in the study areas

Water sources	Location								
	Akure South			Akure North			Total		
	No examined	No positive	Prevalence (%)	No examined	No positive	Prevalence (%)	No examined	No positive	Prevalence (%)
Well	102	20	19.6	102	26	25.5	204	46	22.5
Borehole	102	19	18.6	102	0	0	204	19	9.3
Stream	102	31	30.4	102	55	53.9	204	86	42.2
Rain	102	21	20.6	102	19	18.6	204	40	19.6
Total	408	91	22.3	408	111	27.2	816	191	23.4

For the overall prevalence of parasites in all the water sources from Akure North and South, stream water has the highest prevalence of parasites followed by well water, rain water, and borehole water, with the prevalence of 42.2, 22.5, 19.6, and 9.3% respectively with a significant difference ($p < 0.05$).

A total of fourteen (14) parasites with varying developmental stages (egg, oocyst, cyst, and Larva) were isolated. *Cryptosporidium parvum*, *Schistosoma haematobium*, *Cyclospora cayetanensis*, and *Strongiloides stercoralis* were isolated in the water samples obtained from the two study areas. However, *Entamoeba coli*, *Giardia lamblia*, fluke, round worm, *Enterobium vermicularis*, *Dracunculus medinensis*, and *Naegleria fowleri* were isolated from Akure South only, while *Entamoeba histolytica*, *Giardia intestinalis*, and *Ascaris lumbricoides* were isolated from Akure North (Table 2).

Table 2. Parasites stages found in different drinking water sources in Akure South and North LGAs

Parasite	Location	
	Akure South	Akure North
	Stages	Stages
Cryptosporidium parvum	Oocyst	Oocyst
Entamoeba coli	Cyst	–
Giardia lamblia	Cyst	–
Fluke	Egg	–
Round worm	Larvae	–
Enterobium vermicularis	Larvae	–
Schistosoma haematobium	Egg	Egg
Cyclospora cayetanensis	Cyst	Cyst
Dracunculus medinensis	Larvae	–
Strongyloides stercoralis	Larvae	Larvae
Naegleria fowleri	Egg	–

Entamoeba histolytica	–	Cyst
Giardia intestinalis	–	Cyst
Ascaris lumbricoides	–	Egg

Occurrence and prevalence of parasites in different water samples in the study areas are represented in Table 3. *Cryptosporidium parvum* was observed in all the water sources sampled with a prevalence of 38.4% while *Cyclospora cayetanensis* (1.6%) was found in well and rain water in the South. In Akure North, *Entamoeba histolytica* was found in all the water sources except borehole with a total prevalence of 33.6%, and *Strongyloides stercoralis* (0.9%) was observed in only stream water. Statistical analysis showed significant difference in the occurrence of parasite isolated from well and stream water in the two study areas ($p < 0.05$).

Table 3. Occurrence and Prevalence of Parasites from different water sources in Akure South and Akure North

Parasites found	**Location**									
	Akure South					**Akure North**				
	Well (*n* = 84)	**Borehole (*n* = 33)**	**Stream (*n* = 34)**	**Rain (*n* = 34)**	**Total (*n* = 185)**	**Well (*n* = 29)**	**Borehole (*n* = 19)**	**Stream (*n* = 29)**	**Rain (*n* = 39)**	**Total (*n* = 116)**
Cryptosporidium parvum	32 (38.1%)	29 (87.9%)	6 (17.6%)	4 (11.8%)	71 (38.4%)	11 (37.9%)	0 (0%)	9 (31.0%)	9 (23.1%)	29 (25%)
Entamoeba coli	9 (10.7%)	2 (6.1%)	2 (5.9%)	1 (2.9%)	14 (7.6%)	0 (0%)	0 (0%)	0 (0%)	0 (0%)	0 (0%)
Giardia lamblia	14 (16.7%)	6 (18.2%)	10 (29.4%)	6 (17.6%)	36 (19.5%)	0 (0%)	0 (0%)	0 (0%)	0 (0%)	0 (0%)
Fluke	0 (0%)	0 (0%)	6(17.6%)	1 (2.9%)	7 (3.8%)	0 (0%)	0 (0%)	0 (0%)	0 (0%)	0 (0%)
Round worm	2 (2.4%)	1 (3.0%)	3 (8.8%)	1 (2.9%)	7 (3.8%)	0 (0%)	0 (0%)	0 (0%)	0 (0%)	0 (0%)
Enterobium vermicularis	3 (3.6 %)	0 (0%)	7 (20.6%)	2 (15.9%)	12 (6.5%)	0 (0%)	0 (0%)	0 (0%)	0 (0%)	0 (0%)
Schistosoma haematobium	4 (4.8%)	0 (0%)	2 (5.9%)	0 (0%)	6 (3.2%)	1 (3.4%)	0 (0%)	13 (44.8%)	1 (2.6%)	15 (12.9%)
Cyclospora cayetanensis	2 (2.4%)	0 (0%)	0 (0%)	1 (2.9%)	3 (1.6%)	2 (6.9%)	0 (0%)	5 (17.2%)	3 (7.7%)	10 (8.6%)
Dracunculus medinensis	15 (17.9%)	0 (0%)	12 (35.3%)	4 (11.8%)	31 (16.8%)	0 (0%)	0 (0%)	0 (0%)	0 (0%)	0 (0%)
Strongiloides stercoralis	9 (10.7 %)	0 (0%)	0 (0%)	1 (2.9%)	10 (5.4%)	0 (0%)	0 (0%)	1 (3.4%)	0 (0%)	1 (0.9%)
Naegleria fowleri	0 (0%)	6 (18.2%)	0 (0%)	0 (0%)	6 (3.2%)	0 (0%)	0 (0%)	0 (0%)	0 (0%)	0 (0%)
Entamoeba histolytica	0 (0%)	0 (0%)	0 (0%)	0 (0%)	0 (0%)	6 (20.74%)	0 (0%)	26 (89.7%)	7 (17.9%)	39 (33.6%)
Giardia intestinalis	0 (0%)	0 (0%)	0 (0%)	0 (0%)	0 (0%)	10 (34.5%)	0 (0%)	8 (6.9%)	6 (15.4%)	24 (20.7%)
Ascaris lumbricoides	0 (0%)	0 (0%)	0 (0%)	0 (0%)	0 (0%)	0 (0%)	0 (0%)	2 (6.9%)	0 (0%)	2 (1.7%)

Table 4 shows the seasonal prevalence of parasitic contamination of the different water sources. Result revealed that there was a higher prevalence of contaminants during the wet season (24.0%) when compared to the dry season which had a lower prevalence of

22.7%. However, it was observed that samples gotten from streams (46.5%) and rain water (20.2%) had higher prevalence of parasites in the dry season when compared to wet season (38.1 and 19.1%) respectively. Statistical analysis revealed a significant difference in the seasonal contamination of water samples in both seasons ($p < 0.05$).

Table 4. Seasonal prevalence parasitic contamination of different water sources

Water sources	Seasons					
	Dry season			Wet season		
	No examined	No positive	Prevalence (%)	No examined	No positive	Prevalence (%)
Well	102	18	16.7	102	28	27.5
Borehole	102	7	6.9	102	12	11.8
Stream	99	46	46.5	105	40	38.1
Rain	84	17	20.2	120	23	19.2
Total	387	88	22.7	429	103	24.0

Temperature, pH, and turbidity of the different water sources were measured, and the mean values were expressed (Fig. 2). It was observed that the occurrence of the parasites in the water sources was affected by these parameters. Statistical analysis showed significant difference in the different water parameters ($p < 0.05$)

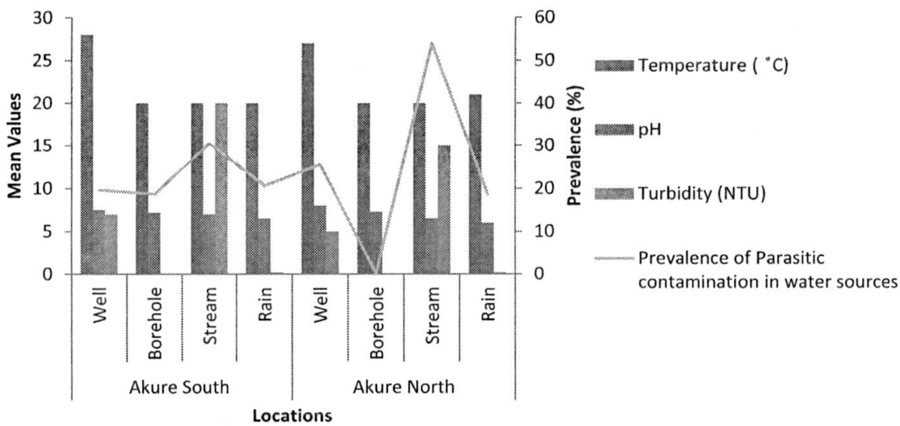

Figure 2. Water parameters in relation to the occurrence of parasite in water sources. Statistical analysis showed significant difference in the different water parameters (p < 0.05).

DISCUSSION

Protozoans and helminths were the main parasites encountered in all the water sources. *Cryptosporidium parvum* recorded the highest prevalence, and it has been known to be an important water-borne disease causative agent associated with several gastrointestinal diseases in human (Razzolini, da Silva Santos, & Bastos, 2010). All water sources across the study areas recorded the presence of *C. parvum*, and this result is in agreement with the findings of Iyaji et al. (2016), who isolated *C. parvum* in borehole water during their study in Okura District, Kogi State, Nigeria. However, it disagrees with the report of Solomon et al. (2013), who recorded 0% parasitic contamination in borehole water during their study in Heipang, a rural community in Plateau State, Nigeria.

Entamoeba histolytica, a protozoan parasite known to cause amoebic dysentery in human, was isolated only in Akure North. *Giardia spp* (*G. intestinalis* found in Akure North and *G. lamblia* found in South) recorded the high prevalence. *Giardia spp* is known to cause giardiasis, a serious gastro intestinal disease. This result is in correlation with the report of Ani and Itiba (2015) who isolated *C. Parvum*, *Giardia spp*, and *E. histolytica* during their study in different sources of drinking water in Abakaliki, Ebonyi State, Nigeria. These three protozoans are known to be part of the major parasites that cause diarrhea (Hernandez & Avendendo, 2001). Tanyuksel, Tachibana, and Petri (2001) also reported these three parasites to be the most common cause of infection globally. Also, Furness et al. (2000) reported *C. parvum* and Giardia *spp.* to induce gastroenteritis and were considered to the leading cause of waterborne diseases in the USA.

Among the helminthes that were isolated from the different water sources, *Dracunculu medinensis* and *Enterobius vermicularis* recorded the high prevalence, although the two parasites were found in Akure South only. However, a high prevalence (12.9%) of *Schistosoma haematobium* was recorded in Akure North compared to South (3.2%). Also, it was observed that *Ascaris lumbricoides* was found in Akure North but absent in the South. The presence of these helminthic parasites in the study area is in conformity with previous reports of other researchers. For instance, Solomon et al. (2013) who worked in a rural community in Nigeria, Ani and Itiba (2015) who worked in Abakaliki, Ebonyi State, Nigeria, and Iyaji et al. (2016) who worked in Okura District, Dekina Local Government, Kogi State, Nigeria, all in their studies, isolated helminthes in the different water samples which they studied. Results obtained from this study indicate that people residing in the study area who depend on all the sources of water are at great risk of contracting water-borne diseases if they fail to treat the water before use. However, residents within Akure North who depend on boreholes as source of water might be at lesser risk of contracting water-borne diseases due to the fact that the all borehole water sources examined in this region were void of parasites.

Of the water sources, stream water has the highest prevalence of parasitic contamination, followed by well water, rain water, and borehole having the lowest prevalence. It was observed that all sampled boreholes in Akure North have no parasitic contamination. The result obtained from Akure North is in agreement with the report of Solomon et al. (2013) who isolated parasites of varying developmental stages in all the water sources they sampled except from boreholes which yielded 0% prevalence. However, it is dissimilar from the report of Ani and Itiba (2015) and Iyaji et al. (2016) who in their respective research isolated parasites from all the water sources they examined including boreholes.

The wet season recorded higher prevalence of parasitic contamination when compared with the dry season. This observation is in line with the result obtained by Pam et al. (2018) in their research at Doma local government area of Nasarawa State, Nigeria, who recorded a higher overall prevalence of 59.38% of parasitic contamination in different water sources during the wet season to a lower overall prevalence of 40.63% during the dry season. Also, they recorded the highest prevalence of contamination in stream samples during both dry and wet season (69.23and 94.74% respectively). The reason for the stream having the highest prevalence could be as a result of human activities such as indiscriminate dumping of waste and defecation into the water body.

Relating the measured water parameters with the abundance of parasites in the water sources, it was observed that stream water which had the highest parasite contamination has a very high turbidity, a moderate pH. and suitable temperature for parasite survival while rain water has low turbidity, slightly low pH. and lower temperature. Rain water is slightly acidic because there is interference of the rain water with CO2 in the atmosphere. Living organisms survive more at neutral to slightly alkaline pH (Odikamnoro, Omowaye, & Uduituma, 2014).

Generally, the presence of different parasites in the various water sources in the study area could be as a result of poor hygiene on people residing in the study area. People defecating close to the stream might have contributed to the contamination of this water source. During fetching of water from wells, the use of unclean contaminated materials might have led to the contamination well water. Leaving wells uncovered after use could have also exposed the well to parasitic contaminants. Stored rain water might also have gotten contaminated though the use of unclean materials and dirty hands dipped into the storage containers. Agricultural activities such as use of manure in which erosion could have washed some parasitic contaminants present in manures into the stream might have been another means through which the stream got contaminated. In some of the streams sampled, *S. haematobium* was isolated; the presence of this parasite could have been as a result of the presence of snail intermediate host in the water body and people engaging in different activities in the stream, and this facilitates the completion of the parasites life cycle. An infected individual urinating into the stream could have also been a source of contamination.

CONCLUSION

From the results obtained from this research, it is apparent that the sampled water sources were contaminated with parasites which indicate that residents in the study areas are at great risk of contracting water-borne parasitic diseases; therefore, it is imperative that water sources in this region should be treated before consumption in other which allays the risk of infection. Also, borehole water sources presented a low prevalence of contamination which could be attributed to the depth, and the engineering work which limits debris and parasites accessibility. Hence, the use of boreholes as source of water should be encouraged. Government should provide borehole water system in every part of study areas which will drastically reduce the chance of contracting water-borne diseases.

ACKNOWLEDGEMENTS

Authors appreciate the effort of Mrs. E. T. Ojo (Chief Technologist, Biology Department, Federal University of Technology, Akure) for her effort and support during the laboratory work of this research.

REFERENCES

1. Ani, O. C., & Itiba, O. L. (2015). Evaluation of the parasitic contamination of local sources of drinking water in Abakaliki, Ebonyi State, Nigeria. *Journal of Dental and Medical Sciences*, *14*(9), 30–34.
2. Anon. (1997). World Health Report. *World Health Forum*, *97*, 181–188.
3. Ayaz, S., Khan, S., Khan, S. N., Bibi, F., Shamas, S., & Akhtar, M. (2011). Prevalence of zoonotic parasites in drinking water of three districts of Khyber Pakhtunkhwa Province, Pakistan. *Pakistan J Life Soc Sci.*, *9*(1), 67–69.

4. Bakir, B., Tanyuksel, M., Saylam, F., Tanriverdis, S., Araz, R. E., Hacim, A. K., & Hasde, M. (2003). Investigation of waterborne parasites in drinking water sources of Ankara, Turkey. *Journal of Microbiology*, *41*(2), 148–151.

5. Bonjoch, X., Balleste, E., & Blanch, A. R. (2004). Multiplex PCR with 16S RNA gene-targeted primers of Bifido-bacterium spp to identify sources of fecal pollution in water. *Applied Environmental Microbiology*, *70*, 3171–3175.

6. Cheesebrough, M. (2006). *District laboratory practice in the tropical countries*, (2nd ed., pp. 39–157). Cambridge, UK: *Cambridge University Press*.

7. Chollom, S. C., Iduh, M. U., Gyang, B. J., idoko, M. A., Ujah, A., Agada, G. O., Okwori, J. A. (2013). Parasitological evaluation of domestic water sources in a rural community in Nigeria. *British Microbiology Research Journal*, *3*(3), 393–399.

8. Dura G, Kambourova V, Simeonova F, (2006). NATO Programme for Security through Science, *Management of Intentional and Accidental Water Pollution.*: Springer;.

9. Furness, B., Beach, M., & Roberts, J. (2000). Giardiasis Surveillance in United States, Morbidity and Mortality. *Weekly Report*, *49*, 1–3.

10. Hernandez, C. F., & Avendendo, L. (2001). Simple Modification of the Baermann method for diagnosis of strongyloidiasis. *Mem Inst. Oswaldo Cruz, Rio de Janeiro.*, *96*, 805–807.

11. Igbekele, A., (2010). Akure City profile.International water management institute. Available at: http://www.google.com.ng/search?hl = en

12. Iyaji, F. O., Lawal, A., Omowaye, O. S., & Yaro, C. A. (2016). Evaluation of parasites of medical importance in drinking water sources in Okura District, Dekina Local Government, Kogi State, Nigeria. *International Journal of Development Research*, *6*(4), 7290–7294.

13. Lv, S., Tian, L. G., Liu, Q., Qian, M. B., Fu, Q., Steinmann, P., et al. (2013). Water-related parasitic diseases in China. *Int J Environ Res Public Health*, *10*(5), 1977–2016.

14. Odikamnoro, O. O., Omowaye, O. S., & Uduituma, S. O. (2014). Parasitic survey of drinking water sources in Ohaukwu Local Government Area, Ebonyi State, Nigeria. *European Journal of Nursing*, *1*(1), 1–5.

15. Okonko, I. O., Ogunnusi, T. A., Adejoye, O. D., & Shittu, O. B. (2008). Microbiological and physicochemical analysis of different water samples use for domestic purposes in Abeokuta, Ogun State and Ojota, Lagos State, Nigeria. *African Journal of Biotechnology*, *7(5)*, 617–621.

16. Oyedeji, O., Olutiola, P. O., & Mononuola, M. A. (2010). Microbiological quality of packaged drinking water brands marketed in Ibadan metropolis and Ile-Ile city in South Western Nigeria. *Journal of Microbiology Research*, *4*(1), 96–102.

17. Pam, V. A., Ombugadu, A., Adejoh, V. A., Idris, A. A., Pam, D. D., Rwang, P. G., Dogo, S. K. (2018). Evaluation of parasitic contamination of local potable water sources in Doma local government Area of Nasarawa State, Nigeria. *Tropical Freshwater Biology*, *27*(2), 31–34.

18. Razzolini, M. T. P., da Silva Santos, T. F., & Bastos, V. K. (2010). Detection of Giardia and Cryptosporidium cysts/oocysts in watersheds and drinking water sources in Brazil urban areas. *Journal of water and health*, *8*(2), 399–404.

19. Sadallah, H., & Al-Najar, H. (2014). *Effectiveness of water supply disinfection system in Um Al-Nasser village as a marginal rural community*. M Sc Thesis: University of Gaza.

20. Solomon, C. C., Michael, U. I., Bitrus, J. G., Micheal, A. I., Aloysius, U., Godwin, O. A., Joseph, A. O. (2013). Parasitological evaluation of domestic water sources in a rural community in Nigeria. *British Microbiology Research Journal*, *3*(3), 393–399.

21. Tanyuksel, M., Tachibana, H., & Petri, W. A. (2001). *Amebiasis, an Emerging Disease; 212.*

INDEX

I

L

M

N

O

P

Q

R

S

T

V

W

X

Z